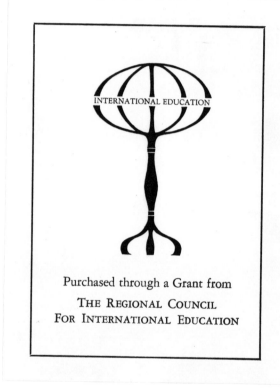

HISTORIANS OF LATIN AMERICA

IN THE UNITED STATES, 1965

HISTORIANS

OF LATIN AMERICA

IN THE UNITED STATES, 1965

Biobibliographies of 680 Specialists

Howard F. Cline, compiler

Published for the Conference on Latin American History

Duke University Press, Durham, North Carolina   1966

CONFERENCE ON LATIN AMERICAN HISTORY
Founded in 1928, incorporated 1964

PERMANENT SECRETARIAT: Hispanic Foundation, Library of Congress

MEMBERSHIP: Persons interested, whether professionally or otherwise, in historical studies of Latin American and related areas are invited to membership. Present membership *ca.* 450. Members annually elect officers by ballot. The Conference is a non-political, autonomous, incorporated, tax-exempt, non-profit society affiliated with the American Historical Association, membership in which is not requisite to joining the Conference.

DUES: There is no initiation or other fee beyond annual regular dues of $1.00, payable January 1 to the Secretary-Treasurer. Payment of dues constitutes membership in the Conference.

MEETINGS: An annual public meeting is held in conjunction with the annual meeting of the American Historical Association, which normally co-sponsors an academic session with the Conference. In addition are the regular Conference luncheon business meeting and other academic sessions approved by the Program Committee of the American Historical Association but planned by the Conference.

PUBLICATIONS: In 1964 the Conference on Latin American History Publications series was established, to include bibliographies, translations of important materials, documents, and similar reference and research tools, but not monographs. The University of Texas Press publishes the series, titles in which may be ordered directly from it. Members receive prepublication discounts. The Secretariat from time to time prepares rosters, directories, and other administrative publications. A *Newsletter* is issued regularly twice a year in the spring and fall, with special numbers as needed.

The Conference does not itself publish the *Hispanic American Historical Review,* sponsored by the Duke University Press (quarterly; $6, U.S.; $4, Canada and Pan-American countries), but co-operates with the Editor and Board of *HAHR* in its publication. Subscriptions to *HAHR* should be directed to the Duke University Press, Durham, North Carolina 27708. Materials for possible publication in the *HAHR* should be submitted to Dr. Robert Quirk, Managing Editor, History Department, Indiana University, Bloomington, Indiana 47405.

PRIZES: The James A. Robertson Memorial Prize of $100 is awarded annually for the best article(s) appearing each year in the *Hispanic American Historical Review.* From funds furnished by the Pan-American Foundation the Herbert E. Bolton Memorial Prize of $300 is awarded for the best book on any aspect of Latin American history published during the previous year (i.e., the 1965 prize for a volume of 1964 imprint). The Conference on Latin American History Prize of $100 is annually awarded for the best article on Latin American history appearing in a journal other than the *Hispanic American Historical Review.* Prizes are awarded by special committees for each prize appointed annually by the Chairman of the Conference. In co-operation with the American Historical Association, which administers the funds, a committee of Conference members

v

AUG 2 3 1967

appointed by the Association recommends award of the Clarence H. Haring Memorial Prize, every five years beginning in 1965, for the best historical work about Latin America by a Latin American during the interval; the stipend varies.

CORRESPONDENCE: Dues, inquiries, and correspondence should be addressed to John Finan, Secretary-Treasurer, Box 164, American University, Washington, D.C. 20016.

CONTENTS

INTRODUCTION

This directory lists 680 persons in the United States whose academic specialty is Latin American history. It is being published for the Conference on Latin American History to facilitate communication among its members and to provide an inventory of research interests in this group of specialists.

The directory grew out of a joint project undertaken by the Conference and the Hispanic Foundation in the Library of Congress. To provide much requested data on Latin Americanists in the United States, the latter undertook to circularize several hundred of them in various fields of knowledge, and to prepare for publication a national directory of such specialists, on funds furnished the Library of Congress by the Office of Education. In this endeavor the Conference on Latin American History aided greatly by urging its members to complete and submit a rather elaborate questionnaire. In early 1966 the general national directory was published by the Government Printing Office.*

The Hispanic Foundation had agreed to make available to the Conference the data collected on historians, for publication by the Conference as a separate volume, this directory. In the course of gathering information, the Hispanic Foundation received completed questionnaires from more than 650 such scholars, of whom 397 met the criteria for inclusion in the published national directory, generally an earned Ph.D. or its equivalent.

The entries of these 397 specialists have been included in this directory, with a few changes of address and academic status. In addition, there are 184 entries for those not included in the national directory. Many of the latter are graduate students who had not completed their work when the national directory was closed; others have terminal M.A. degrees, and yet others are included because of their membership in the Conference on Latin American History. We have tried to include all the latter who were on its rolls at the close of 1965. In some instances where the member has not responded to requests to complete the biobibliographical questionnaire we have

* *National Directory of Latin Americanists: Biobibliographies of 1,884 specialists.* Washington. GPO, 1966. Hispanic Foundation Bibliographical Series, 10. Obtainable from the Superintendent of Documents, GPO, Washington, D.C. 20402, at a cost of $2.00.

listed the name and last known mailing address. In rare instances we were informed that a specialist did not wish to be included either in the national directory or in this one.

Despite earnest efforts on the part of the Hispanic Foundation to provide comprehensive coverage, we are aware of omissions, especially among graduate students recently interested in the specialty. We urge them, and those responsible for them, to furnish the Secretariat of the Conference (Hispanic Foundation, Library of Congress) with their names so that future revisions of this volume will be more complete.

Inevitably some of the data in the various entries are now outdated. In general the questionnaires reflect information gathered during 1963-1964. The magnitude and complexity of the National Directory enterprise prevented continuous follow-up until the initial volumes—the national directory and this one—had been published.

As an aid to users an index to the areas on which various scholars have indicated specialized knowledge follows the main body of entries. When competence in more than one area is indicated, the name is included under each such heading. The area specialities are tabulated (Table 1). Seemingly all Latin American republics but the Dominican Republic and El Salvador have at least one devotee.

Table 1. AREA SPECIALIZATIONS OF 680 HISTORIANS

CARIBBEAN

General	42	
Cuba	29	
Haiti	8	
Puerto Rico	10	
Subtotal		89

MEXICO 195

CENTRAL AMERICA

General	47	
Costa Rica	4	
Guatemala	14	
Honduras	4	
Nicaragua	5	
Panama	11	
Subtotal		85

SOUTH AMERICA

Brazil		83
Rio de la Plata		
General	5	

Argentina	50	
Paraguay	8	
Uruguay	5	
Subtotal		68
Chile		31
Andean		
General	4	
Bolivia	14	
Ecuador	8	
Peru	31	
Subtotal		57
Northern		
Colombia	29	
Venezuela	10	
British Guiana	2	
Subtotal		41

Subtotal 280

INTERNATIONAL RELATIONS 147

RELATED

U.S. Spanish Borderlands 47

Portugal 3

Spain 9

Subtotal 59

TOTAL 855

So far as the information furnished on questionnaires permits, the standard entry contains (in this order) the following information:

Name, birthplace, birthdate;
Major discipline, usually History (in upper case) ;
Degrees, including honorary degrees;
Professional career (with present position in upper case) ;
Fellowships, honors, awards, committees, consultantships;
Membership in professional and honorary organizations;
Research specialties and interests;
Publications (limited to three) ;
Language knowledge (see discussion below) ;
Linguistic studies;
Home and office addresses.

It should be noted that the Hispanic Foundation has not attempted verification of data on the questionnaires. Knowledge of language is an important feature in each biobibliography. The numbers following the language are self-ratings in response to a specially designed question, herewith reproduced from the standard questionnaire:

| 17. | WHAT IS YOUR NATIVE LANGUAGE? *(If bilingual, indicate both languages)* _____ |

PRESENT COMPETENCE IN OTHER LANGUAGES: *(Include English if not a native speaker)*
RATE YOURSELF IN ACCORDANCE WITH THE FOLLOWING LANGUAGE PROFICIENCY CODE IN ALL MODERN FOREIGN LANGUAGES IN WHICH YOU HAVE SOME COMPETENCE.

1. HAVE NO PRACTICAL USABLE PROFICIENCY.

2. ABLE TO READ SIMPLE PROSE WITH DIFFICULTY, TO FOLLOW SIMPLE CONVERSATION, TO USE THE LANGUAGE TO GET AROUND, BUT NOT AS A MEANS OF EXCHANGING IDEAS, TO SPELL OUT SIMPLE PHRASES, BUT NO REAL COMMAND OF GRAMMAR AND SYNTAX.

3. ABLE TO READ NON-TECHNICAL MATERIALS AND TECHNICAL WRITING IN ONE'S FIELD, TO UNDERSTAND ORDINARY NATIVE SPEECH, TO CARRY ON AN EXCHANGE OF IDEAS, THOUGH HALTINGLY, TO WRITE WITH DICTIONARY AND OTHER AIDS.

4. HAVE FLUENCY, ACCURACY AND RANGE ADEQUATE FOR ALL NORMAL PROFESSIONAL AND SOCIAL SITUATIONS.

5. HAVE THE FLUENCY, ACCURACY AND RANGE OF AN EDUCATED NATIVE USER OF THE LANGUAGE.

CHECK THE MOST APPROPRIATE NUMBER IN EACH ASPECT OF EACH LANGUAGE.

LANGUAGES	READING					UNDERSTANDING THE SPOKEN LANGUAGE					SPEAKING					WRITING				
	1	2	3	4	5	1	2	3	4	5	1	2	3	4	5	1	2	3	4	5
SPANISH																				
PORTUGUESE																				
FRENCH																				
OTHERS *(List below)*																				

There remains only to acknowledge, with thanks, help provided by many hands toward this pioneering enterprise. Chairmen of the Conference on Latin American History were uniformly helpful in urging the membership to forward questionnaires. These were processed by a special staff; Miss Helen Hollis and Miss Ruth Ash took special responsibility for entries in this directory. Miss Ash prepared the index of area specializations. On behalf of the Conference I should also like to extend words of appreciation to the Ford Foundation, whose grant to it in 1964 for various activities and projects made possible the preparation and publication of this work.

> Howard F. Cline
> Chairman, Committee on Activities and Projects
> Conference on Latin American History

January 15, 1966

LIST OF ABBREVIATIONS

A.A.	Associate in Arts		Feb.	February
A.B.	Bachelor of Arts		Fla.	Florida
Ala.	Alabama			
A.M.	Master of Arts		Ga.	Georgia
Apr.	April			
Apt.	Apartment		I.H.M.	Order of the Immaculate Heart of Mary
Ariz.	Arizona		Ill.	Illinois
Ark.	Arkansas		Inc.	Incorporated
Assoc.	Associate		Ind.	Indiana
Asst.	Assistant		Instr.	Instructor
Aug.	August			
Ave.	Avenue		Jan.	January
			J.D.	Doctor of Laws
b.	Born		Jur.D.	Doctor of Laws
B.A.	Bachelor of Arts		J.U.D.	Doctor of Canon and Civil Laws
B.Arch.	Bachelor of Architecture		J.S.D.	Doctor of Juristic Science
B.B.A.	Bachelor of Business Administration			
B.C.L.	Bachelor of Civil Law		Kans.	Kansas
B.C.P.	Bachelor of City Planning		Ky.	Kentucky
B.D.	Bachelor of Divinity			
B.Ed.	Bachelor of Education		La.	Louisiana
B.F.A.	Bachelor of Fine Arts		Lectr.	Lecturer
B.F.T.	Bachelor of Foreign Trade		L.H.D.	Doctor of Humanities
Bldg.	Building		Lit.D.	Doctor of Literature
Blvd.	Boulevard		Litt.D.	Doctor of Letters
B.Mus.	Bachelor of Music		LL.B.	Bachelor of Laws
B.S.	Bachelor of Science		LL.D.	Doctor of Laws
B.S.F.S.	Bachelor of Science in Foreign Service		LL.M.	Master of Laws
			Ltd.	Limited
B.S.Met.E.	Bachelor of Science in Metallurgical Engineering		M.A.	Master of Arts
B.S.S.	Bachelor of Social Science		M.A.L.S.	Master of Arts in Library Science
			Mar.	March
Calif.	California		M.Arch.	Master of Architecture
Chmn.	Chairman		Mass.	Massachusetts
Cia	Compania		M.C.P.	Master of City Planning
C.M.	Congregation of the Mission		Md.	Maryland
Coll.	College		M.Ed.	Master of Education
Colo.	Colorado		M.F.	Master of Forestry
Conn.	Connecticut		M.F.A.	Master of Fine Arts
C.S.C.	Congregation of the Holy Cross		Mich.	Michigan
Ct.	Court		Minn.	Minnesota
C.Z.	Canal Zone		Miss.	Mississippi
			M.M.	Maryknoll Missionaries
D.C.	District of Columbia		M.Met.E.	Master of Metallurgical Engineering
Dec.	December		M.Mus.	Master of Music
Del.	Delaware		Mo.	Missouri
Dept.	Department		Mont.	Montana
D.F.	Distrito Federal		M.R.P.	Master of Regional Planning
Dir.	Director		Msgr.	Monseigneur
Div.	Division		M.S.L.S.	Master of Science in Library Science
D.Litt.	Doctor of Literature		M.S.S.	Master of Social Science
Dr.	Drive		M.S.W.	Master of Social Work
D.S.S.	Doctor of Social Science		Mt.	Mount
Dto.	Departamento			
			N.C.	North Carolina
Ed.D.	Doctor of Education		N. Dak.	North Dakota

NE.	Northeast	SE.	Southeast
Nebr.	Nebraska	Sept.	September
Nev.	Nevada	S.J.	Society of Jesus
N.H.	New Hampshire	S.J.D.	Doctor of Juridical Science
N.J.	New Jersey	S.M.	Society of Mary
N. Mex.	New Mexico	S.N.J.M.	Society of the Holy Names of Jesus
Nov.	November		and Mary
NW.	Northwest	Sq.	Square
N.Y.	New York	St.	Street
		S.T.B.	Bachelor of Sacred Theology
Oct.	October	S.T.D.	Doctor of Sacred Theology
O.F.M.	Order of Friars Minor	S.T.L.	Licentiate in Sacred Theology
Okla.	Oklahoma	SW.	Southwest
O.P.	Order of Preachers		
Oreg.	Oregon	Tenn.	Tennessee
O.S.F.S.	Oblate of Saint Francis de Sales	Ter.	Terrace
		Tex.	Texas
Pa.	Pennsylvania	Th.B.	Bachelor of Theology
Ph.B.	Bachelor of Philosophy	Th.D.	Doctor of Theology
Ph.D.	Doctor of Philosophy	Th.M.	Master in Theology
Ph.L.	Licentiate in Philosophy	U.	University
Pl.	Place	UNESCO	United Nations Educational, Scientific, and Cultural Organization
P.R.	Puerto Rico		
Prof.	Professor	U.S.	United States
Rd.	Road	Va.	Virginia
R.F.D.	Rural Free Delivery	V.I.	Virgin Islands
R.I.	Rhode Island	Vis.	Visiting
Rm.	Room	Vt.	Vermont
S.A.	Sociedad Anónima	Wash.	Washington
S.B.	Bachelor of Science	Wis.	Wisconsin
S.C.	South Carolina	W. Va.	West Virginia
S. Dak.	South Dakota	Wyo.	Wyoming

HISTORIANS OF LATIN AMERICA

IN THE UNITED STATES, 1965

ADAMS, ELEANOR BURNHAM, b. Cambridge, Mass. HISTORY. A.B., Radcliffe Coll., 1931; Centro de Estudios Históricos, U. of Madrid, 1931-32. Investigator, historian, Carnegie Institution of Washington, 1934-49; Div. of Manuscripts, Bancroft Library, U. of Calif., Berkeley, 1950; RESEARCH ASSOC. IN HISTORY, U. of N. MEX., 1951- . Research: archival research in Mexico; specialization in New Spain, New Mexico, and Maya area. Author: A Bio-Bibliography of Franciscan Authors in Colonial Central America (1953). Co-author: Don Diego Qijada, Alcalde Mayor de Yucatán (1938); Documentos para la historia del México colonial (1955). Language: Spanish 5,5,4,4; Portuguese 3,3,2,2; French 4,3,3,2; Italian 4,3,3,2; Latin 3,—,—,—. Home: 413 Bryn Mawr Dr., SE., Albuquerque, N. Mex. Office: Library 217, U. of N. Mex., Albuquerque.

ADAMS, HENRY E., b. Ancon, C.Z., July 23, 1940. LINGUISTICS AND BIBLIOGRAPHY. B.S., Georgetown U., 1963. ASST. TO THE EDITOR, HANDBOOK OF LATIN AMERICAN STUDIES, HISPANIC FOUNDATION, LIBRARY OF CONGRESS, 1963- . Membership: Academy of Political Science; American Historical Association; Conference on Latin American History, Inter-American Council (Washington, D.C.). Research: descriptive and applied linguistics; socio-linguistic study of a Brazilian idiolect. Co-contributor: Bibliography and General Works Section (in Handbook of Latin American Studies, 1964, 1965). Language: Spanish 5,5,5,5; Portuguese 5,5,5,5; French 4,4,4,4; Dutch 1,1,1,1; German 2,2,2,1; Italian 3,3,4,4. Linguistic studies: Guaymi; Portuguese. Home: 1603 Fitzgerald Lane, Alexandria, Va. Office: Hispanic Foundation, Library of Congress, Washington, D.C. 20540.

ADAMS, THOMAS RANDOLPH, b. Durham, N.C., May 22, 1921. LIBRARY SCIENCE. B.A., U. of Mich., 1944; M.A., U. of Pa., 1949. Research asst., Library Co. of Philadelphia, 1947-48; asst. curator of rare books, U. of Pa. Library, 1948-50; curator of rare books, U. of Pa. Library, 1950-55; custodian of rare books, Chapin Library, Williams Coll., 1955-57; LIBRARIAN, JOHN CARTER BROWN LIBRARY, BROWN U., 1957- . Guggenheim fellow, 1963. Membership: Conference on Latin American History. Home: 18 Arnold St., Providence, R.I. Office: John Carter Brown Library, Brown U., Providence, 02912.

ADDY, GEORGE MILTON, b. Salt Lake City, Utah, July 6, 1927. HISTORY. B.A., Brigham Young U., 1948; M.A., 1950; Ph.D., Duke U., 1957. Instr., Brigham Young U., 1957-58; asst. prof., 1958-62; ASSOC. PROF., HISTORY, BRIGHAM YOUNG U., 1963- . Institute of International Education fellow, 1956; Angier B. Duke Memorial fellow, Duke U., 1957; American Council of Learned Societies grant-in-aid, 1962. Membership: American Historical Association; Conference on Latin American History. Research: the enlightenment in Hispanic culture and the 18th century. Author: Reforms of 1771: First Steps in the Salamancan Enlightenment (Hispanic American Historical Review, Aug. 1961); The Enlightenment in the University of Salamanca (1966). Language: Spanish 4,3,3,3; French 3,2,2,2; German 3,1,1,1. Home: 1433 Richards St., Salt Lake City, Utah. Office: 320A Maeser Bldg., Brigham Young U., Provo.

AGUILAR, LUIS ENRIQUE, b. Manzanillo, Cuba, June 16, 1926. HISTORY. LL.D., U. of Havana, 1949; LL.D., U. of Madrid, 1950; American U. Prof., Oriente U. (Cuba), 1952-56; prof., Columbia U., 1961-62; PROF., LATIN AMERICAN HISTORY, GEORGETOWN U., 1962- . Membership: American Historical Association. Research: historical and social factors that formed the Cuban nation; role of universities in Latin American political life. Author: Pasado y ambiente en el proceso cubano (1957); La agonía de la democracia en Latina América (Cuadernos, Oct. 1962); The Shadow of Cuba (New Leader, Sept. 1962). Language: Spanish 5,5,5,5; Portuguese 3,3,3,1; French 4,4,4,2. Home: 6836 Tulip Hill Ter., Washington, D.C. 20016. Office: Dept. of History, Georgetown U., Washington, 20007.

ALBRO, WARD S., III. Office: Dept. of History, Wis. State U., Riverfalls, Wis. 54022.

ALDEN, DAURIL, b. San Francisco, Calif., Jan. 12, 1926. HISTORY. A.B., U. of Calif., Berkeley, 1950; M.A., 1952; Ph.D., 1959. Instr., U. of Wash., 1959-60; asst. prof., U. of Wash., 1960-64; vis. asst. prof., U. of Calif., Berkeley, 1962-63; ASSOC. PROF., HISTORY, U. OF WASH., 1964- . Doherty fellow (Brazil), 1957-58; Social Science Research Council fellow, 1958; American Philosophical Society summer grant, 1962. Membership: Conference on Latin American History; Pacific Coast Conference of Latin American Studies. Research: colonial Brazil; administrative and economic history of Brazil; Mexico. Author: Manuel Luis Vieira: An Entrepreneur in Rio de Janeiro during Brazil's Eighteenth Century

3

ALLEN

Agricultural Renaissance (Hispanic American Historical Review, Nov. 1959); The Undeclared War of 1773-1777: Climax of Luso-Spanish Platine Rivalry (Hispanic American Historical Review, Feb. 1961); The Population of Brazil in the Late Eighteenth Century: A Preliminary Study (Hispanic American Historical Review, May 1963). Language: Spanish 4,3,3,3; Portuguese 4,4,4,3; French 3,3,1,1. Home: 8002 38th Ave., NE., Seattle, Wash. Office: Dept. of History, U. of Wash., Seattle 5.

ALLEN, CYRIL G., b. Edgerton, Alberta, Canada, Jan. 23, 1919. HISTORY. B.S., Winona State Teachers Coll., 1941; M.A., U. of Minn., 1946; Ph.D., 1949. Instr., U. of Cincinnati, 1947-49; asst. prof., Extension Div., U. of Minn., 1949-50; PROF., HISTORY, MANKATO STATE COLL., 1950- . Fund for Advancement of Education fellow (Central America, Mexico), 1954-55. Membership: American Historical Association; Conference on Latin American History; Mississippi Valley Historical Association; Society for the History of Discoveries. Research: Central American history, 19th and 20th centuries; United States-Central American relations. Author: U. of Minn. Latin American History Correspondence Study Courses (1952-53); Felix Belly: Nicaraguan Canal Promoter (Hispanic American Historical Review, Feb. 1957). Language: Spanish 4,3,3,2; Portuguese 3,2,1,1; French 3,1,1,1; German 3,2,1,1. Home: Waterville, Minn. Office: Dept. of History, Mankato State Coll., Mankato, Minn.

ALLGOOD, JOHN MASON. Home: Box 266, Carrboro, N.C.

ÁLVAREZ-PEDROSO, ANTONIO, b. Havana, Cuba, June 15, 1910. HISTORY AND SPANISH AMERICAN LITERATURE. LL.D., Havana U., 1934; Ph.D., 1938. Prof., Private School of Law (Havana), 1935-38; prof., Havana Institute, 1938-42; adjunct prof., U. of Havana 1942-44; prof., U. of Villanueva (Havana), 1946-58; asst. prof., U. of Havana, 1952-60; asst. prof., Marshall Coll., 1962-63; ASSOC. PROF., MODERN LANGUAGES, KUTZTOWN STATE COLL., 1963- . Cuban vis. scholar, St. Louis U., 1961-62. Membership: American Association of Teachers of Spanish and Portuguese; Modern Language Association. Research: political and diplomatic relations between the United States and Latin America; Monroe Doctrine and its historic evolution; history and literature of Mexico, Venezuela, Colombia, and Peru. Author: Miguel de Aldama y Alfonso (1948); La civilización maya (Revista de la Habana, May 1946); La civilización azteca (Revista de la Habana, June 1946). Language: Spanish 5,5,5,5. Home: 520 East Walnut St., Kutztown, Pa. Office: Dept. of Modern Languages, Kutztown State Coll., Kutztown.

AMERINGER, CHARLES D., b. Milwaukee, Wis., Sept. 19, 1926. HISTORY. B.A., U. of S. 1949; M.A., Fletcher School of Law & Diplomacy, 1950; Ph.D., 1958. Instr., Suffolk U.,

1950-51; research analyst, U.S. Dept. of Defense, 1951-59; part-time instr., George Washington U., 1954-55; asst. prof., Bowling Green State U., 1959-63; vis. asst. prof., Pa. State U., 1963-64; ASSOC. PROF., HISTORY, PA. STATE U., 1964- . U.S. Dept. of Defense fellow (Mexico), 1956-57; lectr., U.S. Peace Corps, U. of Wis., Milwaukee, 1963. Membership: American Association of University Professors; American Historical Association; Association of Latin American Studies; Conference on Latin American History. Research: United States-Latin American diplomatic history; history of the Caribbean area and the national period; Mexico. Author: The Panama Canal Lobby of Philippe Bunau-Varilla and William Nelson Cromwell (American Historical Review, Jan. 1963). Language: Spanish 4,4,3,4; Portuguese 3,3,3,3; French 2,—,—,—. Office: Dept. of History, Pa. State U., University Park.

ANDERSON, CHARNEL, b. Florine, La., May 30, 1936. HISTORY. B.A., McNeese Coll., 1958; M.A., George Washington U., 1960. Research asst., Human Resources Research Office, George Washington U., 1962-65; U.S. PEACE CORPS VOLUNTEER (BRAZIL), 1965-67. Research: Latin American history; directed cultural change; government of British Guiana, 1953-60. Author: Technology in American Education, 1650-1900 (1963); The Process of Cross Cultural Innovation (International Development Review, July 1964). Language: Spanish 3,3,2,2; Portuguese 2,2,2,1. Home: 314 West College St., Lake Charles, La.

ANDERSON, CONWELL A., b. Sister Bay, Wis., May 24, 1926. HISTORY. B.A., U. of Ala., 1949; M.A., 1950; Ph.D., 1954. Instr. U. of Ala., 1952-54; prof., dean, Mary Hardin-Baylor Coll., 1954-60; prof., president, Judson Coll., 1960-65; president, Md. Baptist Coll., 1965; ASSOC. DIR., INSTITUTE OF HIGHER EDUCATION, U. OF GA., 1966- . U. of Ala. graduate fellow. Membership: Conference on Latin American History; Phi Alpha Theta; Sigma Delta Pi. Research: Central America—18th century. Author: Gibraltar: Fortress or Pawn (Southwestern Social Science Quarterly, Dec. 1958). Office: Institute of Higher Education, 300 Old College, U. of Ga., Athens, Ga.

ANDERSON, EDGAR, b. Tukums, Latvia, June 17, 1920. HISTORY. M.A., U. of Riga; U. of Leiden; U. of Würzburg; Ph.D., U. of Chicago, 1956. Instr., Lake Forest Coll., 1953-57; PROF., HISTORY, SAN JOSE STATE COLL., 1957- . Leader of expedition (Trinidad, Tobago), 1960; Social Science Research Council grant; Hoover Institution of War, Revolution and Peace grant. Membership: American Academy of Political Science; American Association for the Advancement of Slavic Studies; American Historical Association; Conference on British Studies; Institute of Caribbean Studies. Research: educational institutions, history, and political organization of British West Indian islands. Author: Western World and Western Horizon (1949); Cross-Road Country Latvia (1953); Tobago (1962). Language: French

4

4,4,3,3; German 5,5,4,4; Latvian 5,5,4,5; Russian 4,4,3,2; Swedish 5,4,3,3. Office: Dept. of History, San Jose State Coll., San Jose, Calif. 95114.

ANDERSON, RODNEY D. Office: Dept. of History, Fla. State U., Tallahassee, Fla.

ANGUIZOLA, GUSTAVE A., b. Panama, Feb. 28, 1922. HISTORY. B.A., Evansville Coll., 1947; M.A., Ind. U., 1949; M.S., Mich. State U., 1953; Ph.D., Ind. U., 1954. Special asst., public relations, City of Chicago, 1959; prof., chmn., Morris College, 1960-61; vis. prof., State U. of N.Y., Coll. at Geneseo, Summers, 1961, 1962; prof., acting chmn., Elizabeth City State Teachers Coll., 1961-62; supervisor-teacher, Board of Education, Raleigh, N.C., 1962; ASST. PROF., HISTORY, PURDUE U., 1962- . U.S. Dept. of State fellow, 1953. Membership: American Academy of Political Science; American Historical Association; Bolivarian Society of the United States; Conference on Latin American History; Mississippi Valley Historical Association. Research: United States policies in the Caribbean, especially with Panama and Costa Rica. Author: The Unratified Treaty of 1926 (Panama Ministry of Education Bulletin, 1953); Socialistic Enterprises in the Panama Canal Zone (Panama Chamber of Commerce Bulletin, Dec. 1954); The United States and the Latin American Republics (U.S. Senate Sub-committee on Latin America, 1958). Language: Spanish 5,4,3,3. Home: 704 Wentworth Ave., Calumet City, Ill. Office: Box 23, Purdue U., Calumet Campus, Ind.

ANSEL, BERNARD D. Home: 191 Commonwealth Ave., Buffalo, N.Y. 14216.

ARANA, LUIS RAFAEL, b. Ponce, P.R., Sept. 10, 1921. HISTORY. B.A., Inter-American U., 1950; U. of P.R.; M.A., U. of Fla., 1960. Park historian, San Juan National Historic Site (P.R.), U.S. Dept. of Interior, 1951-55; asst. historian, Castillo de San Marcos National Monument, U.S. Dept. of Interior, 1955-57; HISTORIAN, CASTILLO DE SAN MARCOS NATIONAL MONUMENT, U.S. DEPT. OF INTERIOR, 1957- . Membership: Phi Alpha Theta; Southeastern Conference on Latin America. Research: history of Spanish Florida; Latin American history; paleography. Author: List of the Governors of Florida, 1565-1961 (1961); The Day Governor Cabrera Left Florida, 1687 (Florida Historical Quarterly, Oct. 1961); The Alonso Solana Map of Florida, 1683 (Florida Historical Quarterly, Jan 1964). Language: Spanish 5,5,5,5; Portuguese 2,2,1,1; French 3,1,1,1. Home: 35 Coquina Ave., St. Augustine, Fla. 32084. Office: Castillo de San Marcos National Monument, U.S. National Park Service, P.O. Drawer 1431, St. Augustine.

ARBENA, JOSEPH LUTHER, b. Philadelphia, Pa., July 29, 1939. HISTORY. B.A., George Washington U., 1961; U. of Va. National Defense Education Act fellow, U. of Va., 1961-64; Fulbright scholar (Colombia), 1964-66. Membership: American Historical Association; Mississippi Valley Historical Association. Research: Latin American history; United States-Panama relations, 1933-1939. Language: Spanish 4,4,4,4; Portuguese 3,3,2,2. Home: 1001 Jackson Rd., Silver Spring, Md.

ARCE, JOSÉ MARÍA, b. Santo Domingo, Costa Rica, March 23, 1894. SPANISH AMERICAN LITERATURE AND HISTORY. M.A., Columbia U., 1923; Centro de Estudios Históricos and U. of Madrid, 1923-26; Columbia U. Instr., Hunter Coll. and Columbia U. Extension, 1928; instr., Dartmouth Coll., 1928-29; asst. prof., 1929-41; prof., Middlebury Spanish School, Summers 1939-52; prof., Dartmouth Coll., 1941-61; vis. prof., Duke U., Summer 1943; vis. prof., Ohio State U., Summer 1947; chief, Spanish Section, Div. of Language Services, U.S. Dept. of State, 1948; PROF. EMERITUS, SPANISH, DARTMOUTH COLL., 1961- . Corresponding member, Academia Española de la Lengua, 1961; member, Academia Costarricense de la Lengua. Membership: American Association of University Professors; Conference on Latin American History; Instituto Internacional de Literatura Iberoamericana; Modern Language Association of America. Research: Costa Rican history and literature; linguistics. Author: Manuel González Zeledón: Vida, obra, bibliografía antología (1948); Some Letters to Bolívar and to Bello (Hispanic American Historical Review, May 1944). Editor: Cuentos de Manuel González Zeledón (Magón) (1947). Language: Spanish 5,5,5,5; Portuguese 3,3,2,1; French 5,5,5,4; German 3,2,2,1; Italian 5,5,5,4; Latin 4,—,—,—. Linguistic studies: Spanish. Home: Apartado 4139, San José, Costa Rica.

ARENA, CARMELO RICHARD, b. Atlantic City, N.J., May 8, 1925. HISTORY. Universidad Nacional Autónoma de México, Summer 1947; A.B., Temple U., 1951; M.A., Tulane U., 1954; Ph.D., U. of Pa., 1959. Historian, National Park Service, U.S. Dept. of Interior, 1953-58; instr., U. of P.R., 1955-56; instr., Temple U., 1956-60; principal, Columbia Institute-Taylor School (Philadelphia), 1959-60; ASST. PROF., HISTORY, ST. JOSEPH'S COLL., 1960- . Tulane U. fellow (Guatemala), Summer 1951; St. Joseph's Coll. fellow (Mexico), Summer 1963. Membership: Historical Society of Pennsylvania; Phi Alpha Theta; Philadelphia Catholic Historical Society. Research: Spanish Louisiana; Latin American land tenure system; Latin American-United States trade, 1789-1803. Author: Landholding and Political Power in Spanish Louisiana (Louisiana Historical Quarterly, Oct. 1955); Philadelphia-Spanish New Orleans Trade in the 1790's (Louisiana History, Fall 1961); Philadelphia-Mississippi Valley Trade and the Deposit Closure (Pennsylvania History, Jan. 1963). Language: Spanish 4,4,4,4; Portuguese 2,1,1,1; French 3,2,2,2. Home: 5604 Woodcrest Ave., Philadelphia, Pa. 19131. Office: Dept. of History, St. Joseph's Coll., Philadelphia, 19131.

ARNADE, CHARLES W., b. Görlitz, Germany, May 11, 1927. HISTORY. A.B., U. of Mich., 1950; M.A., 1952; Ph.D., U. of Fla., 1955.

Instr., Universidad de San Francisco Xavier (Bolivia), 1953; instr., U. of Fla., 1953-55; asst. prof., U. of Tampa, 1955-56; asst. prof., Fla. State U., 1956-58; asst. prof.-assoc. prof., U. of Fla., 1958-60; PROF., HISTORY, DIR. OF INTERNATIONAL STUDIES, U. OF SOUTH FLA., 1960- . Doherty fellow (Bolivia), 1952-53; consultant, U.S. Peace Corps, 1961- ; book review editor, Hispanic American Historical Review, 1961-65. Membership: Conference on Latin American History. Research: Bolivia; Spanish Florida. Author: The Emergence of the Republic of Bolivia (1957); The Trial of Florida, 1593-1602 (1959). Co-author: El problema del humanista Tadeo Haenke (1960). Language: Spanish 5,5,5,5; Portuguese 3,3,3,3; French 2,2,2,2; German 5,5,5,5; Italian 2,2,2,2; Quechu 2,2,2,2. Home: Box 238, San Antonio, Fla. 33576. Office: Dept. of History, U. of South Fla., Tampa.

ASHBY, JOE C., b. Gatesville, Tex., Aug. 27, 1922. ECONOMICS AND HISTORY. B.S. North Tex. State U., 1943; M.A., U. of Tex., 1950; Ph.D., 1956. Instr.-asst. prof., Tex. Wesleyan Coll., 1947-54; assoc. prof., Lamar State Coll. of Technology, 1954-59; assoc. prof., East Tex. State Coll., 1959-60; PROF., ECONOMICS, ARLINGTON STATE COLL., 1960- . General Education Board fellow, 1952-53. Membership: American Economic Association; Economic History Association; Southern Economic Association; Southwestern Social Science Association. Research: economic development and organized labor of Argentina and Mexico. Author: Labor and the Philosophy of the Argentine Revolution (Inter-American Economic Affairs, Summer 1951); Our Cuban Policy: A Pattern for Latin American Relations? (Ball State Teachers Coll. Forum, Spring 1961); Labor and the Theory of the Mexican Revolution under Lázaro Cárdenas (The Americas, Oct. 1963). Language: Spanish 3,3,2,1; French 2,2,1,1. Home: 1105 West Lovers Lane, Arlington, Tex. Office: Dept. of Economics, Arlington State Coll., Arlington.

AUSTIN, DORIS. Home: 925 25th St., NW., Washington, D.C. 20037.

BACARISSE, CHARLES ALBERT, b. Houston, Tex., Aug. 29, 1925. HISTORY. B.S., U. of Houston, 1948; M.A., 1949; Ph.D., U. of Tex., 1955. Asst. prof., U. of Houston, 1955-58; assoc. prof., 1958-64; vis. prof., U. of Tex., Spring 1962; vis. prof., U. of Wis., Spring 1964; PROF., HISTORY, U. OF HOUSTON, 1964- . National Defense Foreign Language fellow, 1962. Membership: American Historical Association; Conference on Latin American History. Research: early national history of Mexico; Brazilian historiography and nationalism; United States-Latin American policy. Author: Baron de Bastrop (Southwestern Historical Quarterly, Jan. 1955); The Union of Coahuila and Texas (Southwestern Social Science Quarterly, June 1959). Language: Spanish 3,3,3,2; Portugese 3,3,3,2; French 1,1,1,1. Home: 4436 Wheeler St., Houston, Tex. 77004. Office: Dept. of History, U. of Houston, Houston.

BAILEY, HELEN MILLER, b. Modesto, Calif., Mar. 13, 1909. HISTORY. B.A., U. of Calif., Berkeley, 1929; M.A., 1930; Ph.D. U. of Southern Calif., 1934. Teacher, Los Angeles Schools, 1932-46; PROF., CHMN., HISTORY, EAST LOS ANGELES COLL., 1946- . Membership: Phi Beta Kappa. Author: Santa Cruz of the Etla Hills (1958). Co-author: Our Latin American Neighbors (1952); Latin America, the Development of Its Civilization (1960). Language: Spanish 2,3,3,2; French 3,2,1,1. Home: 5229 Palm Dr., La Cañada, Calif. Office: Dept. of Social Sciences, East Los Angeles Coll., Los Angeles 22, Calif.

BAILY, SAMUEL L., b. Philadelphia, Pa., May 9, 1936. HISTORY. A.B., Harvard Coll., 1958; M.A., Columbia U., 1963; Ph.D., U. of Pa., 1964. ASST. PROF., HISTORY, RUTGERS U., 1964- . Rockefeller grant (Argentina), 1963; Argentine Nationalism Project, U. of Pa., 1961-64; chmn., Latin American Committee, American Friends Service. Membership: American Historical Association. Research: nationalism and labor movement in Argentina. Language: Spanish 4,3,3,2; Portuguese 2,1,1,1; French 3,2,1,2. Home: 7057 Cresheim Rd., Philadelphia 19, Pa. Office: Dept. of History, Rutgers U., New Brunswick, N.J.

BAIRD, JOHN E., b. Oakland, Calif., Oct. 1, 1932. HISTORY. B.A., U. of Calif., Berkeley, 1955; M.A., 1956. Instr., U., of Tenn., 1961-62; Instr., Carleton Coll., 1962-65. U. of Calif. research grant (Spain), 1960-61. Membership: American Historical Association; Conference on Latin American History; Phi Alpha Theta; Southern Historical Association; Upper Midwest Historical Association. Research: Latin American history; early modern European history; economic history of Spain; Spanish American empire in the late 17th and 18th centuries. Language: Spanish 5,4,4,3; Portuguese 3,3,3,2; French 3,3,2,2; Italian 3,2,2,1. Home: 5824 Chabot Rd., Oakland, Calif.

BAKER, GEORGE WILLIAM, JR., b. Frederick, Md., Apr. 10, 1931. HISTORY. B.S., Towson State Coll., 1953; M.A., U. of Colo., 1958; Ph.D., 1961. Instr., Mt. Union Coll., 1961; asst. prof., East Carolina Coll., 1961-64; ASST. PROF., HISTORY, RENSSELAER POLYTECHNIC INSTITUTE, 1964- . Conference on Latin American History Prize, 1964. Membership: American Historical Association; Mississippi Valley Historical Association; Southern Historical Association. Research: U.S. relations with Latin America, especially the Wilson, Harding, and Coolidge eras. Author: The Wilson Administration and Cuba (Mid-America, Jan. 1964); Ideals and Realities in the Wilson Administration Relations with Honduras (The Americas, July 1964); Benjamin Harrison and Hawaiian Annexation (Pacific Historical Review, Aug. 1964). Language: Spanish 3,—,—,—; French 3,—,—,—; German 2,—,—,—. Home: 1004 Peoples Ave., Troy, N.Y. 12181. Office: Dept. of History, Rensselaer Polytechnic Institute, Troy, 12181.

BAKER, MAURY DAVISON, b. Waukegan, Ill., July 19, 1912. HISTORY. B.A., U. of Miami, 1939; M.A., Duke U., 1943; Ph.D., 1946. Instr., Duke U., 1943-44; asst. prof., Kent State U., 1947-48; assoc. prof., 1948-55: PROF., HISTORY, CHMN., LATIN AMERICAN AREA STUDIES, KENT STATE U., 1955- . U.S. Dept. of State research grant (Chile), 1948-49. Membership: American Association of University Professors; Conference on Latin American History; Phi Alpha Theta; Phi Beta Kappa. Research: the relationship of highway planning and development to national planning; the history of the Pan American Highway. Author: The Perry Expedition up the Orinoco, 1819 (Hispanic American Historical Review, Nov. 1950); Spanish War Scare of 1816 (Mid-America, Apr. 1963); Damn Yankeeism in Latin America (Social Science, Oct. 1963). Language: Spanish 4,4,4,2; Portuguese 2,1,2,1; French 3,2,2,1; German 2,2,1,1. Home: 1315 Lake Martin Dr., Kent, Ohio. Office: Dept. of History, Kent State U., Kent.

BANNON, JOHN FRANCIS, S.J., b. St. Joseph, Mo., Apr. 28, 1905. HISTORY. A.B., St. Louis U., 1928; A.M., 1929; Ph.D., U. of Calif., Berkeley, 1939. Instr., St. Louis U., 1939-41; asst. prof., 1941-44; assoc. prof. 1944-49; PROF., HISTORY, ST. LOUIS U., 1942- ; CHMN., 1943- . Membership: American Catholic Historical Association; American Historical Association; Conference on Latin American History; Mississippi Valley Historical Association. Research: the church in Latin America and American Southwest; studies on the Patronato Real. Author: Colonial North America (1946); The Mission Frontier in Sonora (1955); History of the Americas (revised edition, 1963). Co-author: Latin America: An Historical Survey (revised edition, 1963). Language: Spanish 4,4,3,2; Portuguese 3,2,2,1; French 4,4,4,3; German 2,1,1,1. Office: Dept. of History, St. Louis U., St. Louis, Mo. 63103.

BARAGER, JOSEPH RUFUS, b. Prince Albert, Canada, May 30, 1914. HISTORY AND GOVERNMENT. B.A., U. of Rochester, 1950; RESEARCH ANALYST, U.S. GOVERNMENT, 1951- ; vis. lectr., U. of Pa., 1964. Harrison fellow, U. of Pa. 1948-49; Doherty fellow, Princeton U., 1949-50; Penfield scholar, U. of Pa., 1949-50; chmn., Bolton Prize Committee, Conference on Latin American History. Membership: American Historical Association; Conference on Latin American History; Council on Foreign Relations (N.Y.); Phi Alpha Theta; Phi Sigma Iota. Research: United States-Latin American relations; Argentina. Author: Historiography of the Río de la Plata area since 1830 (Hispanic American Historical Review, Nov. 1959). Language: Spanish 4,4,3,3; Portuguese 2,2,1,1; French 2,2,1,1. Home: 1416 South Greenbrier St., Arlington, Va.

BARNES, GRANT. Office: U. of Calif., Berkeley, Calif.

BARNHART, DONALD STANFORD, b. St. Louis, Mo., July 18, 1925. HISTORY. A.B.,

San Diego State Coll., 1949; M.A., U. of Chicago, 1950; Ph.D., 1953. Asst. prof., Simpson Coll., 1953-56; assoc. prof., W. Va. U., 1956-59; lectr., U. of Pa., 1959-60; ASSOC. PROF., INTER-DISCIPLINARY STUDIES, SAN FRANCISCO STATE COLL., 1960- . Rotary Foundation fellow (Colombia), 1950; M. Wolfe fellow, U. of Chicago, 1952-53. Membership: Conference on Latin American History; Pacific Coast Council of Latin American Studies. Research: economic development and social change in modern Latin America. Author: Colombian Transport and the Reforms of 1931 (Hispanic American Historical Review, Feb. 1958). Language: Spanish 4,3,3,2; Portuguese 3,1,1,1; French 3,1,1,1. Home: 2270 Hamilton Ave., San Bruno, Calif. Office: Dept. of Inter-disciplinary Studies, San Francisco State Coll., San Francisco 27, Calif.

BARTLETT, RUHL J. Office: Fletcher School of Law and Diplomacy, Tufts U., Medford, Mass. 02155.

BASTERT, RUSSELL HENRY, b. Quincy, Ill., Oct. 1, 1920. HISTORY. B.A., Knox Coll., 1941; M.A., Yale U., 1943; Ph.D., 1952. Instr.-ASSOC. PROF., HISTORY, WILLIAMS COLL., 1948- . Ford Foundation international relations fellow, U. of Calif., Berkeley, 1957-58; Social Science Research Council grant (Argentina, Chile), 1962-63. Membership: American Historical Association; Conference on Latin American History; Mississippi Valley Historical Association. Research: American diplomatic history; inter-American diplomacy. Author: Diplomatic Reversal: Frelinghuysen's Opposition to Blaine's Pan American Policy (Mississippi Valley Historical Review, Mar. 1956); A New Approach to the Origins of Blaine's Pan American Policy (Hispanic American Historical Review, Aug. 1958); The Two American Diplomacies (Yale Review, Summer 1960). Language: Spanish 4,3,3,2; German 4,1,1,2. Home: Grace Ct., Williamstown, Mass. Office: Dept. of History, Williams Coll., Williamstown.

BAUM, EMMI, b. Wetter, Germany. HISTORY. B.A., U. of N. Mex., 1955; M.A., N.Y.U., 1961; Ph.D., 1965. Teacher, União Cultural Brasil-Estados Unidos (Sao Paulo), 1950-51; secretary, International Cooperation Administration (Washington, D.C.), 1955-56; secretary, U.S. Operations Mission to Brazil (Rio de Janeiro), 1956-60; program asst., Fulbright Program for Latin America, Institute of International Education, 1958-60; lectr., Hunter Coll., Spring 1963; LECTR., HISTORY, C.W. POST COLL., 1963- . Inter-American scholar, U. of N. Mex., 1951-54; National Defense Education Act fellow, N.Y.U., 1960-62; U. of Rio Grande (Brazil), Summer 1961. Membership: American Historical Association; Conference on Latin American History; Phi Alpha Theta. Research: Latin American history; Brazilian area studies. Language: Spanish 3,3,3,2; Portuguese 4,4,4,4; French 1,1,1,1; German 5,5,5,5. Home: 567 West 191th St., New York 40, N.Y. Office: Dept. of Social Science, C.W. Post Coll., Greenvale, Long Island, N.Y.

BAUR, JOHN EDWARD, b. Chicago, Ill., Feb. 19, 1922. HISTORY. A.B., U. of Calif., Los Angeles, 1945; A.M., 1947; Ph.D., 1951. Editorial asst., Pacific Historical Review, 1949-53; instr., U. of Calif., Los Angeles, Spring 1954; INSTR., HISTORY, EDUCATION DIV., LOS ANGELES COUNTY MUSEUM, 1954- ; instr., U. of Calif., Los Angeles, Winter 1959-60; instr., Extension Div., 1957- . F. Bancroft Award, 1947; Huntington Library grant-in-aid, 1954. Membership: American Historical Association; California Historical Society; Conference on Latin American History. Research: republican period of Mexico, Haiti, and La Plata areas, 1825-1870; Caribbean history. Author: The Presidency of Nicolas Geffrard of Haiti (The Americas, Apr. 1951); The Welsh in Patagonia, an Example of Nationalistic Migration (Hispanic American Historical Review, Nov. 1954); A Mexican Foreign Trade Policy, 1821-1828 (The Americas, Jan. 1963). Language: Spanish 3,3,2,3; French 3,2,2,2; German 2,1,1,2. Home: 7616 Lexington Ave., Los Angeles 46, Calif. Office: Education Div., Los Angeles County Museum, 900 Exposition Blvd., Los Angeles 7.

BAUSS, RUDOLPH W. Home: 2033 State St., New Orleans, La. 70118.

BAUSUM, HENRY S., b. Annapolis, Md., Feb. 19, 1924. HISTORY. B.A., U. of Md., 1949; M.A., Boston U., 1951; Ph.D., U. of Chicago, 1963. ASSOC. PROF., HISTORY, CARSON-NEWMAN COLL., 1956- . Membership: American Historical Association; Phi Alpha Theta. Research: economic development and ideological structure of Latin America, especially Brazil; expansion of Europe in the Western world. Language: Spanish 3,2,2,1; German 4,3,2,1. Home: 904 George St., Jefferson City, Tenn. Office: Dept. of History, Carson-Newman Coll., Jefferson City.

BEALS, CARLETON, b. Medicine Lodge, Kans., Nov. 13, 1893. HISTORY. B.A., U. of Calif., 1916; M.A., Columbia U., 1917. Dir., English Preparatory Institute (Mexico, D.F.), 1919; principal, American High School (Mexico, D.F.), 1919-20; instr., personal staff of President Carranza (Mexico), 1920; newspaper correspondent in Latin America, 1923-61 (intermittently); lectr., N.Y. Board of Education, 1924; assoc. editor, Mexican Folkways, 1925-37; assoc. editor, Latin American Press Syndicate, 1933-34; lectr., Latin American universities, 1962; RETIRED — . Bonheim Award, 1916, 1917; Bryce History Prize, 1917; Guggenheim fellow, 1931-32; contributing editor, Common Sense, 1933-41, Modern Monthly, 1935-37, Current History, 1939; president, Editorial Board, Latin American Digest, 1934-36; Advisory Board, Better Understanding Foundation; Board of Governors, Academy of Foreign Relations. Membership: American Geographical Society; Foreign Press Club (Mexico); Pi Gamma Mu; Society of American Historians. Research: international affairs. Author: The Long Land: Chile (1948); Latin America: World in Revolution (1963); Eagles of the Andes (1963). Language: Spanish 5,5,5,5; Portuguese 3,2,2,2; French 2,2,2,2; German 3,3,3,2; Italian 4,4,4,2; Nahuatl 2,2,2,1. Home: R.F.D. 2, Box 25, Killingworth, Conn.

BEATTIE, DONALD W., b. Mars Hill, Maine, July 11, 1935. HISTORY. A.B., Gordon Coll., 1958; M.A., Boston U., 1959. Teacher, Bridgewater Classical Academy (Maine), 1959-60; lectr., Barrington Coll., 1961-62; ASST. PROF., HISTORY, BENTLEY COLL., 1962- . Membership: American Historical Association. Research: colonial and modern United States history; modern Latin American history; modern European history. Language: Spanish 3,3,3,3; French 3,3,3,3. Home: 127 Dodge St., Beverly, Mass. Office: Dept. of History, Bentley Coll., 921 Boylston St., Boston, Mass.

BEATTY, W. DONALD, b. South Bend, Wash., Aug. 10, 1907. HISTORY. B.A., U. of Wash., 1933; Ph.D., U. of Minn., 1947. Instr.-asst. prof., U. of Minn., 1946-50; assoc. prof., 1950-60; ASST. CHMN., HISTORY, U. OF MINN., 1960-. Chmn., Latin American Area Committee, U. of Minn.; Doherty fellow (Chile), 1949-50. Membership: American Association of University Professors; American Historical Association; Conference on Latin American History; Hispanic American Historical Association; Mississippi Valley Historical Association. Research: Latin American and United States diplomatic history; recent economic and social history of Chile. Co-author: An Introduction to Hispanic American History (1950). Language: Spanish 4,3,3,1; French 3,2,2,2. Home: 2162 South Rosewood Lane, St. Paul, Minn. Office: Dept. of History, 614-B Social Science Bldg., West Campus, U. of Minn., Minneapolis.

BECK, WARREN ALBERT, b. Minneapolis, Minn., Dec. 9, 1918. HISTORY. A.B., Wayne U., 1947; M.A., 1948; Ph.D., Ohio State U., 1954. Instr., Augustana Coll., 1948-50; prof., chmn., Santa Ana Coll., 1958-61; ASSOC. PROF., HISTORY, ORANGE STATE COLL., 1961- . Membership: American Historical Association; Conference on Latin American History; Mississippi Valley Historical Association; Pacific Coast Council on Latin American Studies. Research: United States policy in Guatemala. Author: A History of New Mexico (1962); Lincoln and Negro Colonization in Central America (Lincoln Quarterly, Sept. 1950). Language: Spanish 4,3,3,2. Home: 1307 West Santa Clara, Santa Ana, Calif. Office: Dept. of History, Orange State Coll., Fullerton, Calif.

BEECHER, DALE FLOYD, b. Brigham City, Utah, Feb. 24, 1937. HISTORY. B.S., Utah State U., 1962; U. of N. Mex. Missionary, Church of Jesus Christ of Latter Day Saints (Uruguay), 1957-60; STUDENT, HISTORY, U. OF N. MEX. National Defense Foreign Language fellow in Spanish, U. of N. Mex., 1963-64. Research: Latin American history; logistical problems of the Conquest. Language: Spanish 5,5,5,5; Portuguese 3,3,3,3; French 2,2,2,2. Home: 473 East 5th St. South, Logan, Utah.

BEILHARZ, EDWIN ALANSON, b. Philippsburg, Kans., June 18, 1907. HISTORY. A.B., Creighton U., 1931; M.A., U. of Nebr., 1934; Ph.D., U. of Calif., 1951. PROF., CHMN., HISTORY, U. OF SANTA CLARA, 1936- . University fellow, U. of Calif.; Heller Memorial scholar, U. of Calif.; sabbatical grant (Spain), 1961-62. Membership: American Historical Association; American Catholic Historical Association. Research: the Spanish frontier in North America; archival research. Author: Communism and History (The Catholic Mind, Nov. 1954); The New Frontier and the Old (U.S. Chamber of Commerce, 1962). Language: Spanish 4,3,2,3; French 4,1,2,1; German 4,2,2,1. Home: 16021 Wood Acres Rd., Los Gatos, Calif. Office: Dept. of History, U. of Santa Clara, Santa Clara, Calif.

BEMIS, SAMUEL FLAGG, b. Worcester, Mass., Oct. 20, 1891. HISTORY. A.B., Clark U., 1912; A.M., 1913; A.M., Harvard U., 1915; Ph.D., 1916. STERLING PROF. EMERITUS, DIPLOMATIC HISTORY AND INTER-AMERICAN RELATIONS, YALE U., 1960- . Pulitzer Award, 1927, 1950; dir., European Mission, Library of Congress, 1927-29; Carnegie vis. prof. (Latin America), 1937-38. Membership: Academia de la Historia (Cuba); American Historical Association; American Antiquarian Society; Sociedad de Geografía e Historia (Mexico). Author: Early Diplomatic Missions from Buenos Aires to the United States, 1811-1824 (1940); The Latin American Policy of the United States, an Historical Interpretation (1943); The United States as a World Power: A Diplomatic History, 1900-1955 (1955). Home: 120 Ogden St., New Haven, Conn. Office: 241 Hall of Graduate Studies, Yale U., New Haven.

BENSON, NETTIE LEE, b. Arcadia, Tex., Jan. 15, 1905. HISTORY AND BIBLIOGRAPHY. B.A., U. of Tex., 1929; M.A., 1935; Ph.D., 1949. Teacher, Instituto Inglés-Español (Monterrey, Mexico), 1925-27; teacher, Ingleside High School (Tex.), 1932-41; LECTR., HISTORY, LIBRARIAN, U. OF TEX., 1942-60, 1962- ; acquisitions, New York Public Library, 1960-62. Membership: American Historical Association; American Library Association; Conference on Latin American History. Research: bibliographical and institutional acquisition of library materials in Latin America. Author: La diputación provincial y el federalismo mexicano (1955). Translator: Report of Ramos Arizpe to the Cortes (1950); The United States versus Porfirio Díaz, by D. Cosío Villegas (1963). Language: Spanish 5,5,4,4; Portuguese 4,3,2,3; French 3,2,2,3. Home: 2834 Shoal Crest, Austin 5, Tex. Office: Latin American Collection, U. of Tex. Library, Austin 12.

BENSUSAN, H. GUY, b. Ewell, Surrey, England, June 19, 1932. HISTORY. B.A., U. of Calif., Los Angeles, 1953. Asst. prof., Northwest Mo. State Coll., 1959-63; ASST. PROF., HISTORY, ARIZ. STATE COLL., 1963- . Del Amo fellow (Spain), 1956-57; O. F. Munson fellow, U. of Calif., Los Angeles, 1958-59. Membership: American Historical Association; Mississippi Valley Historical Association; Sigma Delta Pi. Research: Latin American history; especially that of Brazil and Mexico; the Caribbean. Language: Spanish 4,4,4,4; Portuguese 3,3,2,2; French 3,3,2,2; German 2,2,2,1. Home: 2708 East Elder Dr., Flagstaff, Ariz. Office: Dept. of History, Ariz. State Coll., Flagstaff.

BERBUSSE, EDWARD JOSEPH, S.J., b. Port Chester, N.Y., Nov. 30, 1912. HISTORY AND INTERNATIONAL LAW. B.A., Loyola U. (Chicago), 1938; M.A., Fordham U., 1948; Ph.D., Georgetown U., 1952. Asst. prof., Canisius Coll., 1952-54; asst. prof., Fordham U., 1954-59; rector, Colegio San Ignacio (P.R.), 1959-62; DIR., INSTITUTO IGNACIANO, 1962- . Research: political and cultural history of Puerto Rico. Author: Neutrality Diplomacy of U.S.-Mexico, 1910-11 (The Americas, Jan. 1956); Origins of the McLane-Ocampo Treaty of 1859 (The Americas, Jan. 1958); Aspects in Church-State Relations in Puerto Rico, 1898-1900 (The Americas, Jan. 1963). Language: Spanish 4,4,4,4; French 2,—,—,—; Latin 4,—,—,—. Office: Instituto Ignaciano, 398 Francisco Sein, Hato Rey, P.R.

BERNSTEIN, HARRY, b. New York, N.Y., Oct. 13, 1909. HISTORY. B.A., City Coll. (N.Y.), 1933; M.A., Columbia U., 1934; Ph.D., 1945. PROF., HISTORY, BROOKLYN COLL., 1945- ; vis. prof., N.Y.U., 1960- ; vis. prof., U. of Rochester, Summer 1961; vis. prof., U. of Calif., Berkeley, 1962. Social Science Research Council fellow, 1943-44; Ford Foundation grant, 1953-54; American Philosophical Society grants; consultant, Ford Foundation-N.Y. State Dept. of Education, Summer 1963; consultant, Brazil-Venezuela studies, Special Operations Research Office, American U. Membership: American Historical Association; Conference on Latin American History; Hispanic Society of America; International Congress of Americanists. Research: South America. Author: Making an Inter-American Mind (1961); Emerging Brazil (1964); History of Latin America; Readings on Latin America (1964). Language: Spanish 4,4,4,4; Portuguese 4,4,3,2; French 4,3,3,2; German 4,3,3,3; Italian 4,3,3,3. Home: 191 Lexington Ave., Freeport, Long Island, N.Y. Office: Dept. of History, Brooklyn Coll., Brooklyn, N.Y.

BERNSTEIN, MARVIN DAVID, b. Newark, N.J., Oct. 22, 1923. HISTORY. B.S., City Coll. (N.Y.), 1944; M.A., U. of Mich., 1944; Ph.D., U. of Tex., 1951. Instr., City Coll. (N.Y.), 1946-51; historian, U.S. Dept. of Defense, 1951-53; instr., Mass. State Coll., Worcester, 1954-57; lectr., Clark U., Summers 1955, 1956; vis. prof., U. of Panama, Central U. (Ecuador) 1957-58; vis. asst. prof., U. of Nebr., 1958-59; ASSOC. PROF., SOCIAL STUDIES, STATE U. OF N.Y., COLL. AT FREDONIA, 1959- . Consultant, U.S. Dept. of Justice, 1956-62; Smith-Mundt Act fellow (Panama, Ecuador), 1957-58; State U. of N.Y. grant-in-aid, 1962-64; State U. of N.Y. faculty research fellow, 1964; Bolton Prize Committee,

Conference on Latin American History, 1964. Membership: American Association of University Professors; American Historical Association; Bolivarian Society; Conference on Latin American History. Research: Mexican economic structure and development, specifically in the mining industry and mining law. Author: Economic Organization of the Mexican Coal Industry (Inter-American Economic Affairs, Spring 1952); The OAS: Guardian of Peace or Pawn of Power Politics? (Social Education, Apr. 1961); Colonial Latin America and Revolutionary Movements (in Encyclopaedia Britannica, 1962). Language: Spanish 5,4,4,2; Portugease 2,1,1,1; French 3,2,1,1. Home: 42 Carol Ave., Fredonia, N.Y. 14063. Office: Dept. of Social Studies, State U. of N.Y., Coll., at Fredonia, Fredonia, 14063.

BEYER, ROBERT CARLYLE, b. St. Paul, Minn., Dec. 7, 1915. HISTORY. B.A., Hamline U., 1937; B.A., Oxford U., 1939; M.A., 1943; Ph.D., U. of Minn., 1947. Research, U.S. Bureau of Foreign and Domestic Commerce, 1942; U.S. Naval Reserve (Brazil, 1944), 1942-46; research (Colombia), U.S. Dept. of State, 1946-47; asst. prof., U. of Miami, 1948-50; U.S. Naval Reserve, 1950-52; prof., U. of Miami, 1952-55; economist, Klein & Saks Economic and Financial Mission to Chile, 1955-56; prof., U. of Miami, 1956-65; DIR., HONORS PROGRAM, COLL. OF WILLIAM AND MARY, 1965- . Rhodes scholarship, 1937; coordinator, Hispanic American Studies, U. of Miami. Membership: American Association of University Professors; American Historical Association; Association of American Rhodes Scholars; Phi Alpha Theta; Southeast Conference on Latin American Studies. Research: economic history, development; coffee industry in Colombia. Author: Transportation and the Coffee Industry in Colombia (Inter-American Economic Affairs, Winter 1948); Point Four and Latin America (Miami Law Quarterly, June 1950); Land Distribution and Tenure in Colombia (Journal of Inter-American Studies, Apr. 1961). Language: Spanish 4,4,4,3; Portuguese 3,2,2,3; French 3,3,3,3; German 2,—,—,—. Office: Dir., Honors Program, Coll. of William and Mary, Williamsburg, Va.

BIDWELL, ROBERT LELAND, b. Prairie Grove, Ark., Nov. 30, 1920. HISTORY. A.B., Austin Coll., 1942; A.M., William and Mary Coll., 1948; Ph.D., U. of Va., 1960. Principal, Texas-Mexican Industrial Institute, 1948-54; instr.-asst. prof., Mexico City Coll., 1956-60; asst. prof., East Tex. State Coll., 1960-62; DEAN, U. OF THE AMERICAS (MEXICO), 1962- . Research: National Archives of Mexico; Archives of the Dept. of Defense, Mexico. Language: Spanish 4,5,4,4. Home and office: U. of the Américas, Km. 16, Carretera México-Toluca, México 10, D.F.

BIERCK, HAROLD ALFRED, b. Philadelphia, Pa., Jan. 20, 1916. HISTORY. B.A., U. of Calif., Los Angeles, 1938; M.A., 1940; Ph.D., 1944. Instr., U.S. Navy (Bainbridge, Md.), 1945-46; asst. prof., Carnegie Institute of Tech-

nology, 1946-48; lectr., U. of Pittsburgh, 1947-48; PROF., HISTORY, U. OF N.C., 1948- . Rockefeller Foundation research fellow, 1950-51; Ford Foundation fellow, 1955-56; history consultant, Banco de Venezuela. Membership: American Historical Association; Conference on Latin American History; Pan-American Institute of Geography and History; Southeastern Conference on Latin American Studies; Southern Historical Association. Research: inter-American trade, commerce. Author: Vida pública de don Pedro Gual (1947); Selected Writings of Bolivar (1951); First Instance of U.S. Foreign Aid (Inter-American Economic Affairs Quarterly, Summer 1955). Language: Spanish 4,3,3,3; Portuguese 2,—,—,—; French 2,—,—,—. Home: 1019 Highland Woods, Chapel Hill, N.C. Office: Dept. of History, U. of N.C., Chapel Hill.

BILLINGSLEY, EDWARD BAXTER, b. Melbourne, Ark., June 18, 1910. HISTORY. B.S., U.S. Naval Academy, 1932; M.A., Northwestern U., 1947; Ph.D., U. of N.C., 1964. Jr. officer-rear admiral, U.S. Navy, 1932-59; ASST. PROF., HISTORY, METHODIST COLL., 1964- . Membership: American Historical Association; Hispanic American Society; Naval Historical Foundation; Southeastern Conference on Latin American Studies; Southern Historical Association. Research: U.S. Navy and Latin American independence in Chile and Peru, 1817-1825. Language: Spanish 3,3,3,3; Portuguese 2,1,1,1; French 1,1,1,1; German 3,3,3,3. Home: 1808 Martindale Dr., Fayetteville, N.C. 28304. Office: Dept. of History, Methodist Coll., Fayetteville, 28301.

BILLMAN, CALVIN JAMES, b. Charles City, Iowa, Apr. 21, 1921. HISTORY. B.A., State Coll. of Iowa, 1949; M.A., Tulane U., 1953; Ph.D., 1954. Instr., U. Coll., Tulane U., Summers 1950, 1951, 1952; ASST. PROF., HISTORY, FLA. STATE U., 1954- ; vis. prof., St. Mary's Coll. (Minn.), Summer 1956; dir., Fla. State U. Armed Forces Program (C.Z.), 1957-58. Teaching fellow, Sophie Newcomb Coll., Tulane U., 1951-53; Rockefeller Foundation fellow, 1953. Membership: Conference on Latin American History; Southeastern Committee on Latin American Studies; Southern Historical Association. Research: United States-Latin American diplomatic relations. Language: Spanish 5,3,3,2; Portuguese 2,2,1,1; French 3,3,2,1. Home: 2112 Gibbs Dr., Tallahassee, Fla. Office: Dept. of History, Fla. State U., Tallahassee.

BISHKO, CHARLES JULIAN, b. New York, N.Y., Oct. 6, 1906. HISTORY. B.A., Syracuse U., 1929; M.A., 1930; M.A., Harvard U., 1931; Ph.D., 1937. Asst. prof., U. of Va., 1945-48; assoc. prof., 1948-55; PROF., HISTORY, U. OF VA., 1955- . Francis Parkman fellow, Harvard U., 1932-33; Sheldon traveling fellow (Spain), 1933-34; board of editors, Hispanic American Historical Review; bibliographical editor, American Historical Review; consulting editor, Anuario de estudios medievales; editorial board, Studia Monástica. Membership:

American Historical Association; Conference on Latin American History; Economic History Society; Medieval Academy of America; Sociedad de Estudios Monásticos. Research: colonial Latin America; Luso-Hispanic backgrounds of Latin America. Author: Peninsular Background of Latin American Cattle Ranching (Hispanic American Historical Review, Nov. 1952); Iberian Background of Latin American History (Hispanic American Historical Review, Feb. 1956); Castilian as Plainsman (in The New World Looks at Its History, 1963). Language: Spanish 4,3,3,3; Portuguese, 4,2,3,3; French 4,2,3,3; German 4,2,—,—. Home: "Querencia," 9 Orchard Rd., Charlottesville, Va. Office: Dept. of History, U. of Va., Charlottesville.

BLACK, ROBERT C., III, b. New York, N.Y., Feb. 11, 1914. HISTORY. B.A., Williams Coll., 1937; M.A., U. of Denver, 1947; Ph.D., Columbia U., 1951. Instr., Rensselaer Polytechnic Institute, 1945-48; instr., Trinity Coll., 1950-53; asst. prof., 1953-58; ASSOC. PROF., HISTORY, TRINITY COLL. (CONN.), 1958- . Membership: American Historical Association; Canadian Historical Association; Conference on Latin American History; Southern Historical Association. Research: United States history, especially the Civil War; Canadian history. Author: The Railroads of the Confederacy (1952). Contributor: Essays in American Historiography; Papers Presented in Honor of Allan Nevins (1960). Language: Spanish 2,1,1,1; French 3,3,2,3; German 2,2,2,2. Home: 73 Ledyard Rd., West Hartford 17, Conn. Office: Dept. of History, Trinity Coll., Hartford 6.

BLAISDELL, LOWELL LAWRENCE, b. Chicago, Ill., Nov. 13, 1919. HISTORY. B.A., Elmhurst Coll., 1941; M.A., Rochester U., 1944; Ph.D., U. of Wis., 1949. Asst. prof., Elmira Coll., 1948-49; asst. prof., N. Mex. A. & M. Coll., 1949-53; asst. prof., Ark. Polytechnic Coll., 1954-56; vis. asst. prof., U. of Okla., 1956-57; asst. prof.-PROF., HISTORY, TEX. TECHNOLOGICAL COLL., 1957- . Chmn., History Program Committee, Southwestern Social Science Association, 1962. Membership: American Association of University Professors; American Historical Association; Southwestern Social Science Association. Research: revolutionary history, especially in Mexico. Author: The Desert Revolution (1962); Was It Revolution or Filibustering (Pacific Historical Review, May, 1954); Henry Lane Wilson and the Overthrow of Madero (Southwestern Social Science Quarterly, Sept. 1962). Language: Spanish 4,3,3,2; Portuguese 2,—,—,—; French 3,2,2,1. Home: 2515 24th St., Lubbock, Tex. Office: Dept. of History, Tex. Technological Coll., Lubbock.

BLANCO, RICHARD LIDIO, b. New York, N.Y., May 12, 1926. HISTORY. B.S., U. of Md., 1950; M.A., Western Reserve U., 1956; Ph.D., 1960. Teacher, Cleveland Public Schools, 1954-57; instr., State U. of N.Y., Coll. of Geneseo, 1957-58; instr., Western Reserve U., 1958-59; instr., Duquesne U., 1959-60; asst.

prof.-ASSOC. PROF., HISTORY, MARIETTA COLL., 1960- . Membership: American Association of University Professors; American Historical Association; Hispanic American Association. Research: United States-Caribbean diplomatic relations; contemporary Central America. Language: Spanish 4,4,4,3. Home: 203 Coventry Rd., Marietta, Ohio. Office: Dept. of History, Marietta Coll., Marietta.

BLANE, ANDREW QUARLES, b. San Salvador, El Salvador, Mar. 16, 1929. HISTORY. B.A. Centre Coll., 1950; M.A., Cambridge U., 1960; Leningrad U.; Harvard U.; Ph.D., Duke U., 1964. Director of Student Work, Ky. Baptist Association, U. of Ky., 1953-55; asst. prof., Grinnell Coll., 1963-64; ASST. PROF., HISTORY, SMITH COLL., 1964- . Ford Foundation Foreign Area fellow, Harvard U., 1959-61; Inter-University Committee on Travel grant, Leningrad U., 1961-62; Russian Research Center fellow, Harvard U., 1962-63. Membership: American Association for the Advancement of Slavic Studies; American Historical Association; Conference on Latin American History. Research: Russian history; European history; Latin American history. Language: Spanish 4,4,3,2; Portuguese 3,2,2,1; French 3,1,1,1; German 2,2,2,1; Russian 4,4,3,2. Home: 44A Morton St., New York, N.Y. Office: Dept. of History, Smith Coll., Northampton.

BLOSSOM, THOMAS, b. Dedham, Mass., Feb. 15, 1912. HISTORY. A.B., Amherst Coll., 1934; M.A., Columbia U., 1935; Ph.D., Duke U., 1956. Teacher, Western Carolina Coll., 1941-43; teacher, Indian Service, U.S. Dept. of the Interior, 1941, 1943-44; assoc. prof., The Citadel, 1946-56; assoc. prof., chmn., Southern State Coll. (Ark.), 1956-58; asst. prof., Humanities, U. of Fla., 1958-60; PROF., HISTORY, OLD DOMINION COLL., 1960- . Southern Fellowships grant, Summers 1955, 1958; co-editor, Journal of Latin American Studies, 1960-61; Pan American travel and study grant and U. of Fla. Graduate Council grant (Colombia), 1962. Membership: Caribbean Conferences, 1958-63; Phi Alpha Theta; Southern Historical Association. Research: Colombian independence. Author: New Mexico (in Columbia Encyclopedia, 1940); Antonio Nariño, Precursor of Colombian Independence (South Carolina Historical Association Proceedings, 1952); The Library of a Revolutionary Leader, Antonio Nariño, Precursor of Colombian Independence (Arkansas Academy of Science Proceedings, 1958). Language: Spanish 4,3,3,2; French 4,2,3,2; German 2,2,2,2; Italian 3,2,2,1. Office: Dept. of History, Old Dominion Coll., Norfolk, Va.

BOBB, BERNARD EARL, b. Mitchell, S. Dak., Oct. 21, 1917. HISTORY. B.A., U. of Calif., Los Angeles, 1939; M.A., 1941; Ph.D., 1949. Instr.-PROF., HISTORY, WASH. STATE U., 1949- . History fellow, 1948-49. Membership: Conference on Latin American History; Pacific Coast Council on Latin American Studies. Research: 18th century; Mexico. Author: The Viceregency of Antonio María Bucareli in New

Spain, 1771-1779 (1962); Pedro Sarmiento de Gamboa and the Strait of Magellan (Pacific Historical Review, Aug. 1948); Historiografía mexicanista: Estados Unidos, 1959-60 (Historia Mexicana, Oct.-Dec. 1961). Language: Spanish 3,2,2,3. Home: 412 Grant St., Pullman, Wash. Office: Dept. of History, Wash. State. U., Pullman.

BOEHRER, GEORGE C. A., b. New York, N.Y., June 20, 1921. HISTORY. A.B., Boston Coll., 1942; M.A., Catholic U. of America, 1943; Ph.D., 1951. Instr., Marquette U., 1949-51; lectr., Mexico City Coll., Summer 1950; asst. prof., Marquette U., 1951-55; assoc. prof., Georgetown U., 1955-62; vis. prof., U. of Wis., Summer 1962; cultural attaché (Brazil), U.S. Information Agency, 1962-65; PROF., HISTORY, U. OF KANS., 1965- . U.S. Dept. of State grant (Brazil), 1947; Penfield traveling fellow (Portugal), 1948; Georgetown U. Alumni grant (Portugal), 1957; Social Science Research Council-American Council of Learned Societies grant (Brazil), 1960-61. Membership: American Association of University Professors; American Historical Association; Catholic Historical Association; Conference on Latin American History. Research: 19th century history of Brazil. Author: Da monarquia à república: história do Partido Republicano do Brasil, 1870-1889 (1954); The Flight of the Brazilian Deputies from the Côrtes Gerais of Lisbon, 1822 (Hispanic American Historical Review, Nov. 1960). Translator: Fátima in the Light of History, by J. I. F. de Costa Brochado (1955). Language: Spanish 4,4,3,2; Portuguese 5,5,4,3; French 4,3,2,1; German 3,1,1,1; Italian 3,2,1,1. Office: Dept. of History, U. of Kans., Lawrence, Kans.

BOLD, ERNEST JAMES, b. Titusville, Pa., Dec. 31, 1924. HISTORY. A.B., Gannon Coll., 1948; A.M., U. of Ill., 1949. TEACHER, HEAD, SOCIAL STUDIES, SHALER HIGH SCHOOL (PA.), 1951- . Western Pennsylvania Council for Economic Education scholar, U. of Pittsburgh. Membership: National Council for the Social Studies; National Education Association. Research: Latin American history; church and state in Ecuador under García Moreno, 1860-75. Language: Spanish 2,1,1,3; Portuguese 1,1,1,1. Home: 4343 Beguland Dr., Allison Park, Pa. 15101. Office: Dept. of Social Studies, Shaler High School, 1800 Mt. Royal Blvd., Glenshaw, Pa. 15116.

BONEM, STUART. Home: 7442 Lowell, Skokie, Ill. 60076.

BORAH, WOODROW (WILSON), b. Utica, Miss., Dec. 22, 1912. HISTORY. A.B., U. of Calif., Los. Angeles, 1935; M.A., 1936; Ph.D., U. of Calif., Berkeley, 1940. Instr., Princeton U., 1941-42; analyst, U.S. Office of Stategic Services and U.S. Dept. of State, 1942-47; asst. prof.-prof., U. of Calif., Berkeley, 1948-62; PROF., HISTORY, U. OF CALIF., BERKELEY, 1962- . Guggenheim fellow, 1951-52, 1958-59; Bolton Prize Committee, Conference on Latin American History, 1961. Membership: American Historical Association; Conference on Latin American History; Sociedad Mexicana de Antropología. Research: demographic history; colonial Mexico; socio-economic history of Latin America. Author: New Spain's Century of Depression (1951); Early Colonial Trade and Navigation between Mexico and Peru (1954); The Aboriginal Population of Central Mexico on the Eve of the Spanish Conquest (1963). Language: Spanish 5,4,4,4; Portuguese 4,3,3,2; French 5,4,3,4; German 4,4,3,3; Italian 4,3,3,2. Home: 451 Vincente Ave., Berkeley 4, Calif. Office: Dept. of History., U. of Calif., Berkeley 4.

BORK, ALBERT WILLIAM, b. Prescott, Ariz., Aug. 12, 1906. HISTORY AND SPANISH AMERICAN LITERATURE. B.A., U. of Ariz., 1935; M.A., 1938; Litt.D., Universidad Nacional Autónoma de México, 1944. Asst. prof., State Coll. of Wash., 1944-46; catedrático, Universidad Nacional de México, 1946; asst. prof., U. of Ariz., 1946-50; assoc. prof., dean of undergraduate studies, Mexico City Coll., 1950-53; dir., asst. to vice president, Personnel and Industrial Relations, General Electric, S.A. de C.V. (Mexico), 1953-57; PROF., SPANISH, DIR., LATIN AMERICAN INSTITUTE, SOUTHERN ILL. U., 1958- . Roosevelt scholarship, Institute of International Education (Mexico), 1942-44; American Council of Learned Societies grant, 1943-44; Fulbright lectr., Universidad Nacional Mayor de San Marcos (Peru), 1959-60. Membership: American Association of Teachers of Spanish and Portuguese; American Historical Association; Modern Language Association; Phi Kappa Phi; Sigma Delta Pi; Sociedad Folklórica de México. Research: political and social conditions in Mexico; Mexican literature. Author: Nuevos aspectos del comercio entre Nuevo México y Misuri, 1822-1846 (1944); Doña Inés de Castro y otros motivos del romancero general (Anuario de la Sociedad Folklórica de México, 1944); Mexico—1960 (Arizona Quarterly, Winter 1960). Language: Spanish 5,5,5,5; Portuguese 4,4,4,4; French 3,2,2,2; Catalán 3,2,2,2; German 3,2,2,2. Home: Route 1, Carbondale, Ill. 62901. Office: Latin American Institute, Southern Ill. U., Carbondale, 62903.

BOWSER, FREDERICK PARK, b. Roswell, N. Mex., Dec. 1, 1937. HISTORY. B.A., U. of N. Mex., 1960; M.A., U. of Calif., Berkeley, 1961. STUDENT, HISTORY, U. OF CALIF., BERKELEY. Woodrow Wilson fellow, 1960-62; Foreign Area Fellowship Program fellow, 1962-64; Bancroft Library fellow, 1964-65. Research: colonial Latin American history, especially the Andean area; Negro slavery in colonial Peru. Language: Spanish 4,4,4,4; Portuguese 3,2,2,2; French 2,1,1,1. Office: Dept. of History, U. of Calif., Berkeley, 94720.

BOYD, MAURICE, b. Guthrie, Ky., Apr. 3, 1921. HISTORY. B.A., U. of Mo., 1943; M.A., U. of Mich., 1948; Ph.D., 1951. Assoc. prof., Bradley U., 1950-56; vis. prof., Universidad de Michoacán (Mexico), Summer 1953; prof., U. of Fla., 1956-64; vis. prof., Vanderbilt U., Sum-

mer 1962; PROF., HISTORY, TEX. CHRIS-
TIAN U., 1964- . Membership: American
Historical Association; Association for General
and Liberal Education; Mississippi Valley His-
torical Association; Southern Historical Asso-
ciation. Research: Mexico. Author: Cardinal
Quiroga: Inquisitor General of Spain (1954);
Eight Tarascan Legends (1958); American
Civilization (1964). Language: Spanish 4,4,4,4;
French 4,—,—,3; Latin 4,—,—,3. Office: Tex.
Christian U., Fort Worth, Tex.

BOYD, WILLIS D., b. Santa Monica, Calif., Apr.
30, 1924. HISTORY. B.A., U. of Calif., Los
Angeles, 1945; M.A., 1947; Ph.D., 1954. Instr.,
El Camino Coll., 1951-54; ASSOC. PROF.,
HISTORY, VALPARAISO U., 1954- . Val-
paraiso U. grant (Mexico), 1963-64. Member-
ship: American Historical Association; Midwest
Latin American Council; Phi Beta Kappa. Re-
search: race relations in the Americas; Latin
America in the 20th century. Author: James
Redpath and American Negro Colonization in
Haiti, 1860-62 (The Americas, Oct. 1955);
Negro Colonization in the Reconstruction Era,
1865-1870 (Georgia Historical Quarterly, Dec.
1956); The American Colonial Society and the
Slave Recaptives of 1860-61 (Journal of Negro
History, Apr. 1962). Language: Spanish 4,—,-
—,—; Portuguese 1,1,1,1; French 4,4,4,4; Ger-
man 2,2,2,2. Home: 904 Chicago St., Valparaiso,
Ind. Office: Dept. of History, Valparaiso U.,
Valparaiso.

BRADY, ROBERT L., b. Belmond, Iowa, Apr.
7, 1925. HISTORY. B.A., Loras Coll., 1948;
M.A., State U. of Iowa, 1953; Ph.D., 1965.
CHMN., HISTORY, LORAS COLL., 1955- .
Membership: American Association of Colleges
for Teacher Education; Delta Epsilon Sigma;
Phi Alpha Theta. Research: colonial Latin
American history; Negro in Mexico during
the colonial period. Language: Spanish 3,2,2,2;
Portuguese 2,1,1,1; French 2,1,1,1. Home:
1339 Mt. Pleasant St., Dubuque, Iowa. Office:
Dept. of History, Loras Coll., Dubuque.

BRANDENBURG, FRANK R., b. Faribault,
Minn., July 8, 1926. POLITICAL SCIENCE
AND ECONOMICS. B.A., U. of Calif., 1950;
M.A., U. of Pa., 1951; Ph.D., 1955. Instr.,
U. of Pa., 1951-56; asst. prof., Mich. State U.,
1956-57; prof., Universidad Nacional Autónoma
de México, 1957-62; chmn., Economics, U. of
the Americas (Mexico), 1958-62; staff member,
International Studies, National Planning Asso-
ciation, 1962- ; PROF., SCHOOL OF IN-
TERNATIONAL SERVICE, AMERICAN U.,
1964- ; STAFF MEMBER, COMMITTEE FOR
ECONOMIC DEVELOPMENT, 1964- . Consultant to business in Latin America, 1951-64;
Doherty fellow and Penfield Committee fellow
(Mexico), 1953-54; Ford Foundation fellow,
1955; Social Science Research Council grant,
1957-58. Membership: American Economic Association; American Political Science Association; Conference on Latin American History;
Delta Phi Epsilon; Delta Sigma Pi; Phi
Alpha Theta; Pi Sigma Alpha. Research: public and business policy; politics

in Mexico. Author: The Making of Modern
Mexico (1964); The Development of Latin
American Private Enterprise (1964). Contributor: Government and Politics in Latin America (1958). Language: Spanish 5,5,5,4; Portuguese 5,4,4,3; French 3,3,3,2; Italian 3,3,3,1.
Home: 5001 Battery Lane, Bethesda, Md. Office: Committee for Economic Development,
1000 Connecticut Ave., NW., Washington, D.C.
20006.

BREATHETT, GEORGE, b. Nov. 11, 1925.
HISTORY. B.S., Tenn. State U., 1948; A.M.,
U. of Mich., 1949; Ph.D., U. of Iowa, 1954.
PROF., HISTORY, BENNETT COLL., 1953- .
Research asst., U. of Iowa, 1951-53; coordinator
of summer programs at Tuskegee Institute
under auspices of International Paper Company
Foundation, 1958- . Membership: American
Association of University Professors; American
Historical Association; Association of Social Sci-
ence Teachers; Southern Historical Association.
Research: Haiti and French Caribbean, with
emphasis on church and state relations in the
colonial period. Author: The Socio-Economic
Problem of Haitian Representation in the
French National Assembly, 1789-1790 (Journal
of Social Science Teachers, Aug. 1959); Catholic
Missionary Activity and the Negro Slave in
Haiti (Phylon, Fall 1962); The Jesuits in
Colonial Haiti (The Historian, Feb. 1962).
Language: Spanish 3,1,1,3; French 4,4,4,3.
Home: 1901 Finley St., Greensboro, N.C. 27406.
Office: Dept. of History, Bennett College,
Greensboro, 27402.

BREYMANN, WALTER NORMAN, b. Freeport,
Ill., Apr. 29, 1919. HISTORY. B.S., U. of
Ill., 1941; M.A., 1947; Ph.D., 1950. Teacher,
Drummer Township High School (Ill.), 1941-
42; prof., chmn., Southern State Coll. (Ark.),
1950-56; PROF., CHMN., HISTORY, DRAKE
U., 1956- . Membership: American Association
of University Professors; American Historical
Association; Conference on Latin American History; Instituto Panamericano de Geografia e
Historia; Midwest Association for Latin American Studies; Society for the History of Discoveries. Research: Mexican Revolution of
1910; Mexican positivism in the Díaz era; development of rail transport in Mexico; the
Amazon Valley in the age of exploration and
colonial period. Author: The Científicos, Critics
of the Díaz Regime, 1892-1903 (Arkansas Academy of Science Proceedings, 1954); The
Científicos and the Collapse of the Díaz Regime,
1903-1911 (Arkansas Academy of Science Proceedings, 1955). Language: Spanish 3,3,3,3;
Portuguese 3,1,1,1. Home: 4512 Beaver Crest
Dr., Des Moines 10, Iowa. Office: Dept of
History, Drake U., Des Moines.

BRIDENHAGEN, CLEMENT FRANCIS, b. Stur-
geon Bay, Wis., Mar. 18, 1922. HISTORY.
B.D., U. of Denver, 1948; U. of Edinburgh;
M.A., U. of Denver, 1951; U. of Colo. Instr.,
U. of Denver, 1955-58; taxation consultant,
State of Colo., 1958-60; ASST. PROF., HIS-
TORY, HASTINGS COLL., 1960- . Member-
ship: Missouri Valley Collegiate Teachers of

History. Research: Latin American history; Argentina. Author: Financing Government in Colorado (1959). Language: Spanish 3,—,—,—; French 4,—,—,—. Home: 144 Ringland Rd., Hastings, Nebr. Office: Dept. of History, Hastings Coll., 7th and Turner Sts., Hastings.

BRISTOL, WILLIAM BAKER, b. Philadelphia, Pa., Apr. 13, 1915. HISTORY. B.A., Gettysburg Coll., 1936; M.A., U. of Pa., 1938; Ph.D., 1947. Exchange instr., U. of P.R., 1939-40; instr., Princeton U., 1947-48; asst. prof., Union Coll. (N.Y.), 1948-55; assoc. prof., 1955-62; PROF., HISTORY, UNION COLL. (N.Y.), 1962- . Harrison fellow, U. of Pa., 1940-41; Social Science Research Council fellow, 1941-42; Penfield scholar, U. of Pa., 1946-47; consultant, Choice: Books for College Libraries, 1964. Membership: American Association of University Professors; American Historical Association; Conference on Latin American History; Phi Beta Kappa. Research: Protestant-Catholic relations in Colombia in the 19th and 20th centuries, especially 1948-58; Latin America in the national period. Author: Hispanidad in South America, 1936-1945 (1951); Let's Talk about Cuba; Historical Background: Cuba and the United States (1963); Hispanidad in South America (Foreign Affairs, Jan. 1943). Language: Spanish 4,3,3,3; Portuguese 2,—,—,—; French 2,—,—,—. Home: 135 Rosa Rd., Schenectady, N.Y. 12308. Office: Div. of Social Studies, Union Coll., Schenectady, 12308.

BROMSEN, MAURY AUSTIN, b. New York, N.Y., April 25, 1919. HISTORY AND BIBLIOGRAPHY. B.S.S., City Coll. (N.Y.), 1939; M.A., U. of Calif., Berkeley, 1941; M.A., Harvard U., 1945. Guest lectr., Catholic U. of Chile, 1942; prof., U. of Chile, 1947; lectr., Extension Div., U. of Chile, 1947; editor, Inter-American Review of Bibliography, Dept. of Cultural Affairs, Pan American Union, 1950-53; DIR., MAURY A. BROMSEN ASSOCIATES, INC. Carnegie Endowment for International Peace fellow, U. of Chile, 1942; Buenos Aires Convention fellow (Chile), 1942-43; Social Science Research Council fellow (Chile), 1946-48; Harvard U. Woodbury Lowery travel fellow (Chile), 1946-48; Order of Merit, in rank of Knight Commander (Chile), 1952; advisory editor, Revista Inter-americana de Bibliografía, 1953- . Membership: Academia de Historia Nacional (Buenos Aires); Conference on Latin American History; Sociedad Chilena de Historia y Geografía; Sociedad de Bibliófilos Chilenos (Santiago); Sociedad de Historia Argentina. Research: Latin American history and bibliography; José Toribio Medina and Henry Harrisse. Editor: José Toribio Medina, Humanist of the Americas, an Appraisal (1960). Language: Spanish 5,5,5,4; Portuguese 3,3,3,2; French 3,3,3,2. Home: 195 Commonwealth Ave., Boston 16, Mass. Office: Maury A. Bromsen Associates, Inc., 195 Commonwealth Ave., Boston 16.

BRONNER, FRED, b. Cracow, Poland, July 11, 1925. HISTORY. B.S., City Coll. (N.Y.), 1947; A.M., Teachers' Coll., Columbia U., 1950.

Instr., Columbia U., 1955-61; LECTR., THE NEW SCHOOL FOR SOCIAL RESEARCH, 1961- . Doherty fellow (Peru), 1953-55; consultant teacher on Latin America, Bureau of Curriculum Research, New York City Board of Education, Spring 1963. Membership: American Academy of Political & Social Science; American Association of University Professors; American Geographical Society; American Historical Association; Association for Latin American Studies; Conference on Latin American History. Research: Latin American history; viceroy of Peru; economic history of colonial Spanish America. Author: José de la Riva Agüero (Hispanic American Historical Review, Nov. 1956). Language: Spanish 4,4,4,4; Portuguese 4,4,4,4; French 4,4,4,4; German 4,4,4,4; Italian 4,4,4,4; Polish 4,4,4,4. Home: 520 West 114th St., New York, N.Y. 10025. Office: The New School for Social Research, 66 West 12th St., New York, 10011.

BROOKS, PHILIP COOLIDGE, b. Washington, D.C., Jan. 14, 1906. HISTORY AND ARCHIVAL MANAGEMENT. B.A., U. of Mich., 1928; M.A., U. of Calif., Berkeley, 1930; Ph.D., 1933. Bibliographical asst., American Historical Association, 1933-35; examiner and staff officer, U.S. National Archives, 1935-48; records officer, U.S. National Security Resources Board, 1948-50; archivist, branch chief, U.S. National Archives and Records Service, 1950-57; chief, Federal Records Center (Calif.), 1953-57; DIR., HARRY S. TRUMAN LIBRARY, U.S. NATIONAL ARCHIVES AND RECORDS SERVICE, 1957- . Native Sons of the Golden West fellow, 1932-33; archives and records management adviser, State of Texas, 1950. Membership: American Historical Association; International Council on Archives; Society of American Archivists. Research: United States-Spanish-Latin American diplomatic relations in the early 19th century; evaluation and research use of archives and historical manuscripts; Truman career and administration. Author: Diplomacy and the Borderlands: The Adams-Onis Treaty of 1819 (1939); Public Records Management (1949; Spanish edition, 1952); El manejo de archivos y documentos (1955). Language: Spanish 3,3,3,3; Portuguese 1,—,—,—; French 2,2,—,—. Home: 701 Bellevista Dr., Independence, Mo. 64050. Office: Harry S. Truman Library, Independence.

BROUSSARD, RAY F., b. Lafayette, La., Apr. 22, 1926. HISTORY. B.A., U. of Southwest La., 1949; M.A., U. of Tex., 1952; Ph.D., 1959. Instr., Howard County Jr. Coll. (Tex.), 1955-57; dir., Bi-National Cultural Center (Cartagena, Colombia), U.S. Information Agency, 1959-61; ASST. PROF., HISTORY, MISS. STATE U., 1961- . Specialist on Colombia, Special Operations Research Office, American U., 1962-63; National Defense Foreign Language post-doctoral fellow in Portuguese, 1963; American Philosophical Society research grant (Mexico), 1963. Research: Mexican reform period; filibustering expeditions to Latin America from Mississippi. Author: Correspondence of Ignacio Comonfort with his daughters (Library

Journal of the University of Texas, Spring 1959); Las mocedades de Comonfort (Historia Mexicana, Jan. 1964). Language: Spanish 5,4,-4,3; Portuguese 4,3,3,2; French 4,2,3,2. Home: P.O. Box 203, State College, Miss. 39762. Office: Dept. of History, Miss. State U., State College, 39762.

BROWN JOSEPH ROBERT, b. St. Louis, Mo., June 25, 1926. HISTORY. A.B., Tex. Western Coll., 1948; M.A., U. of Chicago, 1949; Ph.D., La. State U., 1954; Universidad Nacional Autónoma de México, 1959. Bibliographer-researcher, Library of Congress, 1952; instr., Nicholls State Coll., 1952-53; PROF., HISTORY, NORTHEAST LA. STATE COLL., 1953- . Research supervisor, consultant, Louisiana Historical Committee for the Tidelands Project, 1955; sabbatical grant (Mexico), 1959; American Philosophical Society research grant, 1961; Publications Committee, Louisiana History Journal; Board of Directors, Louisiana Historical Association. Membership: Louisiana Historical Association; Louisiana Teachers Association; Southern Historical Association. Research: foreign enterprise in Latin America; United States foreign relations. Author: The Chilean Nitrate Railways Controversy (Hispanic American Historical Review, Nov. 1958); Nitrate Crises, Combinations, and the Chilean Government in the Nitrate Age (Hispanic American Historical Review, May 1963); The Frustration of Chile's Nitrate Imperialism (Pacific Historical Review, Nov. 1963). Language: Spanish 4,2,2,3. Home: 3708 Lafayette St., Monroe, La. Office: Dept. of History, Northeast La. State Coll., Monroe.

BROWN, LYLE CLARENCE, b. Hume, N.Y., Aug. 7, 1926. POLITICAL SCIENCE AND HISTORY. B.A., U. of Okla., 1948; M.A., 1952; Ph.D., U. of Tex., 1964. Instr., Mexico City Coll., Summer 1958; asst. prof., Tex. Coll. of Arts & Industries, 1958-62; asst. prof., Wayland Baptist Coll., 1962-63; ASST. PROF., POLITICAL SCIENCE, BAYLOR U., 1963- . U. of Tex. teaching fellow; Instituto Tecnológico de Monterrey scholar, Summer 1952; Board of Editors, A Journal of Church and State. Membership: Academy of Political Science; American Academy of Political and Social Science; American Association of University Professors; American Historical Association; American Political Science Association; American Studies Association; Mississippi Valley Historical Association; Southwestern Social Science Association. Research: General Lazaro Cárdenas and Mexican presidential politics, 1933-1940; Russian and Latin American government and politics. Author: The Mexican Liberals and Their Struggle against the Díaz Dictatorship, 1900-1906 (in Antología MCC, 1956); Comments on the Closed Ice Box of East Siberia (U.S. Naval Institute Proceedings, Nov. 1961); Party and State in the U.S.S.R. (Social Studies, Feb. 1962). Language: Spanish 5,5,4,4; Portuguese 2,1,1,1; French 5,2,2,2. Home: 1814 South 5th St., Waco, Tex. Office: Dept. of Political Science, Baylor U., Waco.

BROXSON, ELMER RUDOLPH, b. Jacksonville, Fla., Dec. 20, 1934. HISTORY. B.A., City Coll. (N.Y.), 1961; Catholic U. STUDENT, HISTORY, CATHOLIC U. Fulbright scholar (Brazil), 1965-66. Membership: Phi Alpha Theta. Research: Latin American history; Brazil during the 1930's. Language: Spanish 2,2,2,2; Portuguese 4,3,2,2; French 4,3,3,3; German 2,2,2,1. Home: Apt. 3, 116 Fort Dr., NW., Washington, D.C. 20011.

BRUBAKER, GEORGE A., b. Excello, Ohio, Sept. 25, 1928. HISTORY. B.A., U. of Ariz., 1951; M.A., 1952; Ph.D., U. of Tex., 1960. Asst. administrative secretary, U.S. Senator Carl Hayden, 1951-52; instr., Tex. A. & M. Coll., 1955-56; vis. lectr., U. of Ariz., Summer 1959; dir., Bi-National Center (Antofagasta, Chile), U.S. Information Agency, 1959-61; asst. prof., State U. of N.Y., Coll. at Buffalo, 1961-65; PROF., HISTORY, U. OF KY. 1965- . Buenos Aires Convention fellow (Colombia), 1956-57; University fellow, U. of Tex., 1958; Fulbright grant (Colombia), 1964-65. Membership: American Historical Association; Conference on Latin American History. Research: politics in Colombia. Language: Spanish 5,5,4,4; Portuguese 3,2,2,1; French 2,1,1,1. Office: Dept. of History, U. of Ky., Lexington, Ky.

BRUNDAGE, BURR C., b. Buffalo, N.Y., Dec. 15, 1912. HISTORY. A.B., Amherst Coll., 1936; Ph.D., U. of Chicago, 1939. Desk officer, Office of the Coordinator of Inter-American Affairs, U.S. Dept. of State, 1943-44; Peru and Chile desk officer, U.S. Dept. of State, 1944-47; prof., Cedar Crest Coll., 1947-62; PROF., HISTORY, FLA. PRESBYTERIAN COLL., 1962- . Membership: Conference on Latin American History. Research: Incas in the greater Cuzco area of Peru; Oriental history. Author: The Juniper Palace (1951); Empire of the Inca (1963). Language: Spanish 1,3,3,2; French 1,2,2,2; Quechua 4,—,5,—. Home: 4411 Cortez Way St., St. Petersburg, Fla. Office: Dept. of History, Fla. Presbyterian Coll., St. Petersburg.

BRUNETTI, MELVIN E., b. Oakland, Calif., Aug. 30, 1932. HISTORY. A.B., U. of Calif., Berkeley, 1954; M.A., 1955. INSTR., HISTORY, WELLESLEY COLL., 1962- . Center for Latin American Studies grant, U. of Calif., Berkeley, 1961-62. Membership: Phi Alpha Theta. Research: Latin American history; 19th century Brazilian history; Portuguese history. Language: Spanish 4,4,3,3; Portuguese 3,2,2,2; German 3,2,2,2. Home: 4 Weston Ter., Wellesley, Mass. 02181. Office: Dept. of History, Wellesley Coll., Wellesley.

BURKS, DAVID DONALD, b. Duluth, Minn., Feb. 1, 1924. HISTORY. B.A., Earlham Coll., 1945; Ph.D., U. of Chicago, 1952. Asst. prof., Muskingum Coll., 1949-52; asst. prof., Otterbein Coll., 1952-54; assoc. prof., 1955-57; intelligence research specialist, Bureau of Intelligence and Research, U.S. Dept. of State, 1957-60; assoc. prof.-prof., U. of Mich., Dearborn Center, 1960-64; PROF., HISTORY, U. OF IND., 1964- . Council on Foreign Relations research fellow (Mexico, Venezuela, El Salvador, Dominican Republic, Brazil), 1962-63; consultant, U.S. Dept. of State; contributing editor, Handbook of Latin American Studies. Membership: American Association of University Professors; American Historical Association; Conference on Latin American History. Research: Cuba; influence of the Cuban Revolution on other countries. Author: The United States and the Geneva Protocol of 1924: A New Holy Alliance? (American Historical Review, July 1959); Cuba under Castro (Foreign Policy Association Headline Series, June 1964). Coauthor: Evolution or Chaos: Dynamics of Latin American Government and Politics (1963). Language: Spanish 5,5,4,3; Portuguese 4,3,2,1; French 4,2,1,1. Home: 4212 Morningside Dr., Bloomington, Ind. Office: Dept. of History, U. of Ind., Bloomington, 47403.

BURNS, E. BRADFORD, b. Muscatine, Iowa, Aug. 28, 1932. HISTORY. Universidad de San Carlos (Guatemala), 1953; B.A., State U. of Iowa, 1954; M.A., Tulane U., 1955; U. of Lisbon, 1955-56; Ph.D., Columbia U., 1963. Instr., Rutgers U., 1961-62; guest lectr., United States-Brazilian Cultural Institute (Brazil), 1962; guest lectr., U. of Paraná (Brazil), 1963; ASST. PROF., HISTORY, STATE U., OF N.Y., COLL. AT BUFFALO, 1963- . Venezuelan Government Pan-American award, Universided Central de Caracas, 1959-60; Mexican Government award; Andrew Carnegie fellow; Rotary Foundation fellow; Lydia C. Roberts fellow; National Defense Education Act fellow; Cordell Hull grant; Doherty fellow. Membership: American Association of University Professors; Conference on Latin American History; Phi Beta Kappa; Phi Sigma Iota; Society for the History of Discoveries. Research: Brazilian history; United States-Brazilian diplomatic relations. Author: The Sixteenth Century Jesuit Letters of Brazil (Mid-America, July 1962); Introduction to the Brazilian Jesuit Letters (Mid-America, July 1962); Rio-Branco visto pelos seus contemporâneos norteamericanos (Jornal de Comércio, Aug. 1963). Language: Spanish 5,4,4,4; Portuguese 5,5,5,4; French 2,1,1,1. Home: 215 Mary Pl., Muscatine, Iowa. Office: Dept. of History, State U. of N.Y., Coll. at Buffalo, N.Y. 14214.

BURR, ROBERT N., b. Rochester, N.Y., Oct. 15, 1916. HISTORY AND INTERNATIONAL RELATIONS. B.A., U. of Rochester, 1939; Ph.D., U. of Pa., 1948. Instr., Rutgers U., 1946-48; asst. prof.-PROF., HISTORY, U. OF CALIF., LOS ANGELES, 1948- . Penfield fellow (Colombia), 1942-43; Social Science Research Council grant, 1947-48; Doherty fellow (Chile), 1951-52; Eisenhower exchange fellow (South America), 1957; Rockefeller Foundation grant, 1961-62; chmn., Joint Committee on Latin American Studies, American Council of Learned Societies-Social Science Research Council, 1959- ; consultant, Foreign Area Fellowship Program, 1961- . Membership: American Historical Association; Conference on Latin American History; Pacific Coast Council on Latin American Studies; Pan American Insti-

tute of Geography and History. Research: history and international relations of South American nations. Author: The Stillborn Panama Congress: Power Politics and Chilean-Colombian Relations during the War of the Pacific (1962). Co-author: Documents on Inter-American Cooperation, 1810-1948 (1955). Language: Spanish 4,4,3,3; Portuguese 3,1,1,1; French 4,1,1,1. Home: 10856 Wellworth Ave., Los Angeles 24, Calif. Office: Dept. of History U. of Calif., Los Angeles 24.

BURRUS, ERNEST JOSEPH, S.J., b. El Paso, Tex., Apr. 20, 1907. HISTORY. A.B., Gonzaga U. (Wash.), 1931; M.A., 1932; Loyola U. (La.), 1933; Litt.D. (honoris causa), U. of St. Louis, 1960. Instr., Loyola U. (La.), 1932-35, 1939-50; dean, 1947-50; staff member, Jesuit Historical Institute (Rome), 1950- ; DIR., HISTORY, JESUIT HISTORICAL INSTITUTE (U.S.), 1960- . Carnegie grant-in-aid (Mexico), 1945-50; Guggenheim fellow (Italy), 1957-59; American Council of Learned Societies grant, 1961-62. Membership: American Jesuit Historians; Instituto Panamericano. Research: New Spain; archival research in Mexico; research in Italian archives on Hispanic American sources. Editor: Historia de México (1949). Translator: Kino Reports to Headquarters, by E. F. Kino (1954); Historia de la Provincia de la Compañía de Jesús de Nueva España, 1566-1767 (1956-60). Language: Spanish 5,5,-5,5; Portuguese 5,2,2,2; French 5,5,5,5; German 5,5,5,5; Italian 5,5,5,5; Latin 5,—,—,5. Home and office: Via dei Penitenzieri 20, Rome 6, Italy; in U.S., Dept. of History, St. Louis U., St. Louis 3, Mo.

BUSHNELL, CLYDE GILBERT, b. Sioux City, Iowa, June 6, 1912. HISTORY. B.A., Union Coll. (Nebr.), 1933; M.A., Universidad Nacional de México, 1948; Ph.D., U. of Tex., 1958. President, Training Coll. (Colombia), 1948-49; high school principal and supervisor of education, Seventh-Day Adventist Church (P.R.), 1949-52; CHMN., COMMUNICATIONS DIV., SOUTHERN MISSIONARY COLL., 1952- . Southern Fellowship grant, U. of Tex. Membership: American Association of Teachers of Spanish and Portuguese; Southeastern Latin Americanists. Research: social conditions in Mexico prior to Santa Ana's overthrow in 1855. Language: Spanish 4,4,4,4; Portuguese 2,2,2,1; French 3,2,2,2; German 3,3,3,3; Italian 3,2,2,2. Home: Collegedale, Hamilton County, Tenn. Office: Communications Div., Southern Missionary Coll., Collegedale.

BUSHNELL, DAVID, b. Philadelphia, Pa., May 14, 1923. HISTORY. A.B., Harvard U., 1943; A.M., 1948; Ph.D., 1951. Research analyst, Latin American Div., U.S. Office of Strategic Services, 1944-45; research analyst, U.S. Dept. of State, 1944-46; instr.-asst. prof., U. of Del., 1949-56; historian, U.S. Air Force Missile Development Center (N. Mex.), 1956-61; chief, Historical Div., Office of Aerospace Research, 1961-63; ASSOC. PROF., HISTORY, U. OF FLA., 1963- . Sheldon traveling fellow, 1943; Social Science Research Council fellow, 1948-

49; contributing editor, Handbook of Latin American Studies, 1955- . Bolton Prize Committee, Conference on Latin American History, 1962. Membership: American Historical Association; Conference on Latin American History. Research: independence period of Spanish South America; 19th and 20th century Colombia; development of scientific research in Latin America. Author: The Santander Regime in Gran Colombia (1954); Two Stages in Colombian Tariff Policy: The Radical Era and the Return to Protection (Inter-Amcrican Economic Affairs, Spring 1956). Co-author: Space Biology (1960; 1962). Language: Spanish 5,4,4,4; Portuguese 4,2,2,3; French 4,2,2,3; German 3,2,2,1. Home: 620 NW. 34th St., Gainesville, Fla. Office: Dept. of History, U. of Fla., Gainesville.

BUTLER, RUTH LAPHAM, b. Chicago, Ill., Dec. 19, 1896. HISTORY AND BIBLIOGRAPHY. A.B., Northwestern U., 1918; M.S., 1919; Ph.D., 1925; LL.D., Loyola U. (Ill.), 1962. Asst., Bibliography and Book Selection Dept., Newberry Library, 1920-22; research dir., William Smith Mason Franklin Collection, 1922-25; prof., Hillsdale Coll., 1925-26; curator, E. E. Ayer Collection, Newberry Library, 1927-62; HONORARY CONSULTANT, LIBRARY, KALAMAZOO COLL., 1962- . History fellow, Northwestern U., 1919-20. Membership: American Historical Association; Conference on Latin American History. Research: bibliographical history; colonial Latin American history. Author: Dr. Franklin, Postmaster General (1932); A Check List of Manuscripts in the Edward E. Ayer Collection (1937); Guide to the Hispanic American Historical Review (1950). Language: Spanish 3,3,3,1; Portuguese 3,3,1,1; French 3,3,1,1; German 2,1,1,1; Italian 3,1,1,1. Home: 806 East Michigan, Paw Paw, Mich. Office: Library, Kalamazoo Coll., Kalamazoo, Mich.

CADENHEAD, IVIE EDWARD, JR., b. Montgomery, Ala., Nov. 23, 1923. HISTORY. B.S., Auburn U., 1946; M.S., 1947; Ph.D., U. of Mo., 1950. Asst. instr., U. of Mo., 1948-50; PROF., HISTORY, U. OF TULSA, 1950- . Membership: American Studies Association; Conference on Latin American History; Mid-Continent American Studies; Southern Historical Association. Research: 19th century Mexican history. Author: González Ortega and the Presidency of Mexico (Hispanic American Historical Review, Aug. 1952); American Socialists and Mexican Revolution (Southwestern Social Science Quarterly, Sept. 1962); Flores Magón y el periódico "The Appeal to Reason" (Historia Mexicana, Sept. 1963). Language: Spanish 3,2,1,1; German 2,1,1,1. Office: Dept. of History, U. of Tulsa, Tulsa 4, Okla.

CAIN, GEORGE WILLIAM, JR., b. Fort Wayne, Ind., April 25, 1939. HISTORY. A.B., Princeton U., 1963; Tulane U. STUDENT, HISTORY, TULANE U. National Defense Education Act fellow in Latin American History, Tulane U. Research: Latin American history. Language: Spanish 3,3,2,2; Portuguese 2,1,1,1;

French 2,1,1,1. Home: Apt. 802, 6440 South Claiborne Ave., New Orleans, La. 70125.

CALLAGHAN, MARY CONSUELA, I.H.M., b. Philadelphia, Pa., June 19, 1908. HISTORY. B.S., U. of Pa., 1932; M.A., 1934; Ph.D., 1951. Teacher, Philadelphia School District, 1932-37; McDevitt High School (Pa.), 1938-40; instr. Immaculata Coll., 1940-42; head, Social Studies, J. W. Hallahan High School (Pa.), 1942-53; dir., Teacher Education, Immaculata Coll., 1954-59; CHMN., HISTORY, IMMACULATA COLL. (PA.), 1959- . Corporation grant (Peru), 1962; U.S. coordinator for Villa María Coll. (Peru). Membership: American Historical Association; Catholic Historical Association; Conference on Latin American History; National Council for the Social Studies. Research: social situations in Peru. Author: The Sisters of the Immaculate Heart in Peru (Catholic Historical Bulletin, 1964). Language: Spanish 5,4,4,3. Office: Dept. of History, Immaculata Coll., Immaculata, Pa.

CALLCOTT, WILFRID HARDY, b. Guadalupe County, Tex., Nov. 12, 1895. HISTORY. A.B., Southwestern U., 1919; M.A., Columbia U., 1920; Ph.D., 1926. Assoc. prof., U. of S.C., 1923-28; PROF., HISTORY, U. OF S.C., 1928- ; vis. prof., U. of Tex., 1961-62. Fulbright lectr., Oxford U., 1963-64; lecture tour (Yugoslavia, Italy), 1964; lectr., Miami U. and George Washington U. Membership: American Historical Association; Deans of Southern Graduate Schools; South Carolina Historical Association; Southern Historical Association. Research: hemisphere policy of the United States; Mexican history and relations. Author: Santa Ana, An Enigma That Once Was Mexico (1926, 1964); Liberalism in Mexico, 1857-1929 (1931); Caribbean Policy of the United States, 1890-1920 (1942). Language: Spanish 5,4,3,3; French 4,3,2,—. Home: 1718 College St., Columbia, S.C. 29208. Office: Dept. of History, U. of S.C., Columbia, 29208.

CAMPA, DAVID L., b. El Paso, Tex., Oct. 8, 1903. HISTORY. M.A., U. of N. Mex., 1930; Universidad Nacional de México, 1930-32; Ph.D., U. of Calif., Berkeley, 1940. Teacher, American High School (Mexico. D.F.), 1930-33; teacher, Santa Fe Public Schools, 1933-36; asst. prof., N. Mex. State U., 1939-42; LATIN AMERICAN POLITICAL RESEARCH, U.S. GOVERNMENT, 1942- ; dir., Education Program for Latin American Educators, U.S. Government, 1944-47. U. of Calif. teaching fellow, 1936-39; adviser and liaison officer, U.S. Delegation, Inter-American Economic Conference (Brazil), 1954, (Argentina), 1957. Membership: American Association of University Professors; Instituto Internacional de Literatura Iberoamericana; Inter-American Bibliographical and Library Association; Phi Alpha Theta. Research: Mexican history and literature; political and sociological research on Latin America. Language: Spanish 5,5,5,5; Portuguese 4,4,3,—; French 4,3,2,—. Home: 7708 Granada Dr., Bethesda, Md. 20034.

CANEDO, LINO GÓMEZ, O.F.M., b. Laracha, Spain, June 24, 1908. HISTORY. Diploma on Paleography and Archives, State Archives (Rome), 1937; Diploma of Librarian, Vatican Library, 1937; Ph.D., Gregorian U., 1938. Editor, Archivo Ibero-Americano (Madrid), 1940-47; RESIDENT MEMBER, ACADEMY OF AMERICAN FRANCISCAN HISTORY, ASST. EDITOR, THE AMERICAS, 1952- . Junta de Relaciones Culturales, Spanish Foreign Office research grant (archives and libraries of America), 1947-49; Creole Foundation and Organization of American States fellow (Venezuela), 1958-59; research of Puerto Rican historical archives for U. of P.R., 1960. Membership: Academia Colombiana de Historia; Junta Mexicana de Estudios Históricos; Real Academia de la Historia (Madrid). Research: sources and archives in Latin America; historiography. Author: Los estudios hispánicos en los Estados Unidos (1947); Crónica Franciscana de las Provincias del Perú (1957); Los archivos de la historia de América (1961). Language: Spanish 5,5,5,5; Portuguese 4,4,4,3; French 4,3,3,3; German 2,—,1,1; Italian 4,—,4,3. Home: Convento San Francisco, Santiago de Compostela, Spain. Office: Academy of American Franciscan History, Box 5850, Washington, D.C. 20014.

CANTWELL, MARY KAREN, b. East St. Louis, Ill., Aug. 24, 1942. HISTORY. B.A., Webster Coll., 1964; Georgetown U. Bibliographer, Hispanic Foundation, Library of Congress, 1964-65; STUDENT, LATIN AMERICAN AREA STUDIES, GEORGETOWN U. Webster Coll. scholar, 1960-64; Universidad Jaime Balmas summer scholar (Saltillo, Mexico), 1963; Georgetown U. fellow, 1965-66; Fulbright fellow (Chile), 1966-67. Membership: Conference on Latin American History. Research: Latin American educational planning and administration; Mexican revolution. Language: Spanish 4,3,3,3; Portuguese 2,1,1,1; French 2,2,1,1; German 2,1,1,1. Home: 1601 Grape Ave., St. Louis, Mo.

CARDOZO, MANOEL, b. Ribeiras, Pico, Azores, Dec. 24, 1911. HISTORY. A.B., Stanford U., 1931; A.M., 1934; Ph.D., 1939. CURATOR, OLIVEIRA LIMA LIBRARY, CATHOLIC U. OF AMERICA, 1940- ; lectr., Catholic U. of America, 1940-44; asst. prof., 1944-47; assoc. prof., 1947-54; PROF., HISTORY, CATHO-LIC U. OF AMERICA, 1954- ; HEAD, 1961- . Social Science Research Council grant, 1941; consultant, Library of Congress, 1950-51; American Philosophical Society grant, 1953; Smith-Mundt lectr. (Portugal), 1958; Organization of American States fellow, 1963; Advisory Committee, Who's Who in Latin America; Cavaleiro, Ordem Nacional do Cruzeiro do Sul (Brazil); Rio Branco Medal (Brazil). Membership: Academy of American Franciscan History; American Association of University Professors; American Catholic Historical Association; American Historical Association; Conference on Latin American History; Council for Basic Education; Institute of Ibero-American Studies; Instituto do Ceará; Instituto Histórico da Terceira (Azores); Instituto Histórico e Geográfico (São Paulo); Instituto Histórico e Geográfico do Maranhão; Inter-American Council; Phi Alpha Theta; Sigma Delta Pi; Sociedad Peruana de Historia; Sociedade de Geografia (Lisbon). Research: church-state relations in Brazil; 18th century Brazil; biography of Oliveira Lima. Author: The Holy See and the Question of the Bishop-Elect of Rio, 1833-1839 (The Americas, July 1953); The Idea of History in the Portuguese Chroniclers of the Age of Discovery (Catholic Historical Review, Apr. 1963). Editor: Impressões da América Espan-Abstract of Latin America, 1963. Language: Spanish 5,5,5,5; Portuguese 5,5,5,5; French 3,3,3,3; Italian 3,3,3,3. Home: 325 Franklin St. NE., Washington, D.C. 20002. Office: Dept. of History, Catholic U. of America, Washington, 20017.

CAREY, JAMES CHARLES, b. Bancroft, Nebr., Apr. 1, 1915. HISTORY. A.B., Nebr. State Teachers Coll., 1937; M.A., U. of Colo., 1940; Universidad de San Marcos (Peru), 1942; Ph.D., U. of Colo., 1948. Dir., Colegio Americano (Peru), 1941-45; instr., U. of Colo., 1947-48; PROF., HISTORY, KANS. STATE U., 1948- ; vis. prof., Colegio Pan Americano (Mexico), 1953-54. U. of Colo. fellow; dir., Biblioteca Pública del Callao (Peru); consultant for U.S. Senator Gale McGee. Membership: American Association of University Professors; American Historical Association; Mississippi Valley Historical Association; Phi Alpha Theta. Research: United States diplomacy in Latin America; Peru. Author: United States Policy in Peru, 1919-1930 (Bulletin: U. of Colo. Studies, 1951); Mexico's Hands-Off Policy (The Midwest Quarterly, Spring 1962); Lord Cochrane: Critic of San Martin's Campaign (The Americas, Apr. 1962). Language: Spanish 4,4,4,4; Portuguese 2,1,1,1; French 3,2,1,1. Home: 332 North 15th St., Manhattan, Kans. Office: Dept. of History, Kans. State U., Manhattan.

CARL, GEORGE EDMOND, b. Los Angeles, Calif., Apr. 11, 1937. HISTORY. B.S., Southwest Mo. State Coll., 1960; U. of Tex., 1960-61; M.A., U. of Calif., Berkeley, 1962; Tulane U. STUDENT, HISTORY, TULANE U., 1962- . Woodrow Wilson fellow, 1960; Center for Latin American Studies fellow, U. of Calif., Berkeley, 1961; Tulane U. scholar, 1962; National Defense Foreign Language fellow in Spanish, Tulane U., 1963; National Defense Foreign Language-Fulbright Hays Award (Venezuela), 1964. Research: Latin American history; Brazilian history; British economic influence in Latin America. Language: Spanish 4,4,4,4; Portuguese 3,3,3,3; French 1,1,1,1. Home: 11521 Carvarillo St., North Hollywood, Calif. 91602.

CASSIN, RICHARD CLARK, b. Albany, N.Y., Apr. 11, 1941. HISTORY. B.A., U. of the Americas, 1962; Syracuse U.; U. of N. Mex. Instr., Peace Corps Training Center for Latin America, U. of N. Mex.; STUDENT, HISTORY, U. OF N. MEX. Membership: Phi Alpha Theta. Research: Latin American history; Mexico; community development. Language: Spanish 5,5,5,5; Portuguese 3,3,3,3; French 3,3,3,3; Italian 2,2,2,2. Home: 211 San Pasquale, SW., Albuquerque, N. Mex.

CASTRO, DONALD STEVEN, b. Bakersfield, Calif., June 27, 1940. HISTORY. A.B., U. of Calif., Los Angeles, 1962; M.A., 1964. STUDENT, HISTORY, U. OF CALIF., LOS ANGELES. National Defense Foreign Language fellow, U. of Calif., Los Angeles, 1964-65. Membership: Phi Alpha Theta; Pi Gamma Mu. Research: Latin American political and social history; growth of radical political philosophies in Argentina. Author: Statistical Abstract of Latin America, 1963. Language: Spanish 5,5,5,5; Portuguese 3,3,2,3; French 2,2,2,2. Home: Apt. 10, 1661 Federal Ave., Los Angeles, Calif. 90025.

CAUGHEY, JOHN W., b. Wichita, Kans., July 3, 1902. HISTORY. B.A., U. of Tex., 1923; M.A., U. of Calif., 1926; Ph.D., 1928. Asst. prof., U. of Calif., Los Angeles, 1930-47; PROF., HISTORY, U. OF CALIF., LOS ANGELES, 1947- . Native Sons of the Golden West fellow; Rockefeller Foundation fellow; American Council of Learned Societies fellow; Shreve fellow, Princeton U.; consultant, Dept. of Justice, State of Calif.; consultant, Dept. of Water and Power, City of Los Angeles. Membership: American Association of University Professors; American Historical Association; American Civil Liberties Union; California Historical Society; Mississippi Valley Historical Association. Research: western America. Author: History of the Pacific Coast (1933); Bernardo de Gálvez in Louisiana, 1776-1783 (1934). Editor: The Indians of Southern California in 1852 (1952). Language: Spanish 3,3,1,—; Portuguese 2,—,—,—; French 3,2,1,—. Home: 1897 Mango Way, Los Angeles 49, Calif. Office: Dept. of History, U. of Calif., Los Angeles 24.

CHAMBERLAIN, ROBERT S., b. Canton, Ohio, Oct. 19, 1903. HISTORY. A.B., Stanford U., 1925; B. Sc. in Ed., Ohio State U., 1927; Ph.D., Harvard U., 1936. Staff member, Historical Research Div., Carnegie Institution of Washington, 1936-47; cultural relations officer (Guatemala), U. S. Dept. of State, 1941-45; assoc. prof., U. of Miami, 1947-48; U.S. GOVERNMENT, 1948- . Woodbury Lowery fellow (Spain), 1932-34. Membership: American Franciscan Academy of History; American Historical Association; Conference on Latin American History; Hakluyt Society (England); Pan American Institute of Geography and History; Sociedad de Geografía e Historia (Guatemala); Sociedad de Geografía e Historia (Honduras). Research: Hispanic colonial history. Author: The Castilian Backgrounds of the Repartimiento-Encomienda (1939); The Governorship of the Adelantado Francisco de Montejo in Chiapas, 1539-1544 (1947); The Conquest and Colonization of Yucatan, 1517-1550 (1948); The Conquest and Colonization of Honduras, 1502-1550 (1953). Language: Spanish 5,4,4,4; Portuguese 4,3,2,1; French 4,2,1,1; German 3,—,—,1. Home: 804 Grand View Dr., Alexandria, Va.

CHAMBERLIN, EUGENE KEITH, b. Gustine, Calif., Feb. 15, 1916. HISTORY. B.A., U. of Calif., Berkeley, 1939; M.A., 1940; Ph.D., 1949. Teacher, Calif. Public Schools, 1941-45; prof., Mont. State U., 1948-54; PROF., HISTORY, SAN DIEGO CITY COLL., 1954- . Rockefeller-Huntington Library grant, Summer 1952; chmn., Baja California Historical Materials Committee, Library, U. of Calif., San Diego. Membership: American Association of University Professors; Conference on Latin American History; American Historical Association; Pacific Coast Council on Latin American Studies; Phi Alpha Theta. Research: Mexican northwest area and Baja California; United States-Mexican relations. Author: Mexican Colonization versus American Interests in Baja California (Pacific Historical Review, Feb. 1951); Baja California after Walker: The Zerman Enterprise (Hispanic American Historical Review, May 1954); Nicholas Trist and Baja California (Pacific Historical Review, Feb. 1963). Language: Spanish 3,3,3,3; Portuguese 1,1,1,1; French 2,1,1,1; German 2,1,1,1. Home: 3033 Dale St., San Diego, Calif. 92104. Office: Dept. of History, San Diego City Coll., 1425 Russ Blvd., San Diego, 92101

CHANDLER, DAVID LEE, b. New Plymouth, Idaho, Oct. 9, 1938. HISTORY. B.S., Brigham Young U., 1963; M.A., Tulane U., 1965. STUDENT, HISTORY, TULANE U., 1964- . National Defense Education Act fellow. Research: Latin American history. Language: Spanish 3,3,3,3; German 2,2,2,2. Home: New Plymouth, Idaho.

CHAPMAN, MARY P., b. Los Angeles, Calif., Aug. 20, 1917. HISTORY. B.A., Stanford U., 1939; M.A., 1942; Ph.D., 1950. Analyst, Hoover Library, Stanford U., 1948-49; research asst., Prof. Hubert Herring, Claremont Graduate School, 1950-52; research analyst, U.S. Dept. of State, 1955-59; DIPLOMATIC HISTORIAN, HISTORICAL OFFICE, U.S. DEPT. OF STATE, 1959- . Membership: American Historical Association; Conference on Latin American History; Phi Alpha Theta. Research: past and current United States-Latin American relations. Author: The Mission of Elisha O. Crosby to Guatemala, 1861-1864 (Pacific Historical Review, Aug. 1955); The Mission of Lansing Bond Mizner to Central America (The Historian, Aug. 1957). Language: Spanish 4,4,4,3; French 2,1,1,1. Home: 2117 E St. NW., Apt. 816, Washington, D.C. 20037. Office: Historical Office, U.S. Dept. of State, Washington 25, D.C.

CHARDIET, ARMANDO. Office: Fairfield U., Fairfield, Conn. 06430.

CHATELAIN, VERNE ELMO, b. Waco, Nebr., July 22, 1895. HISTORY. B.A., Nebr. State Coll., 1917; M.A., U. of Chicago, 1925; Ph.D., U. of Minn., 1943. Prof., chmn., Nebr. State Coll., 1925-31; chief historian, Branch of Historic Sites and Buildings, U.S. National Park Service, 1931-36; research asst., dir., St. Augustine Program (Fla.), Carnegie Institution of

Washington, 1936-42; liaison administrative officer, U.S. Government, 1942-45; PROF., HISTORY, U. OF MD., 1945- . U. of Minn fellow, 1928-29; consultant on St. Augustine Program, State of Florida; National Advisory Committee on the Program for Spanish Florida, Carnegie Institution; Committee for National Parks and Monuments, U.S. Dept. of Interior. Membership: American Bar Association; American Historical Association; Mississippi Valley Historical Association; Pan American Institute of Geography and History. Research: Spanish Florida. Author: The Defenses of Spanish Florida, 1565-1763 (1941); The St. Augustine Historical Restoration (1958); Spanish Contributions to American Culture (Florida Historical Quarterly, Jan. 1941). Language: Spanish 4,3,2,4; French —,2,2,3. Home: 1206 Noyes Dr., Silver Spring, Md. Office: Dept. of History, U. of Md., College Park.

CHILDS, JAMES B. Home: 1221 Newton St., NE., Washington, D.C. 20017.

CHIPMAN, DONALD EUGENE, b. Hill City, Kans., Nov. 19, 1928. HISTORY. B.A., Fort Hays Kans. State Coll., 1955; M.S., 1958; Ph.D., U. of N. Mex., 1962. Vis. prof, U. of Wash., Summer 1962; ASST. PROF., HISTORY, FORT HAYS KANS. STATE COLL., 1962-64. University fellow, U. of N. Mex., 1960-61; American Council of Learned Societies grant-in-aid (Spain), Summer 1963. Membership: American Historical Association; Conference on Latin American History. Research: paleography; Spanish archival research; Mexican history. Author: New Light on the Career of Nuño de Guzmán (The Americas, Apr. 1963). Language: Spanish 4,3,3,2; French 2,1,1,1. Office: Box 5191 NT Station, Denton, Tex.

CHRISTIAN, PERCY W. Office: Pacific Union Coll., Angwin, Calif.

CHRISTIANSEN, PAIGE W., b. Miles City, Mont., July 7, 1923. HISTORY. B.A., Mich. State U., 1949; M.A., U. of N. Mex., 1954; Ph.D., U. of Calif., Berkeley, 1959. Instr., U. of Calif., Berkeley, 1949; ASST. PROF., HISTORY, N. MEX. INSTITUTE OF MINING AND TECHNOLOGY, 1959- . Advisory Council, New Mexico State Archives and Records Center. Membership: American Association of University Professors; Phi Alpha Theta. Research: Mexico; inter-American affairs. Author: Pascual Orozco: Chihuahua Rebel (New Mexico Historical Review, Apr. 1961); A Brief History of Socorro County (New Mexico Geological Society, Oct. 1963); Hugo Oconor's Inspection of Nueva Vizcaya and Coahuila, 1773 (Louisiana Studies, Fall 1963). Language: Spanish 5,3,3,4. Home: 8 North Dr., Socorro, N. Mex. Office: Dept. of Humanities, N. Mex. Institute of Mining and Technology, Socorro.

CLAXTON, ROBERT HOWARD, b. Buffalo, N.Y., July 18, 1942. HISTORY. A.B., Houghton Coll., 1962; M.A., State U. of N.Y. Coll. at Buffalo, 1964; Tulane U. STUDENT, HISTORY, TULANE U., 1964- ; interim instr., Houghton Coll., Summer 1965. National Defense Foreign Language fellow in Spanish, Tulane U., 1964-65. Membership: American Historical Association; Hispanic American Historical Association. Research: Latin American history; inter-American relations in the thought of Eugenio Maria de Hostos. Language: Spanish 3,2,2,2; Portuguese 3,1,1,1; French 1,1,1,1. Home: 1900 Porterville Rd., East Aurora, N.Y. 14052.

CLEGERN, WAYNE M., b. Edmond, Okla., Nov. 28, 1929. HISTORY. A.B., U. of Okla., 1951; M.A., 1954; Ph.D., U. of Calif., Berkeley, 1959. Asst. prof., La. State U., 1959-62; asst. prof., acting chmn., 1962-63; ASSOC. PROF., CHMN., HISTORY, LA. STATE U., NEW ORLEANS, 1963- . Doherty fellow (Central America), 1958-59. Membership: American Historical Association; Conference on Latin American History; Louisiana Historical Association. Research: international disputes; British Honduras. Author: Maudslay's Central America (1962); New Light on the Belize Dispute (American Journal of International Law, Apr. 1958); A Guatemalan Defense of the British Honduras Boundary of 1859 (Hispanic American Historical Review, Nov. 1960). Language: Spanish 3,—,—,—; Portuguese 2,—,—,—; German 2,—,—,—. Home: 4653 Kendall Dr., New Orleans 26, La. Office: Dept. of History, La. State U., New Orleans 22.

CLENDENEN, CLARENCE C., b. Colorado Springs, Colo., June 8, 1899. HISTORY. B.S., U.S. Military Academy, 1920; M.A., Mich. State U., 1953; Ph.D., Stanford U., 1959. Second lieutenant-colonel, U.S. Army, 1918-1954; instr., Stanford U., 1959-60; instr., Menlo Coll., 1960-63; RESEARCH ASST. AND MILITARY CURATOR, HOOVER INSTITUTION ON WAR, REVOLUTION AND PEACE, STANFORD U., 1963- . Membership: American Historical Association; American Military Institute; Naval Historical Foundation. Research: revolutionary history of Mexico. Author: The United States and Pancho Villa (1961); Dan Showalter—California Secessionist (California Historical Society Quarterly, Dec. 1961); A Confederate Spy in California (Southern California Quarterly, Sept. 1963). Language: Spanish 4,4,3,4; German 2,1,1,2. Home: 1587 Dennis Lane, Mountain View, Calif. Office: Hoover Institution on War, Revolution and Peace, Stanford U., Stanford, Calif.

CLINE, HOWARD FRANCIS, b. Detroit, Mich., June 12, 1915. HISTORY, ANTHROPOLOGY, AND GEOGRAPHY. S.B., Harvard Coll., 1939; A.M., Harvard U., 1942; Ph.D., 1947. Asst. dean, Harvard Coll., 1943-46; instr. Harvard U., 1946-47; instr., Yale U., 1947-49; asst. prof., Northwestern U., 1949-52; DIR., HISPANIC FOUNDATION, LIBRARY OF CONGRESS, 1952- . Sheldon Prize fellow, 1939; Social Science Research Council fellow, 1942-43; Woodbury Lowery fellow, 1947; Social Science Research Council grant-in-aid, 1951, 1955; chmn., Conference on Latin American History,

1964. Membership: American Anthropological Association; American Historical Association; Conference on Latin American History; Phi Beta Kappa. Research: Mexico; Middle American ethnohistory; Mexican pictorial documents. Author: The United States and Mexico (1953); Mexico: Revolution to Evolution, 1940-1960 (1962); Colonial Lienzos and Communities of the Mazatec Indians, Oaxaca, Mexico (in Ancient Oaxaca, by J. Paddock, 1964). Language: Spanish 4,4,4,2; Portuguese 4,3,3,1; French 4,2,2,1; German 4,3,3,1; Italian 3,2,2,1; Maya 2,2,1,1. Linguistic studies: Chinantec. Home: 1701 North Patrick Henry Dr., Arlington, Va. Office: Hispanic Foundation, Library of Congress, Washington, D.C. 20540.

CLINTON, RICHARD LEE, b. Cookeville, Tenn., Sept. 20, 1938. HISTORY. B.A., Vanderbilt U., 1960; M.A. in History, 1964; M.A. in Latin American Studies, 1964. Instr., Spanish, Vanderbilt U., Summer, Fall 1960; instr., English, Instituto Cultural Peruano-norteamericano (Lima, Peru), 1961; EXECUTIVE TRAINEE, OVERSEAS DIV., FIRST NATIONAL CITY BANK OF N.Y., 1964- . National Defense Education Act fellow in Latin American Studies, Vanderbilt U., 1961-64; Buenos Aires Convention grant (Peru), 1961-62. Membership: Southeastern Conference on Latin American Studies. Research: Latin American history, especially that of Bolivarian nations and Peru; political thought of Manuel González Prada. Author: La Universidad de San Cristóbal de Huamanga at Ayacucho (Andean Airmail and Peruvian Times, July 14, 1961); Paramonga: Blueprint for Progress (Andean Airmail and Peruvian Times, Nov. 17, 1961). Language: Spanish 5,5,5,5; Portuguese 2,2,1,1; French 3,3,3,3; German 2,2,2,2. Home: 1015 East Amelia Ave., Orlando, Fla. 32803. Office: First National City Bank of N.Y., 399 Park Ave., New York, 10022.

COBB, GWENDOLIN B. Office: Dept. of History, Fresno State Coll., Fresno, Calif. 93726.

COLEMAN, WILLIAM JACKSON, M.M., b. Shelby, Ohio, Mar. 29, 1911. HISTORY. Maryknoll Seminary (N.Y.), 1935-39; M.A., Catholic U. of America, 1942; Ph.D., 1950. Prof., Maryknoll Coll., 1947-50; dir., Colegio Gonzalo Correa (Chile), 1950-56; prof., Maryknoll Seminary (N.Y.), 1956-61; PROF., HISTORY, MARYKNOLL SEMINARY (ILL.), 1961- . Catholic Foreign Mission Society research fellow, Vatican Archives, 1945-47. Membership: American Historical Association; Catholic Historical Association; Interamerican Conference. Research: Latin American church and mission history, especially the early national period. Author: The First Apostolic Delegation in Rio de Janeiro and Its Influence in Spanish America (1950); La restauración del episcopado chileno en 1828 según fuentes vaticanas (1954); Latin American Catholicism (1958). Language: Spanish 4,—,—,—; Portuguese 3,—,—,—; French 3,—,—,—; Italian 3,—,-—,—. Office: Maryknoll Seminary, Glen Ellyn, Ill. 60137.

COLLINS, JOHN C., b. Schenectady, N.Y., June 25, 1902. HISTORY. B.S., Union Coll., 1922; M.S., Coll. of St. Rose, 1959; Harvard Law School, 1923-25. Teacher, Greene Central School (N.Y.), 1957-64; instr., Broome Technical Community Coll., 1962-64; ASST. PROF., HISTORY, BROOME TECHNICAL COMMUNITY COLL., 1964- . Membership: Conference on Latin American History; Schenectady County Bar Association. Research: Latin American history. Language: Spanish 2,1,1,1; Portuguese 1,1,1,1; French 2,1,1,1; German 2,1,1,1. Home: 90 Genesse St., Greene, N.Y. Office: Broome Technical Community Coll., Binghamton, N.Y.

CONRAD, DAVID E., b. Marietta, Okla., Aug. 22, 1928. HISTORY. B.A., U. of Okla., 1952; M.A., 1957; Ph.D., 1962. ASSOC. PROF., HISTORY, SOUTHWEST TEX. STATE COLL., 1957- . Southern Fellowships Fund grant-in-aid, 1959, fellow, 1961. Membership: Agricultural History Association; Mississippi Valley Historical Association. Research: Mexican-American border area. Author: The Whipple Expedition on the Great Plains (Great Plains Journal, Spring 1963). Language: Spanish 3,3,2,2; French 3,2,2,2. Home: R.F.D. 2, Box 474-A, San Marcos, Tex. Office: Dept. of History, Southwest Tex. State Coll., San Marcos.

COOK, SHERBURNE F., b. Springfield, Mass., Dec. 31, 1896. HISTORY, DEMOGRAPHY, AND ECOLOGY. A.B., Harvard U., 1919; M.A., 1923; Ph.D., 1925. PROF., PHYSIOLOGY, U. OF CALIF., BERKELEY, 1928- . Guggenheim fellow, 1939, 1946. Research: Mexican archeology, soils and ethnography. Author: Soil Erosion and Population in Central Mexico (1949). Co-author: Population of Central Mexico in the 16th Century (1948); The Aboriginal Population in Central Mexico on the Eve of the Spanish Conquest (1962). Language: Spanish 4,3,3,3; French 4,2,2,2; German 4,3,3,4. Home: 105 Grand Ave., Pacific Grove, Calif. Office: Dept. of Physiology, U. of Calif., Berkeley.

COOK, WARREN L., b. Spokane, Wash., July 29, 1925. HISTORY AND ANTHROPOLOGY. Bachillerato de Humanidades, Universidad de San Marcos (Peru), 1950; Litt.D., 1955; M.A., Yale U., 1957; Ph.D., 1960. Bibliographical research, Universidad de San Marcos, 1950-52; instr., 1953; asst. prof., Castleton State Coll., 1960-63; ASSOC. PROF., SOCIAL SCIENCE, CASTLETON STATE COLL., 1963- . Membership: American Anthropological Association; American Association of University Professors; American Historical Association; Conference on Latin American History; Northern New England Historian's Conference. Research: Andean history; Spanish period of the American West; Mexico. Author: Fray Buenaventura de Salinas y Córdova, su vida y su obra (Revista del Museo Nacional, Lima, 1955; revised edition, in Memorial de las Historias del Nuevo Mundo Perú, 1957). Language: Spanish 5,5,5, 4; Portuguese 4,3,3,2; French 4,3,2,2; German

3,3,3,2. Box 195, Castleton, Vt. Office: Dept. of Social Science, Castleton State Coll., Castleton.

COOPER, DONALD BOLON. b. Columbus, Ohio, Aug. 20, 1931. HISTORY. B.A., Ohio State U., 1957; M.A., 1958; Ph.D., U. of Tex., 1963. Asst. prof., Okla. State U., 1961-63; ASST. PROF., HISTORY, TULANE U., 1963- . Woodrow Wilson fellow, 1957-58; University fellowships, U. of Tex., 1958-60, 1961; Doherty fellow (Mexico), 1960; U.S. Public Health Service fellow, 1962; National Defense Foreign Language post-doctoral fellow in Portuguese, Summer 1963. Membership: American Association of University Professors; Phi Alpha Theta; Phi Beta Kappa; Pi Sigma Alpha. Research: history of Brazil, particularly social, municipal, and medical history; Mexico. Author: A Cycle of Sickness: The Fight Against Epidemics in Mexico City, 1761-1813 (1964); A Selective List of the Colonial Manuscripts in the Department of Health and Welfare, Mexico City, 1564-1800 (Hispanic American Historical Review, Aug. 1962); The Withdrawal of the United States from Haiti, 1928-1934 (Journal of Inter-American Studies, Jan. 1963). Language: Spanish 3,3,3,2; Portuguese 3,2,2,1; French 2,1,—,—. Home: 595 Gordon Ave., New Orleans 23, La. Office: Dept. of History, Newcomb Coll., Tulane U., New Orleans, 70118.

CORBITT, DUVON CLOUGH, b. Atkinson County, Ga., July 4, 1901. HISTORY. A.B., Asbury Coll., 1923; M.A., Emory U., 1926; Ph.D., U. of N.C., 1938. Dept. head, Candler Coll. (Cuba), 1927-29, 1931-43, 1945-46; chmn., History, Columbia Coll. (S.C.), 1943-45; vis. prof., Fla. State U., Summer 1944, Ohio State U., Summer 1944, U. of Omaha, Summer 1945; CHMN., DIV. OF SOCIAL STUDIES, ASBURY COLL., 1946- ; lectr., National Defense Education Act Language Institute, Vanderbilt U., 1963. Membership: Academia de la Historia de la Medicina; Southern Historical Society. Research: history of Cuba and the Caribbean; archival research in Cuba; documents from Spanish archives concerned with the Southwest of the United States. Author: The Chinese in Cuba (Research Bureau for Post-War Economics, 1944); Historical Publications of the Martí Centennial (Hispanic American Historical Review, Aug. 1954); Cuban Revisionist Interpretations of Cuba's Struggle for Independence (Hispanic American Historical Review, Aug. 1963). Language: Spanish 5,4,4,3; Portuguese 3,3,3,1; French 4,3,2,1. Home: 205 East Morrison Ave., Wilmore, Ky. Office: Div. of Social Studies, Asbury Coll., Wilmore.

CORTÉS, CARLOS ELISEO, b. Oakland, Calif., Apr. 6, 1934. HISTORY. M.S., Columbia U., 1957; B.F.T., American Institute for Foreign Trade, 1962; M.A., U. of N. Mex., 1965. Executive editor, Phoenix Sun (Ariz.), 1959-61; reporter, Associated Press (Phoenix), 1961; programmer, Learning, Inc. (Tempe, Ariz.), 1961-62; STUDENT, HISTORY, U. OF N. MEX., 1962- . National Defense Foreign Language fellow, U. of N. Mex., 1962-65; So-

cial Science Research Council foreign area fellow (Brazil), 1965-66. Membership: Sigma Delta Chi; Phi Beta Kappa. Research: Latin American history; Brazilian political literature; post-World War II politics of Brazil. Language: Spanish 4,4,3,3; Portuguese 4,4,4,3; French 2,1,1,1. Home: Apt. 1, 1340 San Mateo SE., Albuquerque, N. Mex.

CORWIN, ARTHUR F., b. Raton, New Mex., Nov. 10, 1924. HISTORY. B.A., Trinity Coll. (Dublin), 1950; M.A., Mexico City Coll., 1952; Ph.D., U. of Chicago, 1958. Conferencista, U. of P.R., 1956; catedrático, Universidad de Nuevo León (Mexico), 1958-62; vis. prof., U. of Texas, 1962-63; ASST. PROF., HISTORY, U. OF KY., 1963- . U. of Chicago-U. of Madrid exchange fellow, 1954-55; consultant, General Education Program, Universidad del Valle (Colombia), Apr. 1961. Membership: Hispanic American Society. Research: economic history of Latin America. Author: Contemporary Mexican Attitudes toward Poverty and Population (1963); The Spanish Abolition Law of 1870 (Revista de Ciencias Sociales, U. of P.R., Mar. 1960). Co-editor: Evolución de la civilización contemporánea (U. of Nuevo León, Sept. 1963). Language: Spanish 5,5,5,5; Portuguese 3,2,2,2; French 3,3,2,3. Home: 1917 Oxford Circle No. 5, Lexington, Ky. Office: Dept. of History, U. of Ky., Lexington.

COTNER, THOMAS EWING, b. Dallas, Tex., Oct. 26, 1916. HISTORY AND EDUCATION. A.B., Baylor U., 1937; A.M., U. of Tex., 1939; Ph.D., 1947. Teacher, Brownwood High School (Tex.), 1937-39; dir., History Div., Tex. Memorial Museum, 1939-40; instr., U. of Tex., Summer 1940; instr., Tulane U., 1940-41; specialist, American Republics Section, U.S. Office of Education, 1942-43; DIR., TECHNICAL ASSISTANCE AND EXCHANGE PROGRAM, DIV. OF INTERNATIONAL EDUCATION, U.S. OFFICE OF EDUCATION, 1946- ; lectr., George Washington U., 1948-53. Graduate fellow, U. of Tex., 1939-40, 1941-42; Superior Service Award from the Secretary of U.S. Dept. of Health, Education, and Welfare, 1961. Membership: Academy of Political Science; Alpha Chi; American Historical Association; National Education Association; Phi Kappa Sigma; Texas Historical Society. Research: history of Mexico; international exchange of students, teachers, and professors. Author: The Military and Political Career of President José Joaquín de Herrera, 1792-1854 (1946); International Educational Exchange: A Selected Bibliography (1961). Editor: Essays in Mexican History (1958). Language: Spanish 4,4,3,3; Portuguese 2,—,—,—; French 2,—,—,—; Italian 2,—,—,—. Home: 228 Buxton Rd., Falls Church, Va. Office: Div. of International Education, U.S. Office of Education, Washington, D.C. 20202.

COTTON, DONNA LILLIAN, b. Grosse Pointe Farms, Mich., Dec. 18, 1931. HISTORY. B.A., U. of Md., 1953; M.A., George Washington U., 1959. Teacher, Fairfax County, Va., 1956-59; teacher, Mobil Oil Company (Puerto

Cabello, Venezuela), 1959-63; STUDENT, HIS-
TORY, GEORGE WASHINGTON U., 1963- ;
instr., Peace Corps Training Center, Springfield Coll., Summer 1965. Membership: American Historical Association; Brazilian-American
Cultural Institute; Middle East Institute. Research: Latin American history, government
and economics; the fall of the Ibáñez government in Chile; history of the modern Middle
East. Language: Spanish 4,4,4,4; Portuguese
2,2,2,2. Home: 24 South Aberdeen St., Arlington, Va. 22204.

CRAHAN, MARGARET ELLEN, b. Catskill,
N.Y., June 2, 1939. HISTORY. A.B., Coll. of
New Rochelle, 1960; M.A., Georgetown U.,
1963; Columbia U. Reference librarian, Riggs
Library, Georgetown U., 1960-61; researcher,
Hispanic Foundation, Library of Congress,
Summer 1962; STUDENT, HISTORY, CO-
LUMBIA U. Walter Ross Martin fellow, Co-
lumbia U., 1961-62; National Defense Foreign
Language fellow, 1962-63; Fulbright scholar
(Spain), 1963-64. Membership: American His-
torical Association; Conference on Latin Amer-
ican History. Research: Latin American colo-
nial legal history; viceroyalty of Duque de la
Palata, viceroy of Peru, 1681-1689. Language:
Spanish 4,4,4,4; Portuguese 3,3,3,3; French
2,2,2,2. Home: 380 Riverside Dr., Apt. 2C,
New York, N.Y. 10025.

CRAMER, BETTY NESBITT, b. Jacksonville,
Tex., Oct. 7, 1927. HISTORY. U. of Pa.;
M.A., Radcliffe Coll., 1965. Instr., East Tex.
State Coll., 1959-60; instr., Wellesley Coll.,
1960-61. Membership: Phi Beta Kappa. Re-
search: Latin American history; political history
of Argentina; Union Cívica Radical of Argen-
tina. Language: Spanish 1,3,2,3; French 3,4,-
—,—. Home: Apt. 605, 1201 South Scott St.,
Arlington, Va.

CRAMPTON, C. GREGORY, b. Kankakee, Ill.,
Mar. 22, 1911. HISTORY. A.B., U. of Calif.,
Berkeley, 1935; M.A., 1936; Ph.D., 1941. Special agent, Federal Bureau of Investigation,
U.S. Dept. of Justice, 1943-45; historian, Calif.
Quartermaster Depot, U.S. War Dept., 1944-
45; PROF., HISTORY, U. OF UTAH, 1945- ;
vis. asst. prof., Northwestern U., Summer 1946;
vis. prof., U. of Panama, 1955; prof., Overseas
Program (Europe), U. of Md., 1956-57; vis.
lectr., Eastern Mont. Coll. of Education, Sum-
mer 1961. Rockefeller Foundation traveling
fellow (Latin America), 1941-42; Rockefeller
Foundation fellow, 1948-49. Membership:
American Historical Association; Mississippi
Valley Historical Association; Phi Alpha Theta.
Research: Mexico and Central America; west-
ern United States. Author: Historical Sites in
Glen Canyon, Mouth of San Juan River to Lee's
Ferry (1960); Historical Sites in Glen Canyon,
Mouth of Hansen Creek to Mouth of San Juan
River (1962). Editor: The Mariposa Indian
War, Diaries of Robert Eccleston: The Cali-
fornia Gold Rush, Yosemite and the High
Sierra (1957). Language: Spanish 4,4,4,2; Por-
tuguese 3,3,3,1; French 2,2,2,1. Home: 327
South 12th East, Salt Lake City, Utah. Office:

Dept. of History, U. of Utah, Salt Lake City,
84112.

CRISCENTI, JOSEPH THOMAS, b. Detroit,
Mich., Aug. 7, 1920. HISTORY. Ph.B., U. of
Detroit, 1942; A.M., Harvard U., 1947; Ph.D.,
1956. ASSOC. PROF., HISTORY, BOSTON
COLL., 1955- . Pan American World Airways
traveling fellow (Argentina and Uruguay),
1950-52; Robertson Prize, 1961; American
Philosophical Society grant (Argentina and
Uruguay), 1963. Membership: American Historical Association; Conference on Latin American History. Research: 19th century developments in the Río de la Plata area—Argentina,
Uruguay, Brazil; economic, political and international factors contributing to the formation
of the Argentine state, 1810-1880. Author: The
Campaign against Rosas: Minutes of Conferences on Military Plans, June 1851 (Hispanic
American Historical Review, Feb. 1954); Argentine Constitutional History, 1810-1852: A Re-
examination (Hispanic American Historical Review, Aug. 1961). Language: Spanish 5,5,5,4;
Portuguese 3,4,3,2; French 4,3,2,2; Italian
4,4,3,2. Home: 28 Richard Rd., Needham,
Mass. Office: Dept. of History, Boston Coll.,
Chestnut Hill 67, Mass.

CRONON, E(DMUND) DAVID, b. Minneapolis,
Minn., Mar. 11, 1924. HISTORY. B.A.,
Oberlin Coll., 1948; M.A., U. of Wis., 1949;
Ph.D., 1953. Instr.-asst. prof., Yale U., 1953-
59; assoc. prof.-prof., U. of Nebr., 1959-62;
PROF., HISTORY, U. OF WIS., 1962- . Fulbright fellow, U. of Manchester (England),
1950-51; Henry L. Stimson grant (Mexico),
Summer 1955; fellow, Yale U., 1958-59. Membership: American Historical Association; Mississippi Valley Historical Association. Research:
United States contemporary history and foreign
relations. Author: Black Moses: The Story of
Marcus Garvey and the Universal Negro Improvement Association (1955); Josephus Daniels
in Mexico (1960); The Cabinet Diaries of
Josephus Daniels (1963). Language: Spanish
2,2,1,1; French 2,2,2,2; German 2,2,2,2. Home:
5601 Varsity Hill, Madison 5, Wis. Office:
Dept of History, U. of Wis., Madison 6.

CROWLEY, FLORENCE JOSEPH, b. New York,
N.Y., June 12, 1937. HISTORY. B.A., Brook-
lyn Coll., 1959; M.A., 1960; Ph.D., U. of Fla.,
1963. U.S. ARMY, 1963-1965. Research: intel-
lectual history of Mexico; Argentina; Brazil.
Language: Spanish 4,4,4,4; Portuguese 2,2,2,2;
French 2,2,2,2. Home: 1933 Batchelder St.,
Brooklyn 29, N.Y.

CULVER, JOHN WILLIAM, b. Mountain Home,
Idaho, Nov. 12, 1906. HISTORY. B.A., U. of
Wis., 1932; Ph.D., 1938. Instr., U. of Wis.,
1937-41; dir., União Cultural Brasil—E.E.U.U.
(São Paulo, Brazil), 1942-45; dir., Instituto
Chileno-Norteamericano de Cultura (Santiago),
1945-48; vis. prof., U. of Chile, 1947; assoc.
prof., Western Reserve U., 1948-51; ASSOC.
PROF., HISTORY, CASE INSTITUTE OF
TECHNOLOGY, 1951- ; vis. prof., U. of
P.R., Summer 1956; dir., Jr. Year in Brazil

Program, N.Y.U., 1960-61. Regents' fellowship, teaching fellow, U. of Wis.; consultant, Champion Paper Co., 1958. Membership: American Historical Association; Conference on Latin American History; Pen International; Phi Delta Kappa. Research: Brazil. Language: Spanish 5,5,4,3; Portuguese 5,5,5,3; French 4,3,3,2; German 3,2,2,1; Italian 3,2,2,1. Home: 1838 Wymore, East Cleveland, Ohio. Office: Dept. of History, Case Institute of Technology, Cleveland 6.

CUMBERLAND, CHARLES CURTIS, b. Kingsville, Tex., May 6, 1914. HISTORY. B.A., Tex. Coll. of Arts & Industries, 1936; M.A., 1938; Ph.D., U. of Tex., 1949. Asst. prof., Princeton U., 1946-48; asst. prof., Rutgers U., 1948-55; PROF., HISTORY, MICH. STATE U., 1955- . Doherty fellow (Mexico); Social Science Research Council grant-in-aid; Fulbright lectr. (Spain). Membership: American Historical Association; Conference on Latin American History; Texas Historical Association. Research: 20th century Latin American revolutions; modern Mexican history and United States-Mexican relations. Author: Mexican Revolution: Genesis under Madero (1952); Twentieth Century Revolutions in Latin America (Centennial Review, Fall 1962). Co-author: U.S. University Cooperation in Latin America (1960). Language: Spanish 4,4,4,4; Portuguese 3,2,1,1; French 3,1,1,1. Home: 2216 Iroquois Rd., Okemos, Mich. Office; Dept. of History, Mich. State U., East Lansing.

CUMMINS, LEJEUNE, b. San Diego, Calif., Nov. 18, 1924. HISTORY AND INTERNATIONAL RELATIONS. A.B., U. of Calif., Berkeley, 1950; M.A., 1951; Ph.D., 1964. Instr., Imperial Valley Coll., 1951-52; instr., Berkeley Unified School District, 1953-59; ASST. PROF., HISTORY, CALIF. STATE COLL., HAYWARD, 1963- . Woodrow Wilson traveling grant, 1962. Membership: American Historical Association; Hispanic American Society, Mississippi Valley Historical Association; Phi Alpha Theta; Phi Beta Kappa. Research: Pan Americanism; United States diplomatic history. Author: Quijote on a Burro, Sandino and the Marines: A Study in the Formulation of Foreign Policy (1958); Antonelli, the Younger, First Engineer of the Indies (Mid-America, Jan. 1956). Language: Spanish 4,4,3,3; Portuguese 2,1,1,1; French 2,1,1,1. Home: 3505 Isla Vista, San Diego 5, Calif. Office: Dept. of History, Calif. State Coll., Hayward, 94542.

CUNNINGHAM, JAMES STEWART, JR., b. San Francisco, Calif., Apr. 25, 1911. HISTORY. A.B., U. of Calif., Berkeley, 1934; M.A., 1936; Ph.D., 1946. Asst.-assoc. prof., Goucher Coll., 1946-51; research specialist and acting chief, American Republics Div., U.S. Dept. of State, 1951-57; prof., Foreign Service Institute, U.S. Dept. of State, 1953; second-first secretary, Embassy (Tegucigalpa, Honduras), U.S. Dept. of State, 1958-60; first secretary, chief, Political Section, Embassy (Asunción, Paraguay), U.S. Dept. of State, 1961-63; first secretary and chief, Political Section, Embassy (Montevideo,

Uruguay), U.S. Dept. of State, 1963-66; HISTORIAN, HISTORICAL OFFICE, U.S. DEPT. OF STATE, 1966- . Editor, Latin American Section, American Historical Review, 1946-51; Seminar on Latin American Studies, Social Security Research Council, Stanford U., 1963. Research: United States policy and diplomacy in Latin America; political and social change in modern Latin America. Author: Spanish Colonization in Patagonia, 1778-1783 (in Greater America, Essays in Honor of Herbert Eugene Bolton, 1945). Co-author: Brazil (in Britannica Book of the Year, 1939, 1940, 1941); Colombia (in Britannica Book of the Year, 1939). Language: Spanish 4,3,3,3. Home: 1823 Dalmation Dr., McLean, Va. Office: U.S. Dept. of State, Washington, D.C.

CUTTER, DONALD COLGETT, b. Chico, Calif., Jan. 9, 1922. HISTORY. A.B., U. of Calif., Berkeley, 1943; M.A., 1947; Ph.D., 1950. Instr., San Diego State Coll., 1950-51; asst. prof.-prof., U. of Southern Calif., 1951-61; PROF., HISTORY, U. OF N. MEX., 1962- . Native Sons of the Golden West fellow, 1947-48; U. of Calif. teaching fellow, 1948-49; Social Science Research Council fellow (Mexico), 1949-50; Del Amo fellow (Spain), 1953; Social Science Research Council faculty research fellow, 1956-59; Fulbright scholar (Spain), 1961-62; chief historical research consultant, Council of California Indians, 1953-56; Board of Editors, The Americas, The American West, Arizona and the West, Journal of the West. Membership: American Historical Association; Pacific Coast Council of Latin American Studies; Phi Alpha Theta; Sigma Delta Pi; Western History Association. Research: Spanish colonial history in California and American West; explorations; Spanish naval history. Author: The Diary of Ensign Gabriel Moraga's Expedition of Discovery in the Sacramento Valley, 1808 (1957); Malaspina in California (1960); Documentos para la historia de Sonora (1964). Language: Spanish 4,4,4,4; Portuguese 3,3,2,2; French 3,3,2,3; German 2,2,1,2; Italian 2,2,2. Home: 2508 Harold Pl., Albuquerque, N. Mex. Office: Dept. of History, U. of N. Mex., Albuquerque.

DABBS, JACK AUTREY, b. Mercury, Tex., Jan. 31, 1914. HISTORY AND LINGUISTICS. B.A., U. of Tex., 1935; M.A., 1936; Ph.D., 1950. Teacher, Tex. Wesleyan Academy, 1936-37; teacher, Lockhart High School (Tex.), 1937-38; instr., St. Edward's U., 1938-40, 1948-50; dir., American Language Institute (Iraq), 1957-58; PROF., MODERN LANGUAGES, TEX. A. & M. U., 1950- . Institute of Latin American Studies, U. of Tex., summer research grants, 1956, 1959, 1961, 1962, 1963; Ford Foundation grant (East Pakistan), 1960. Membership: American Name Society; Linguistic Society of America; Modern Language Association. Research: anthropology; literature; Mexican history and documents; namelore. Author: Catalog of the Manuscripts in the Manuel E. Gondra Manuscript Collection (1953); Independent Mexico in Documents (1955); The French Army in Mexico, 1861-1867 (1963). Co-author:

Guide to Latin American Manuscripts in the University of Texas Library (1940). Language: Spanish 5,4,4,4; Portuguese 3,3,2,2; French 5,4,3,4; Bengali 2,2,2,2; German 3,3,3,3; Russian 2,2,2,2. Home: 1011 Edgewood, Bryan, Tex. Office: Dept. of Modern Languages, Tex. A. & M. U., College Station.

DAHL, VICTOR CHARLES, b. Dickinson, N. Dak., Dec. 11, 1928. HISTORY. B.A., Mont. State U., 1950; M.A., 1951; Ph.D., U. of Calif., 1959. Asst. prof., Portland State Coll., 1959-61; ADMINISTRATIVE ASST., PRESIDENT'S OFFICE, PORTLAND STATE COLL., 1961- . Membership: American Historical Association; Montana Historical Society; Pacific Coast Council on Latin American Studies. Research: Mexico; Uruguay. Author: Alien Labor on the Gulf Coast of Mexico, 1880-1900 (The Americas, July 1960); Business Influence in the Anglo-Mexican Reconciliation of 1884 (Latin American Economic Affairs, Aug. 1961). Language: Spanish 4,3,3,3; Portuguese 3,2,1,1; German 3,2,2,1. Home: 13138 SW. 63rd Pl., Portland 19, Oreg. Office: P.O. Box 751, Portland State Coll., Portland.

DAUPHINEE, BEDE ANTHONY, REVEREND, b. Concord, N.H., Nov. 6, 1918. HISTORY. M.A., Georgetown U., 1959; Ph.D., 1965. Resident member, Academy of American Franciscan History, 1950-60; lectr., Brazilian Div., Institute of Inter-Cultural Communication (Anapolis, Brazil), 1960-61. Research: Latin American history; spoliation of church property in Mexico; Franciscan history. Language: Spanish 4,3,3,3; Portuguese 3,1,1,1; French 3,1,1,1. Home: Holy Name Coll., 14th and Shepherd Sts., NE., Washington, D.C. 20017.

DAVIES, ARCHIBALD PUTNAM, b. Oriskany Falls, N.Y., Jan. 14, 1923. HISTORY. A.B., Colgate U., 1948; M.A., Columbia U., 1949. Teacher, Instituto Chileno-norteamericano de Cultura (Santiago), 1951-53; Spanish master, Church Farm School for Boys (Panoli, Pa.), 1953-55; ASST. PROF., HISTORY AND LANGUAGES, U.S. MERCHANT MARINE ACADEMY, 1955- . Doherty fellow (Chile), 1950-51. Membership: American Association of University Professors; American Historical Association; Conference on Latin American History. Research: Latin American history; comparative culture of United States and Latin America; Latin American colonial institutions. Language: Spanish 4,4,4,3; Portuguese 2,2,2,1; French 2,2,2,1. Home: 15 Beach Rd. (1-U), Great Neck, N.Y. Office: Dept. of History and Languages, U.S. Merchant Marine Academy, Kings Point, N.Y.

DAVIS, HAROLD EUGENE, b. Girard, Ohio, Dec. 3, 1902. HISTORY AND POLITICAL SCIENCE. B.A., Hiram Coll., 1924; M.A., U. of Chicago, 1927; Ph.D., Western Reserve U., 1933. Prof., Hiram Coll., 1927-44; dean, 1944-47; dir., Div. of Educational and Teacher Aids, Office of the Coordinator of Inter-American Affairs, U.S. Govt., 1943-46; instr., U.S. Army U. (France), 1945-46; prof., chmn., Div. of Social Sciences, American U., 1947-52; dir., American Language Center, 1952-53; dean, Arts & Sciences, 1953-58; PROF., CHMN., LATIN AMERICAN AREA STUDIES, SCHOOL OF INTERNATIONAL SERVICE, AMERICAN U., 1958- . Washington Evening Star Research Award, 1958; Fulbright prof., U. of Chile, 1958-59; Survey of U. of Asunción (Paraguay) for U.S. Dept. of State, 1959; consultant for reviews of books for U.S. Information Agency, Operations & Policy Research, Inc.; consultant in general education, Calif. State Coll. (Pa.). Membership: American Historical Association; American Political Science Association; American Society of International Law; Instituto de la Historia del Derecho (Buenos Aires); Instituto Interamericano Indigenista; Inter-American Council (Washington, D.C.). Research: history of Latin American social thought; the presidency in Latin America; inter-American relations. Author: The Americas in History (1953); Latin American Social Thought (1961). Co-author: Government and Politics in Latin America (1958). Language: Spanish 4,4,4,4; Portuguese 4,3,3,2; French 4,3,3,2. Home: 4842 Langdrum Lane, Chevy Chase, Md. 20015. Office: School of International Service, American U., Washington, D.C. 20016.

DAVIS, ROBERT HENRY, b. Jacksonville, Ill., Feb. 15, 1939. HISTORY. B.A., Ill. Coll., 1961; M.A., Vanderbilt U., 1964. STUDENT, HISTORY, VANDERBILT U. National Defense Education Act fellow in Latin American History, Vanderbilt U., 1961-64. Membership: American Historical Association; Conference on Latin American History; Southeastern Conference on Latin American Studies. Research: Latin American history; early national period of Colombian history. Language: Spanish 3,2,-2,2; Portuguese 3,2,2,2. Home: 1117 Maplehurst Ave., Nashville, Tenn. 37204.

DAVIS, THOMAS BRABSON, JR., b. Hillsboro, Tex., Aug. 3, 1905. HISTORY. B.A., North Tex. State Teachers Coll., 1925; M.A., U. of Tex., 1928; Ph.D., Yale U., 1942. PROF., HISTORY, HUNTER COLL., 1942- . U.S. Dept. of State travel grant (Argentina), 1941. Membership: American Association of University Professors; American Historical Association; Conference on Latin American History. Research: early diplomatic relations between Argentina and the United States. Author: Carlos de Alvear, Man of Revolution (1955); James Monroe and Carlos de Alvear (Hispanic American Historical Review, Dec. 1942). Language: Spanish 4,4,4,4. Home: 22 Francis Lane, Port Chester, N.Y. Office: Dept. of History, Hunter Coll., 695 Park Ave., New York 21, N.Y.

DAVIS, WILLIAM COLUMBUS, b. Birmingham, Ala., Aug. 28, 1910. HISTORY AND POLITICAL SCIENCE. A.B., U. of Ala., 1931; M.A., 1932; M.A., Harvard U., 1943; Ph.D., 1948. Instr. U. of Ala., 1931-32; asst. prof., U. of Ga., 1948-51; research analyst, U.S. Central Intelligence Agency, 1951-52; PROF., LATIN AMER-

ICAN HISTORY, DIR., LATIN AMERICAN STUDIES, GEORGE WASHINGTON U., 1951- ; prof., Political Affairs, The National War College, 1963- . Research: recent political and economic developments in Latin America. Author: The Last Conquistadores (1950). Co-author: Soviet Bloc Latin American Activities and Their Implications for United States Foreign Policy (1960). Editor: Index to the Writings on American History, 1902-1940 (1956); The American Historical Association Guide to Historical Literature (1960). Language: Spanish 4,4,4,4; Portuguese 4,—,—,—; French 4,—,—,—. Home: 5100 Darnall Dr., McLean, Va. Office: Dept. of History and Political Science, George Washington U., Washington 6, D.C.

DEAN, WARREN KEMPTON, b. Passaic, N.J., Oct. 17, 1932. HISTORY. B.A., U. of Miami, 1953; M.A., U. of Fla., 1961; Ph.D., 1964. Translator, Instituto de Estudos Soçiais e Econômicos (São Paulo), 1962; POST-DOCTORAL FELLOW, U. OF TEX., 1964-65. Foreign Area training fellow, 1962-64; Interamerican U. Foundation, Brazilian Student Seminars, Harvard U., 1964. Membership: American Historical Association. Research: economic development; Brazilian entrepreneurship and economic nationalism; Cuba; international economic relationships, 1870- . Language: Spanish 4,4,3,3; Portuguese 5,5,4,4; French 3,2,2,1. Home: 4619-B Bull Creek Rd., Austin Tex., 78731. Office: Graduate School, U. of Tex., Austin, 78712.

DE ARMOND, LOUIS CUSHMAN, b. Orland, Calif., June 2, 1918. HISTORY. A.B., U. of Calif., Berkeley, 1940; M.A., 1947; Ph.D., 1950. Foreign Service (Chile), U.S. Dept. of State, 1942-44; PROF., HISTORY, DIR., INSTITUTE OF LATIN AMERICAN STUDIES, LOS ANGELES STATE COLL., 1950- . Ford Foundation Fund for the Advancement of Education grant (South America), 1954-55. Membership: American Historical Association; Conference on Latin American History; Pacific Coast Council on Latin American Studies. Research: colonial history and contemporary problems of Latin America; the activities of some United States groups in Latin America, such as the San Domingo Improvement Company. Author: Justo Sierra O'Reilly and Yucatecan-United States Relations, 1847-1848 (Hispanic American Historical Review, Aug. 1951); Frontier Warfare in Colonial Chile (Pacific Historical Review, May 1954). Language: Spanish 4,4,4,4; Portuguese 3,3,2,1; French 2,1,1,1; Japanese 1,2,—,—. Home: 436 East Benwood, Covina, Calif. Office: Institute of Latin American Studies, Los Angeles State Coll., 5151 State College Dr., Los Angeles 32, Calif.

DEARTH, JOHN A(RTHUR), b. Framingham, Mass., Mar. 5, 1907. HISTORY. A.B., Dartmouth Coll., 1929; M.A., Clark U., 1932; Ph.D., U. of Colo., 1954. Instr., Santiago Coll. (Chile), 1940-42; lectr., Chile-American Cultural Institute, 1942; instr., Drake U., 1946-49; asst. prof., Mission House Coll., 1955-56; assoc.

prof., Cottey Coll., 1956-58; assoc. prof., Nebr. State Teachers Coll., Peru, 1958-61; PROF., SOCIAL SCIENCES, SLIPPERY ROCK STATE COLL., 1961- . Membership: American Association of University Professors; American Historical Association; National Education Association. Research: colonial Hispanic American history; Mexico. Language: Spanish 3,3,3,3; Portuguese 1,—,—,—; French 3,3,3,3. Home: 363 Franklin St., Slippery Rock, Pa. Office: Dept. of Social Sciences, Slippery Rock State Coll., Slippery Rock.

DE CONDE, ALEXANDER, b. Utica, N.Y., Nov. 13, 1920. HISTORY. B.A., San Francisco State Coll., 1943; M.A., Stanford U., 1947; Ph.D., 1949. Instr., Stanford U., 1947-48; asst. prof.-assoc. prof., Whittier Coll., 1948-52; asst. prof., Duke U., 1952-57; assoc. prof., U. of Mich., 1957-61; assoc. prof., Stanford U., Summer 1960; PROF., HISTORY, U. OF CALIF., SANTA BARBARA, 1961- . CHMN., 1964- . Social Science Research Council grants, 1950, 1956; Guggenheim fellow, 1959-60; American Philosophical Society grant, 1963. Membership: American Association for the United Nations; American Association of University Professors; American Historical Association; Mississippi Valley Historical Association. Research: history and development of United States foreign policy. Author: Herbert Hoover's Latin American Policy (1951); Entangling Alliance: Politics and Diplomacy under George Washington (1957); History of American Foreign Policy (1963). Home: 1105 North Ontare Rd., Santa Barbara, Calif. Office: Dept. of History, U. of Calif., Santa Barbara.

DE GRUMMOND, JANE LUCAS, b. Bellefonte, Pa., Dec. 27, 1905. HISTORY. A.B., American U., 1929; M.A., La. State U., 1943; Ph.D., 1946. Teacher, Colegio Robinson (P.R.), 1925-28; teacher, Tyrone High School (Pa.), 1929-42; PROF., HISTORY, LA. STATE U., 1942- . Membership: Conference on Latin American History; Historical Society of Pennsylvania. Research: influence of sea power in Latin America's wars for independence; Bolivar and his admirals. Author: Envoy to Caracas (1951); Caracas Diary (1954); Baratarians and the Battle of New Orleans (1961). Language: Spanish 5,5,3,3; French 3,—,—,—. Home: 354 Albert Hart Dr., Baton Rouge 8, La. Office: Dept. of History, La. State U., Baton Rouge.

DELANEY, ROBERT W., b. Macon County, Mo., Oct. 5, 1918. HISTORY. A.B., B.S., Northeast Mo. State Teachers Coll., 1948; M.A., U. of N. Mex., 1950; Ph.D., 1955. Assoc. prof., Nebr. State Teachers Coll., 1955-57; CHMN., DIV. OF HUMANITIES, FORT LEWIS A. & M. COLL., 1957- . Consultant, U.S. Peace Corps Peruvian Projects, U. of Denver, 1963. Membership: American Association of University Professors; American Historical Association; Conference on Latin American History; Conference of Western Historians. Research: colonial and national periods in Latin America. Author: Matamoros, Port for Texas during the Civil War (Southwestern Historical Quarterly,

Apr. 1955); General Miller and the Confederación Perú-Boliviana (The Americas, Jan. 1962). Language: Spanish 4,3,3,3; French 3,2,2,2. Home: 1549 West Third Ave., Durango, Colo. Office: Div. of Humanities, Fort Lewis A. & M. Coll., Durango.

DELANEY, WILLIAM V., b. Falmouth, Ky., Mar. 16, 1923. HISTORY. B.A., Xavier U. (Ohio), 1948; M.A., 1950; St. Louis U. Part-time instr., Webster Coll., 1951-52; ASSOC. PROF., HISTORY, OUR LADY OF CINCINNATI COLL., 1954- . Xavier U. fellow, 1949-50. Membership: Cincinnati Council for World Affairs; Diocesan Papal Volunteers for Latin America; Peace Corps Council of Cincinnati. Research: Latin American history; history of the Maynas or the upper Amazon region. Home: 132 Roger Lane, Florence, Ky. Office: Dept. of History, Our Lady of Cincinnati Coll., Edgecliff-Walnut Hills, Cincinnati 6, Ohio.

DEL DUCA, GEMMA MARIE, SISTER, b. Greensburg, Pa., Apr. 1, 1932. HISTORY. B.A., Seton Hill Coll., 1962; M.S.S., Pontifical Institute, Regina Mundi (Rome), 1959; U. of N. Mex.; Teacher, St. Leo School (Altoona, Pa.), 1952-55; St. Luke High School (Carnegie, Pa.), 1955-56; Sacred Heart High School (Pittsburgh), 1959-60; Holy Innocents School (Pittsburgh), 1960-61; STUDENT, IBERO-AMERICAN STUDIES, U. OF N. MEX., 1962- . National Defense Education Act fellow. Membership: Latin American Secretariat for Academic Services; Phi Alpha Theta; Phi Sigma Iota. Research: Christian socialism in Latin America; 19th century Cuba. Language: Spanish 5,5,4,3; Portuguese 4,4,3,3; French 4,4,3,3; Italian 5,5,4,4. Home: Seton Hill Coll., Greensburg, Pa. 15601.

DELLA CAVA, RALPH S., b. Yonkers, N.Y., Sept. 11, 1934. HISTORY. B.S.S., Fordham U., 1956; Ph.D., Columbia U., 1965. Latin American representative, U.S. National Student Association, 1956-58; asst. secretary general, Latin American Area, World Assembly of Youth (Belgium), 1958-60. International Fellows Program, Columbia U., 1960-61; National Defense Foreign Language grant, 1961-62, 1962-63, 1963-64; Foreign Area Fellowship Program grant (Brazil), 1963-64; Board of Directors, Commission for International Development. Membership: Conference on Latin American History. Research: student movements, labor, and politics in Latin America; reform movements in the Brazilian Northeast, 1889-1930. Language: Spanish 5,5,5,4; Portuguese 5,5,4,4; French 5,5,5,4; Italian 5,5,4,4; Russian 3,3,3,2. Home: 4634 Garden Pl., New York 70, N.Y.

DE VORE, BLANCHE BLUE, b. May 19, 1912. HISTORY. B.S., Appalachian State Teachers Coll., 1939; Ph.D., U. of Southern Calif., 1963. Teacher, Blowing Rock High School (N.C.), 1941-43; teacher, San Diego County Public Schools (Calif.), 1943-48; teacher, Los Angeles County Public Schools (Calif.), 1953-63;

INSTR., HISTORY, RIO HONDO JUNIOR COLL., 1963- . Membership: Phi Alpha Theta. Research: the Mexican Revolution; international relations. Language: Spanish 3,2,-2,2; Portuguese 1,1,1,1; French 3,2,2,1; German 3,2,2,2. Home: 14711 Valeda Dr., La Mirado, Calif. Office: Dept. of History, Rio Hondo Junior Coll., Whittier, Calif.

DÍAZ-SOLER, LUIS M., b. San Juan, P.R., Nov. 12, 1916. HISTORY. B.A., U. of P.R., 1939; M.A., La. State U., 1947; Ph.D., 1950. Clerk, U.S. Engineer Office, 1940-41; head, District Div., U.S. Censorship Office, 1941-43; PROF., HISTORY, U. OF P.R., 1943- . Vice president, IV Reunión de Consulta, Instituto Pan Americano de Geografía e Historia, 1959. Membership: Institute International de Civilisations Differents (Belgium). Research: history of Puerto Rico and the Caribbean. Author: Historia de la Esclavitud Negra en Puerto Rico (1953); Rosendo Matienzo Cintrón (1960). Language: Spanish 5,5,5,5; Portuguese 1,1,—,—; French 1,—,—,—. Home: 110 Janer St., Río Piedras, P.R. Office: Box 22133, University, San Juan, P.R. 00931.

DIFFIE, BAILEY, W., b. Detroit, Tex., June 27, 1902. HISTORY. A.B., Southeastern Teachers Coll., 1923; M.A., Tex. Christian U., 1926; Ph.D., Central U. (Spain), 1929. Instr., Tex. Christian U., 1926-27; instr., City Coll. (N.Y.), 1930-36; asst. prof., 1936-46; vis. lectr., Cornell U., 1943; economic analyst, Foreign Economics Administration, 1943-44; assoc. prof., City Coll. (N.Y.), 1946-47; vis. lectr., Yale U., 1946-47; PROF., HISTORY, CITY COLL. (N.Y.), 1951- ; vis. prof., N.Y.U., 1962; vis. prof., Columbia U., 1963-64. Rotary Club grant (Spain), 1926-27; American Fund for Public Service grant, 1929-30; Editorial Board, Hispanic American Historical Review, 1946- ; grants from Social Science Research Council and American Philosophical Society, 1948-49, 1952, 1958-59, 1960, 1962. Membership: American Historical Association; Amigos de España; Conference on Latin America History. Research: history of Portugal and Brazil to 1808. Author: Porto Rico: A Broken Pledge (1931); Latin American Civilization: Colonial Period (1945); Prelude to Empire: Portugal Overseas before Henry the Navigator (1960). Language: Spanish 4,—,4,4; Portuguese 4,—,4,4; French 4,—,3,3; Italian 3,—,2,—. Home: 181-41 Kruger Rd., Jamaica, N.Y. Office: Dept. of History, City Coll., Convent Ave. at 139th, New York 31, N.Y.

DILLON, DOROTHY R., b. New York, N.Y., Apr. 10, 1917. HISTORY. A.B., Hunter Coll., 1939; A.M., Columbia U., 1940; Ph.D., 1947. Instr., Sweet Briar Coll., 1942-44; instr., Rutgers U., 1944-48; dir., Latin American Bibliographical Project for the United Nations, Library of Congress, 1948-49; Latin American intelligence officer, U.S. Government, 1949-51; Latin American research officer, U.S. Dept. of State, 1951-54; chief, Latin American Research Bureau, deputy chief, Worldwide Research Div., U.S. Information Agency, 1954-61; planning staff, Bureau of Educational and Cultural Affairs, U.S. Dept. of State, 1961-63; cultural attaché (Guatemala), U.S. Information Agency, 1963-66; COORDINATOR, LATIN AMERICAN BOOK PROGRAM OF THE INFORMATION CENTER SERVICE, U.S. INFORMATION AGENCY, 1966- . Rutgers U. Faculty Research Council fellow (Uruguay), 1947. Membership: American Association of University Women; American Historical Association; Conference on Latin American History. Research: politics, education, and culture in Latin America. Author: The New York Triumvirate (1949); Latin America: A Selected Bibliography (1950); International Communism and Latin America (1962). Language: Spanish 4,4,3,3; Portuguese 3,2,1,1; French 4,3,1,1. Home: 5809 MacArthur Blvd., N.W., Washington, D.C. 20016. Office: U.S. Information Agency, Washington, D.C.

DODD, THOMAS J., b. Washington, D.C., Mar. 29, 1935. HISTORY. B.S.F.S., Georgetown U., 1957; M.A., George Washington U., 1961. Public relations officer, Pan American Union, 1958-59; salesman, Encyclopaedia Britannica (Mexico), 1960; INSTR., HISTORY, GEORGE WASHINGTON U., 1964- . Membership: Pi Gamma Mu. Research: Latin American history; United States diplomatic history; European history since 1789. Language: Spanish 3,4,4,3; French 3,2,2,2. Home: 1401 31st NW., Washington, D.C. Office: Dept. of History, George Washington U., Washington.

DOLKART, RONALD HOWARD, b. Los Angeles, Calif., Oct. 12, 1933. HISTORY. B.A., U. of Calif., Los Angeles, 1955; M.A., U. of Calif., Berkeley, 1958; U. of Calif., Los Angeles. ASST. PROF., HISTORY, U. OF N. MEX., 1966- . National Defense Foreign Language fellow in Spanish, 1962-63; Foreign Area fellow (Argentina), 1963-64. Research: modern Argentine history. Co-editor: Statistical Abstract of Latin America, 1961 (1962). Language: Spanish 4,4,3,3; Portuguese 3,2,2,2; French 3,3,2,2. Office: Dept. of History, U. of N. Mex., Albuquerque.

DONOHUE, JOHN AUGUSTINE, S. J., b. San Francisco, Calif., Aug. 28, 1916. HISTORY. M.A., Gonzaga U. (Wash.), 1941; S.T.L., Alma Coll., 1948; Ph.D., U. of Calif., Berkeley, 1957. Teacher, librarian, St. Ignatius High School (San Francisco), 1941-43; instr., U. of San Francisco, 1943-44; asst. pastor, Roman Catholic Church (México, D.F.), 1953-54; ASSOC. PROF., HISTORY, LOYOLA U. OF LOS ANGELES, 1955- . Research: history of Mexico; archival research. Author: Unlucky Jesuit Mission of Bac (Arizona and the West, Summer 1960). Language: Spanish 3,3,3,3; French 3,1,1,1; Latin 4,3,3,3. Office: Dept. of History, Loyola U., 7101 West 80th St., Los Angeles, Calif. 90045.

DORN, GEORGETTE MAGASSY, b. Budapest, Hungary, Aug. 13, 1936. HISTORY. U. of Buenos Aires, 1954-56; B.A., Creighton U., 1959; M.A., Boston Coll., 1961. Cataloger,

Foreign Language Section, Descriptive Cataloging, Library of Congress, 1962-65; HISPANIC REFERENCE SPECIALIST, HISPANIC FOUNDATION, LIBRARY OF CONGRESS, 1965- . Boston Coll. scholar, 1959-60. Membership: Conference on Latin American History. Research: Latin American history; the United Provinces of Rio de la Plata as seen by the contemporary American press, 1828-1835; Spanish and Mexican land grants, 1695-1848. Language: Spanish 5,5,5,5; Portuguese 3,2,1,1; French 5,5,4,4; German 5,5,4,4; Hungarian 5,5,5,4; Italian 4,3,2,1. Home: 2126 37th St., N.W., Washington, D.C. 20007. Office: Hispanic Foundation, Library of Congress, Washington, D.C. 20540.

DOZER, DONALD MARQUAND, b. Zanesville, Ohio, June 7, 1905. HISTORY. B.A., Wooster Coll., 1927; M.A., Harvard U., 1930; Ph.D., 1936. Instr. U. of Md., 1937-41; research analyst, Latin American Div., U.S. Office of Strategic Services, 1941-43; liasion officer, U.S. Government research analyst, asst. chief, Div. of American Republics, U.S. Dept. of State, 1944-46; asst. chief, assoc. chief, acting chief, Div. of Research for American Republics, 1946-51; asst. to chief, Historical Div., 1951-56; lectr., American U. and U. of Md., 1956-59; assoc. prof.-PROF., HISTORY, U. of CALIF., SANTA BARBARA, 1959- . Consultant on Latin America, Brookings Institution, 1950-51; Latin American fellow, Relm Foundation, 1963. Membership: American Historical Association; Conference on Latin American History; Delta Sigma Rho; Omicron Delta Kappa; Pacific Coast Council on Latin American Studies; Phi Beta Kappa. Research: inter-American relations; Latin American policy of the United States; Panama. Author: Are We Good Neighbors (1959); Latin America: An Interpretive History (1962); Roots of Revolution in Latin America (Foreign Affairs, Jan. 1949). Language: Spanish 5,5,4,4; Portuguese 4,3,—,—; French 3,3,3,—. Home: 421 Miramonte Dr., Santa Barbara, Calif. Office: Dept. of History, U. of Calif., Santa Barbara.

DREIER, JOHN CASPER, b. Brooklyn, N.Y., Dec. 27, 1906. POLITICAL SCIENCE AND HISTORY. A.B., Harvard Coll., 1928. Latin American Bureau, U.S. Dept. of State, 1941-50; U.S. Ambassador to Organization of American States, 1950-60; VIS. PROF., INTERNATIONAL RELATIONS, DIR., INTER-AMERICAN CENTER, SCHOOL FOR ADVANCED INTERNATIONAL STUDIES, JOHNS HOPKINS U., 1961- . Consultant, U.S. Dept. of State, 1963; political science panel member, Seminar on Latin American Studies, American Council of Learned Societies-Social Science Research Council, 1963. Membership: American Political Science Association; Inter-American Council. Research: the inter-American system; U.S. policy in Latin America; Mexico, Central America, Colombia, and Chile. Author: The Organization of American States and the Hemisphere Crisis (1962); The OAS and U.S. Policy (1963). Editor: The Alliance for Progress (1962). Language: Spanish 4,4,4,3;

Portuguese 3,2,1,1; French 3,2,1,1; German 3,3,2,1. Home: 3511 Lowell St., N.W., Washington, D.C. 20016. Office: School of Advanced International Studies, 1740 Massachusetts Ave., NW., Washington, D.C. 20036.

DUIN, EDGAR CHARLES, b. St. Paul, Minn., Mar. 13, 1918. HISTORY. B.Sc., U. of Minn., 1941; M.A., Georgetown U., 1950; Ph.D., 1955. Captain, U.S. Army, 1942-49; POLITICAL ANALYST, DEPT. OF THE ARMY, U.S. GOVERNMENT, 1949- . Membership: American Historical Association; Minnesota Historical Society. Research: United States-Dominican diplomatic history; Russian history. Author: Settlers' Periodical: Eugene Smalley and the Northwest Magazine (Minnesota History, Spring 1952). Language: German 4,4,-4,4; Russian 3,2,2,3. Home: 1511 Pinecastle Rd., Falls Church, Va. Office: 1717 H St., NW., Washington, D.C.

DULLES, JOHN WATSON FOSTER, b. Auburn, N.Y., May 20, 1913. HISTORY AND ENGINEERING. A.B., Princeton U., 1935; M.B.A., Harvard Business School, 1937; B.S. Met. E., U. of Ariz., 1943; M. Met. Eng., 1951. Engineer, asst. general manager, executive vice president, Cia. Minera de Peñoles, S.A. (Mexico), 1943-59; vice president, Cia. de Mineração Novalimense (Brazil), The Hanna Mining Company (Cleveland), 1959-62; PROF., LATIN AMERICAN STUDIES, HUMANITIES RESEARCH CENTER, U. OF TEX., 1962- . Organization of American States grant (Brazil), Summer 1963. Research: political history; Brazil; Mexico. Author: Yesterday in Mexico (1961). Language: Spanish 5,4,3,3; Portuguese 5,4,3,3. Home: 1904 Hill Oaks Ct., Austin, Tex. Office: Box 7934, University Station, U. of Tex., Austin 12.

DUNCAN, ROLAND E., b. Detroit, Mich., Oct. 31, 1922. HISTORY. B.A., Wayne State U., 1944; M.A., U. of Calif., Berkeley, 1949; Ph.D., 1960. Dir., Foreign Microfilm Project in Great Britain, Bancroft Library, U. of Calif., Berkeley, 1951-53; dir., German Foreign Ministry Archives Microfilm Project, General Library, 1953; assoc. in history, U. of Calif., Davis, 1957-59; vis. asst. prof., Ind. U., 1961-62; ASST. PROF., HISTORY, U. OF TENN., 1960- ; vis. asst. prof., dir., Junior Year in Peru Program, Ind. U., 1964. Robertson Prize Committee, Conference on Latin American History, 1963. Membership: American Association of University Professors; American Historical Association; Phi Alpha Theta. Research: biography of William Wheelwright. Author: William Wheelwright: Early Plans and Projects for Pacific Steam Navigation, 1820-35 (Atlantic and Pacific Breezes, Spring, Summer 1960); Batista and Castro in Cuba (Indiana Alumni Magazine, Jan. 1962); Latin America: Past and Present (Indiana Review, Nov. 1962). Language: Spanish 4,3,3,3; Portuguese 2,1,1,1; French 2,1,1,1. Home: 6411 Kingston Pike, Knoxville 19, Tenn. Office: Dept. of History, U. of Tenn., Knoxville.

DUSENBERRY, WILLIAM HOWARD, b. Carmichaels, Pa., June 6, 1908. HISTORY. A.B., Waynesburg Coll., 1932; M.A., U. of Mich., 1936; Ph.D., 1941. Teacher, Pa. Public Schools, 1930-38; instr., Fresno State Coll., Spring 1942; instr., U. of Calif., Los Angeles, 1946-48; assoc. prof., U. of Pittsburgh, 1948-61; CHMN., SOCIAL SCIENCES, WAYNESBURG COLL., 1962- . U. of Pittsburgh grant (Mexico), 1949, 1952. Membership: Agricultural History Society; American Association of University Professors; American Historical Association. Research: the role of the vaquero in the development of Mexican society. Author: The Mexican Mesta: The Administration of Ranching in Colonial Mexico (1963); Foot-and-Mouth Disease in Mexico, 1946-1951 (Agricultural History, Apr. 1955); Juan Manuel de Rosas as viewed by American Diplomats (Hispanic American Historical Review, Nov. 1961). Language: Spanish —,—,—,3; French 3,—,—,—. Home: 53 South Morris St., Waynesburg, Pa. Office: Dept. of Social Sciences, Waynesburg Coll., Waynesburg.

DUTRA, FRANCIS ANTHONY, b. New York, N.Y., Apr. 29, 1938. HISTORY. B.A., St. Bonaventure U., 1960; M.A., N.Y.U., 1963. Instr., St. Bonaventure U., 1963-65. National Defense Foreign Language fellow in Portuguese, 1962-63; Summer 1963. Membership: American Historical Association; Hispanic American Society; Mississippi Valley Historical Society. Research: Brazilian history and civilization; United States-Brazilian diplomatic relations; Catholicism in Brazil. Language: Spanish 4,4,3,2; Portuguese 5,5,4,4; French 4,3,3,2; German 3,2,2,1. Home: c/o Cultural Section, American Embassy, Lisbon, Portugal.

EALY, LAWRENCE ORR, b. Ocean City, N.J., Sept. 17, 1915. HISTORY AND POLITICAL SCIENCE. A.B., Temple U., 1934; LL.B., U. of Pa., 1937; A.M., 1947; Ph.D., 1951. Asst. prof., Temple U., 1947-54; lectr., Rutgers U., 1954-55; assoc. prof., Temple U., 1955-58; prof., U.S. Naval War Coll., 1958-59; provost, prof., Hobart Coll., 1959-62; DEAN, PROF., HISTORY, RIDER COLL., 1962- . Consultant, Area Handbook for Panama for U.S. Dept. of Defense, Special Operations Research Office, American University, 1962. Membership: American Academy of Political and Social Science; American Bar Association; American Conference of Academic Deans; American Historical Association; Conference on Latin American History; World Affairs Council. Research: international relations and law. Author: The Republic of Panama in World Affairs (1951); The Development of an Anglo-American System of Law in the Panama Canal Zone (American Journal of Legal History, Oct. 1958); The Monroe Doctrine and International Law (Social Science, Jan. 1963). Language: Spanish 4,3,3,4; French 2,2,2,2. Home: 25 Vander Veer Dr., University Park, Trenton, N.J. 08638. Office: Dept. of History, Rider Coll., Trenton.

EISENBERG

EISENBERG, PETER LOUIS, b. New York, N.Y., Jan. 16, 1940. HISTORY. B.A., Yale Coll., 1961; M.A., Stanford U., 1962; Columbia U. STUDENT, HISTORY, COLUMBIA U. National Defense Foreign Language fellow in Spanish, 1962-63. Membership: Society for International Development. Research: Latin American history of the 19th and 20th centuries; economic development. Author: Honduras (Collier's Encyclopedia Yearbook, 1961); Nicaragua (Collier's Encyclopedia Yearbook, 1961, 1962); Cuba and Nicaragua (World Mark Encyclopedia, 1964). Language: Spanish 4,4, 4,3; Portuguese 4,4,4,3; French 4,4,4,3; German 3,3,3,2. Home: 17 Ogden Rd., Scarsdale, N.Y.

ELIZABETH ANN, SISTER, O.P. Office: Barry Coll., 11300 NE. Second Ave., Miami, Fla. 33161.

ELLIS, JOSEPH ALBERT, b. Springfield, Pa., Aug. 28, 1930. HISTORY. B.S., Temple U., 1952; A.M., Columbia U., 1953; Universidad Nacional Autónoma de México, 1956-57; Ph.D., Columbia U., 1961. Asst. prof., dir., Latin American studies program, St. Francis Coll. (N.Y.), 1957-64; ASSOC. PROF., HISTORY, CITY COLL. (N.Y.), 1964- ; lectr., Brooklyn Coll., 1959-60; lectr., Iona Coll., 1962-63; Mexican Government grant, 1955-56; group leader, Experiment in International Living (Mexico and Central America), 1962; St. Francis Coll. research grant (Chile). Summer 1963; consultant, University Work Projects (Mexico and Peru), 1962-1963. Membership: American Catholic Historical Association; American Historical Association; Association of International Clubs; Bolivarian Society; Conference on Latin American History. Research: the national period, institutional structure, and contemporary trends. Author: Toward Progress and Unity in Latin America (Proceedings, Association of International Relations Clubs, 1962). Language: Spanish 4,4,4,4; Portuguese 3,3,2,1; French 2,2,1,1. Home: 215 Willoughby Ave., Brooklyn, N.Y. Office: Dept. of History, City Coll. of New York, New York, 10010.

ELSASSER, EDWARD ORR, b. Oak Park, Ill., Feb. 16, 1918. HISTORY. B.A., Bethany Coll., 1942; M.A., Clark U., 1948; Ph.D., U. of Chicago, 1954. Lectr., Roosevelt U., 1954-55; asst. prof., Western Mich. U., 1955-59; ASSOC. PROF., HISTORY, WESTERN MICH. U., 1959- . Fulbright research grant (Argentina), 1963. Membership: American Association of University Professors; American Historical Association; Midwest Council, Association for Latin American Studies; Conference on Latin American History; Mississippi Valley Historical Association. Research: Argentine history; United States-Latin American relations. Author: Argentina and the Export-Import Bank, 1934-1945 (Inter-American Economic Affairs, Spring 1955). Language: Spanish 3,4,2,2. Home: 301 Edgemoor, Kalamazoo, Mich. Office: Dept. of History, Western Mich. U., Kalamazoo.

ELY, ROLAND TAYLOR, b. Philadelphia, Pa., Sept. 27, 1924. HISTORY AND ECONOMICS.

A.B., Princeton U., 1947; A.M., Harvard U., 1949; Universidad Nacional de México, Summer 1949; Ph.D., Harvard U., 1959. Instr., Rutgers U., 1957-59; master, Laurenceville School (N.J.), 1958-59; asst. prof., Rutgers U., 1959-63; vis. asst. prof., Stanford U., Summer 1963; ASST. PROF., HISTORY, RUTGERS U., 1963- . 12th Annual Global Strategy Discussions, Naval War College, Newport, 1960; Congreso de Instituciones Hispánicas, Sección Económica, Madrid, 1963; officer, Orden Nacional al Mérito (Ecuador), Orden de Mayo al Mérito (Argentina), Ordem Nacional do Cruzeiro do Sul (Brazil). Membership: Academy of Political and Social Sciences; Academy of Political Science; American Association of University Professors; American Brazilian Association; American Economic Association; American Historical Association; Conference on Latin American History; Newcomen Society; Pan American Society. Research: economic development and contemporary problems in Latin America. Author: La economía cubana entre las dos Isabeles, 1492-1832 (1960); Economic Integration in Latin America (Financial Analysts Journal, July-Aug. 1962). Language: Spanish 4,4,4,4; French 3,3,2,2. Home: 215 S. 16th St., Philadelphia, Pa. 19102. Office: Dept. of History, NCAS, Rutgers U., 42 James St., Newark 2, N.J.

ERVIN, DWAIN T., b. Craig, Colo., Feb. 14, 1918. HISTORY. B.A., U. of Colo., 1942; M.A., 1945; Ph.D., 1953. Instr., Boise Junior Coll., 1946-47; asst. prof., N. Dak. State U., 1947-57; prof., History, chmn., Social Science, Central Methodist Coll., 1957-65; PROF., HISTORY, SOUTHERN COLO. STATE COLL., 1965- . U. of Colo. research fellow, 1950-51; Doherty fellow (Argentina), 1954-55. Membership: American Historical Association; Conference on Latin American History; Hispanic American Society; Midwest Council, Association for Latin American Studies; Mississippi Valley Historical Association. Research: Argentine history, particularly the period of the wars of independence, 1810-1820. Language: Spanish 4,3,3,3; Portuguese 2,1,1,1; French 3,2,2,—. Office: Dept. of History, Southern Colo. State Coll., Pueblo, Colo. 81005.

ESPINOSA, JOSÉ MANUEL, b. Chicago, Ill., Feb. 2, 1909. HISTORY AND EDUCATION. B.A., Stanford U., 1930; M.A., 1931; Ph.D., U. of Calif., Berkeley, 1934. Instr.-asst. prof., St. Louis U., 1934-39; assoc. prof., Loyola U. (Ill.), 1939-44; DEPUTY DIR., OFFICE OF INTER-AMERICAN PROGRAMS, BUREAU OF EDUCATIONAL AND CULTURAL AFFAIRS, U.S. DEPT. OF STATE, 1944- . American Folklore Society research grant, 1951; advisory editor, The Americas and Mid-America. Membership: Royal Spanish Academy of History. Research: Spanish borderlands of the United States; international education exchange programs. Author: First Expedition of Vargas into New Mexico (1939); Spanish Folktales from New Mexico (1937); Crusaders of the Rio Grande (1942). Language: Spanish 5,5,4,4;

Portuguese 3,4,—,—; French 3,4,—,—. **Home:** 13 Vassar Circle, Glen Echo, Md.

ESQUENAZI-MAYO, ROBERTO, b. Havana, Cuba. Apr. 22, 1920. SPANISH AMERICAN LITERATURE AND HISTORY. Litt. D., U. of Havana, 1941; Columbia U. Foreign correspondent at United Nations for El Mundo (Havana), and El Tiempo (Bogotá), 1946-48; instr., Sweet Briar Coll., 1948-49; editor, Americas, Pan American Union, 1949-52; Board of Editors, Time-Life International, 1952-59; asst. prof., Columbia U., 1960-61; DIR., LATIN AMERICAN AREA STUDIES, ASST. PROF., ROMANCE LANGUAGES, U. OF NEBR., 1961- . Cuban National Prize for Literature, 1951; Latin American Committee, Overseas Press Club; Board, Instituto de la España; contributing editor, Handbook of Latin American Studies; Board of Editors, Revista Iberoamericana de Literatura and Cuadernos. Membership: American Association of Teachers of Spanish and Portuguese; American Association of University Professors; Instituto Internacional de Literatura Iberoamericana; International Association of Hispanists; Modern Language Association. Research: the essay; origin of the Latin American novel; cultural development of Latin America; parallel literary movements in Latin America and the United States. Author: Memorias de un estudiante soldado (1951); Ensayos y apuntes (1954); Historiografía de la guerra entre México y los Estados Unidos (Duquesne Hispanic Review, Autumn-Winter 1962). Language: Spanish 5,5,5,5; Portuguese 4,4,4,4; French 4,4,4,4; Italian 3,3,3,3. Home: 1212 South 20th, Lincoln 2, Nebr. Office: Dept. of Romance Languages, U. of Nebr., Lincoln 8.

ESTEP, RAYMOND, b. Purcell, Okla., July 23, 1910. HISTORY. B.S., East Central State Coll., 1937; M.A., Okla. A. & M. Coll., 1938; Ph.D., U. of Tex., 1942; U. of Mexico, Summer 1946. Instr., historian, Intelligence Div., Army Air Force, 1942-46; asst. prof., Okla. A. & M. Coll., 1946; PROF., LATIN AMERICAN HISTORY, AEROSPACE STUDIES INSTITUTE, AIR U., 1946- ; instr., U. of Ala., Montgomery Center, 1950-51; 1962-63. Fellowship, U. of Tex., 1940-41, advanced fellowship, 1941-42. Membership: Hispanic American Society; Southeastern Conference on Latin American Studies; Southern Historical Association; Texas State Historical Association. Research: archival research in Mexico. Author: Lorenzo de Zavala: profeta del liberalismo mexicano (1952); The Military and Diplomatic Services of Alexander Le Grand for the Republic of Texas, 1836-1837 (Southwestern Historical Quarterly, Oct. 1950). Editor: The Removal of the Texas Indians and the Founding of Fort Cobb: Lieutenant William E. Burnet Letters (1961). Language: Spanish 4,4,3,3; Portuguese 2,2,1,1; French 2,1,-1,1. Home: 3420 Cleveland Ave., Montgomery, Ala. 36105. Office: Air U., Aerospace Studies Institute, Maxwell Air Force Base, Montgomery.

EVANSON, PHILIP NORMAN, b. Minneapolis, Minn., May 18, 1939. HISTORY. B.A., Hamline U., 1961; U. of Va. STUDENT, HIS-

TORY, U. OF VA. National Defense Education Act fellow in Latin American History, 1961-64; Foreign Area fellow, 1964-65. Research: Latin American history; Brazilian history. Author: Winston Churchill and the Sinews of Peace (Georgia Review, Fall 1963); The Third Dominican-Haitian War (Caribbean Studies, Apr. 1964). Language: Spanish 4,3,3,3; Portuguese 3,3,3,3. Home: 3448 NE. Buchanan St., Minneapolis 18, Minn.

EWING, FLOYD FORD, JR., b. Lockney, Tex., Sept. 21, 1915. HISTORY. B.S., West Tex. State Coll., 1936; M.A., U. of Tex., 1950; Ph.D., 1952. Teacher, principal, Cameron County Public Schools (Tex.), 1936-49; PROF., CHMN., HISTORY, GRADUATE DEAN, MIDWESTERN U., 1952- ; vis. prof., U. of Mo., Summer 1960. Membership: American Historical Association; Great Plains Historical Association; Hispanic American Society; Rocky Mountain Council for Latin American Studies; Southwestern Social Science Association; Texas State Historical Association; West Texas Historical Association. Research: history of the American Southwest and Mexico; United States-Latin American relations. Language: Spanish 3,2,2,2; French 2,1,1,1. Home: 3507 Sheridan, Wichita Falls, Tex. Office: Dept. of History, Midwestern U., Wichita Falls.

EWING, RUSSELL CHARLES, b. Manhattan, Kans., Feb. 16, 1906. HISTORY. B.A., U. of Calif., Berkeley, 1929; M.A., 1931; Ph.D., 1934. Regional historian, National Park Service, U.S. Dept. of the Interior, 1935-37; asst. prof.-PROF., CHMN., HISTORY, U. OF ARIZ., 1937- ; lectr., U. of Andes (Colombia), 1956-57. Smith-Mundt fellow (Colombia), 1956-57; participant, American Assembly on Latin America, 1959. Membership: American Historical Association; Rocky Mountain Council of Latin American Studies. Research: history of Mexico and the Spanish borderlands, 1513-1848. Author: The Pima Outbreak in November, 1751 (New Mexico Historical Review, Oct. 1938); The First Histories and Historians of the Southwest (Arizona Quarterly, Winter 1946); The Spanish Past (in Arizona, Its People and Resources, 1960). Language: Spanish 5,5,4,2; Portuguese 4,2,2,1; French 5,3,2,1; German 2,2,1,1. Home: 2804 East 9th St., Tucson, Ariz. Office: Dept. of History, U. of Ariz., Tucson.

FAGG, JOHN EDWIN, b. San Saba, Tex., Nov. 21, 1916. HISTORY. B.A., U. of Tex., 1938; M.A., U. of Chicago, 1939; Ph.D., 1942; PROF., CHMN., HISTORY, DIR., PORTUGUESE LANGUAGE AND AREA CENTER, WASHINGTON SQUARE COLL., N.Y.U., 1946- ; asst. dean, Graduate School of Arts & Sciences, 1950-56. Special consultant, U.S. Air Force, 1946-51, 1956-57; Latin American consultant, Crowell-Collier Publications; National Woodrow Wilson Fellowship Committee. Membership: American Historical Association. Research: colonial Latin America. Author: The Republican Movement in Spain (1944); Introduction to Letters of Christopher Columbus (1961); Latin America: A General History (1963). Language: Spanish 5,4,4,3; Portuguese 2,2,2,2; French 2,2,2,2. Home: 40 Washington St., East Orange, N.J. Office: Dept. of History, N.Y.U., New York 3.

FAULK, ODIE B., b. Winnsboro, Tex., Aug. 26, 1933. HISTORY. B.S., Tex. Technological Coll., 1958; M.A., 1960; Ph.D., 1962. Teacher, Lubbock Public Schools (Tex.); instr., Tex. A. & M. U., 1962-63; ASST. EDITOR, ARIZONA AND THE WEST, 1963- . Membership: American Historical Association; Arizona Pioneer's Historical Society; Hispanic American Historical Association; Texas State Historical Association; Western History Association. Research: history of Spanish borderlands of Mexico; Spanish Arizona and Sonora. Author: Tom Green: A Fightin' Texan (1963); The Last Years of Spanish Texas, 1778-1821 (1964). Co-author: Lancers for the King (1965). Language: Spanish 3,3,3,3. Office: Dept. of History, U. of Ariz., Tucson.

FELL, MARIE LÉONORE, S.C., b. New York, N.Y., Dec. 16, 1907. HISTORY. A.B., Coll. of Mt. St. Vincent, 1932; M.A., Catholic U., 1936; Ph.D., 1941. Instr.-PROF., CHMN., HISTORY, COLL. OF MT. ST. VINCENT, 1940- ; prof., Catholic U., Summer 1948. Anne Hope Hudson scholar, Catholic U.; Executive Committee, American Catholic Historical Association. Membership: American Academy of Political and Social Science; American Historical Association; Conference on Latin American History; Foreign Policy Association; National Council of Social Studies; Pi Gamma Mu. Research: United States history; European history; political and social structures of Brazil. Author: The Foundations of Nativism in American Textbooks, 1783-1860 (1941); Pan-Americanism (Alumnae Record of the College of Mt. St. Vincent, 1944); A "Boa Viagem" to South America—Brazil in Particular (Alumnae Record, 1955). Language: Spanish 2,2,1,1; Portuguese 2,2,2,1; French 4,3,3,2; German 3,3,2,1; Latin 3,—,—,—. Office: Dept. of History, Coll. of Mt. St. Vincent, Bronx, N.Y. 10471.

FELT, JEREMY POLLARD, b. Miami, Fla., Dec. 26, 1930. HISTORY. A.B., Duke U., 1951; M.A., 1956; Ph.D., Syracuse U., 1959. ASST. PROF., HISTORY, U. OF VT., 1959- . University fellow in history, Syracuse U., 1956-57. Membership: American Historical Association; Conference on Latin American History; Mississippi Valley Historical Association; Northern New England Historians Conference; Phi Beta Kappa. Research: United States-Latin American relations. Author: Lucius B. Northrop: The Confederacy's Subsistence Department (Virginia Magazine of History & Biography, Apr. 1961). Language: Spanish 3,3,3,3; Portuguese 1,1,1,1; French 2,2,2,2. Home: Star Route, Essex Junction, Vt. Office: Dept. of History, U. of Vt., Burlington.

FIELDS, HAROLD B. Office: Mich. State U., 406 Morrill Hall, East Lansing, Mich. 48823.

FINAN, JOHN JOSEPH, b. St. Louis, Mo., Sept. 1, 1925. HISTORY. A.B., Washington U., 1945; M.A., 1947; Ph.D., Harvard U., 1956. Latin American specialist, Manuscripts Div., Library of Congress, 1953-55; political officer, Embassy (Colombia), U.S. Dept. of State, 1958-61; ASSOC. PROF. OF LATIN AMERICAN STUDIES, SCHOOL OF INTERNATIONAL SERVICE, AMERICAN U., 1961- . University scholar, Harvard U., 1949-50; Buenos Aires Convention fellow (Mexico), 1951-52; Brown University President's Fellow in Argentina, 1956-58. Membership: American Historical Association; Conference on Latin American History. Research: rural history in colonial Mexico and 19th century Argentina; contemporary agrarian problems of Latin America. Author: Maize in the Great Herbals (1951). Language: Spanish 4,4,4,4; Portuguese 3,3,2,1; French 4,3,2,3. Home: 6007 Milo Dr., Washington, D.C. 20016. Office: School of International Service, American U., Washington, D.C. 20016.

FISCHMAN, JEROME, b. New York, N.Y., Aug. 2, 1928. HISTORY. B.S.S., City Coll. (N.Y.), 1951; M.A., 1952; Ph.D., N.Y.U., 1962. Instr. U. of P.R., 1955-58; instr., Hofstra U., 1958-62; lectr., Universidad de Caracas, Summer 1962; ASST. PROF., HISTORY, LEHIGH U., 1962- . Membership: American Historical Association. Research: Caribbean area; political parties in Puerto Rico; the church in politics in Puerto Rico. Language: Spanish 5,5,5,5; Portuguese 4,4,4,4; French 3,3,3,3. Home: 1910 Aripine Ave., Bethlehem, Pa. Office: Dept. of History, Lehigh U., Bethlehem.

FLACCUS, ELMER WILLIAM, b. Pittsburgh, Pa., Apr. 12, 1909. HISTORY. A.B., Washington & Jefferson Coll., 1932; M.A., 1933; Ph.D., U. of Tex., 1951. PROF., HISTORY, AUSTIN COLL., 1951- ; chmn., 1958-63. Danforth Summer Fellowship, 1959; Southern Association Fellowship, 1960; Austin Coll. sabbatical (England), 1963-64. Membership: Conference on Latin American History; East Texas Historical Society; Hispanic American Historical Association; Southwestern Social Science Association. Research: Mexico in the 1820's. Author: Commodore David Porter and the Mexican Navy (Hispanic American Historical Review, Aug. 1954). Language: Spanish 3,—, —,—; Portuguese 1,—,—,—; French 2,—,—,—. Home: 1102 West College St., Sherman, Tex. Office: Dept. of History, Austin Coll., Sherman.

FLEMION, PHILIP FREDERICK, b. Findlay, Ohio, July 5, 1935. HISTORY. B.A., B.S., Ohio State U., 1957; M.A., 1958; U. of Fla. Asst. dir., Center for Latin American Studies, U. of Fla., 1962-65; ASST. PROF., HISTORY, SAN DIEGO STATE COLL., 1965- . Editor, Southeastern Latin Americanist, 1962- . Membership: Conference on Latin American History; Phi Alpha Theta; Southeastern Conference on Latin American Studies. Research:

Central American history. Author: Survey of Investigations in Progress in the Field of Latin American Studies (1962). Language: Spanish 4,3,3,3; Portuguese 2,2,1,1. Office: Dept. of History, San Diego State Coll., San Diego, Calif.

FLICKEMA, THOMAS ORIN, b. Muskegon, Mich., Jan. 26, 1938. HISTORY. B.A., Hope Coll., 1960; M.A., Wayne State U., 1962. Instr. Henry Ford Community Coll., 1963-65; ASST. PROF., WAYNE STATE COLL., 1965- . Membership: American Association of University Professors; American Historical Association; Hispanic American Historical Association; Mississippi Valley Historical Association. Research: Latin American history; international relations of Latin America; American-Paraguayan diplomatic relations, 1843-1870; modern Colombian history. Language: Spanish 4,3,3,3; Portuguese 2,1,1,1; French 4,2,1,1. Office: Div. of Social Sciences, Wayne State Coll., Wayne, Nebr.

FLOYD, TROY SMITH, b. Rampart, Alaska, Jan. 31, 1920. HISTORY. B.J., U. of Mo., 1948; A.M., 1949; Ph.D., U. of Calif., Berkeley, 1959. ASST. PROF., HISTORY, U. OF N. MEX., 1959- . American Philosophical Society grant (Guatemala), 1962. Membership: Conference on Latin American History. Research: colonial Central America. Author: The Guatemala Merchants, the Government, and the Provincianos, 1750-1800 (Hispanic American Historical Review, Feb. 1961); Bourbon Palliatives and the Central American Mining Industry, 1765-1800 (The Americas, Oct. 1961). Language: Spanish 4,4,4,3; Portuguese 4,2,2,2; French 1,1,1,1; German 1,1,1,1. Home: 10124 Propps Dr., NE., Albuquerque, N. Mex. Office: Dept. of History, U. of N. Mex., Albuquerque.

FOLKMAN, DAVID I., JR., b. Elyria, Ohio, Mar. 9, 1929. HISTORY. B.S., Brigham Young U., 1954; M.A., U. of Utah, 1962. Captain, U.S. Air Force; asst. prof., U.S. Air Force Academy, 1962-64. Membership: American Historical Association; Conference on Latin American History; Western Historical Association. Research: Latin American history; Nicaragua. Language: Spanish 3,2,—,—; German 3,—,—,—. Home: 2034 Hubbard Ave., Salt Lake City, Utah.

FORBES, JACK DOUGLAS, b. Long Beach, Calif., Jan. 7, 1934. HISTORY AND ANTHROPOLOGY. A.B., U. of Southern Calif., 1955; M.A., 1956; Ph.D., 1959. Lectr., U. of Southern Calif., 1958-59; instr., Citrus Coll., 1959-60; ASST. PROF., HISTORY, SAN FERNANDO VALLEY STATE COLL., 1960- . Social Science Research Council research fellow (Spain), 1957-58; Social Science Research Council grant-in-aid, 1961-62; Guggenheim fellow, 1963-64; Board of Editors, Journal of the West, 1962- . Membership: American Indian Ethnohistoric Conference; Pacific Coast Council on Latin American Studies; Phi Beta Kappa; Western History Association. Research: ethnohistory; Indian-European contact studies; the Indians of Chihuahua, 1560-1750; the Chumash of

California. Author: Apache, Navaho and Spaniard (1960); The Quechans: Warriors of the Colorado (1964); Melchior Díaz and the Discovery of Alta California (Pacific Historical Review, Fall 1958). Language: Spanish 3,3,3,3; German 2,2,1,1. Home: 1461 Vaquero Dr., Simi, Calif. Office: Dept. of History, San Fernando Valley State College, Northridge, Calif.

FORREST, FREDERICK AUGUST, b. Buenos Aires, Argentina, Dec. 27, 1914. LIBRARY SCIENCE AND HISTORY. B.A., San Jose State Coll., 1947; M.A., Stanford U., 1948; Ph.D., 1951; B.L.S., U. of Calif., Berkeley, 1955. Cataloger, Long Beach State Coll., 1955-58; head librarian, asst. prof., History, Southern Ill. U., 1958-60; dean of libraries and communication arts, Inter American U. (P.R.), 1960-64; CURATOR, LATIN AMERICAN COLLECTION, STERLING LIBRARY, YALE U., 1964- . Institute of International Education travel fellow (Argentina), 1952-53; Argentine Congress research fellow. Research: Latin American archives; Argentine history. Language: Spanish 5,5,5,5; Portuguese 5,4,4,4; French 4,3,3,3; Italian 4,4,4,4. Office: Sterling Library, Yale U., New Haven, Conn.

FRANKEL, BENJAMIN ADAM, b. New York, N.Y., Jan. 4, 1918. HISTORY. M.A., U. of Calif., Berkeley, 1948; Ph.D., 1964. Teacher, Academia Milton (Mexico, D.F.), 1938-42; PROF., HISTORY, ST. MARY'S COLL. OF CALIF., 1949- ; prof., San Francisco State Coll., 1953-57. Fundación John Boulton fellow (Caracas, Venezuela); North American Association of Venezuela grant; Woodrow Wilson grant-in-aid. Membership: American Association of University Professors; American Historical Association; Pacific Historical Association. Research: caste relationships in Latin America as a basis for evaluation of the role of socioeconomic factors in political developments; United States-Latin American cultural relations; newspaper and radio; Mexico, Venezuela, and Colombia. Author: Bolivar and the Role of the Colored Castes in the Wars of Independence (Academia Nacional de la Historia de Venezuela, 1949); Venezuela y los Estados Unidos: ayuda, alianza, y asociación (Boletín Histórico, Caracas, May 1964). Language: Spanish 5,5,5,5; Portuguese 4,4,3,2; French 4,3,2,2; German 4,4,4,3. Home: 1 Rochdale Way, Berkeley, Calif. 94708. Office: Dept. of History, St. Mary's Coll. of Calif., St. Mary's College, Calif.

FRAZER, ROBERT WALTER, b. Sacramento, Calif., Dec. 19, 1911. HISTORY. B.A., U. of Calif., Los Angeles, 1936; M.A., 1940; Ph.D., 1941. Asst. prof., Adams State Coll., 1940-42; prof., chmn, History, U. of Wichita, 1946-64; vis. prof., U. of Calif., Los Angeles, 1961-62. Membership: American Geographical Society; Conference on Latin American History; Hispanic American Society; Mississippi Valley Historical Association; Western History Association. Research: Mexican history; American West; inter-American relations. Author: Maximilian's Propaganda Activities in the United

States, 1865-1866 (Hispanic American Historical Review, Feb. 1944); The Truce of Altmark (The Municipal University of Wichita Bulletin, Aug. 1947); The Role of the Lima Congress, 1864-65, in the Development of Pan-Americanism (Hispanic American Historical Review, Aug. 1949). Language: Spanish 4,4,3,4; Portuguese 3,2,2,3; French 3,2,2,2. Home: 2410 Gaffey St., San Pedro, Calif.

FRAZIER, CHARLES EDWARD, JR., b. Pine Bluff, Ark., July 15, 1925. HISTORY. Biarritz American U., 1945; B.A., U. of Tenn., 1949; M.A., N.Y.U., 1949; Ph.D., U. of Tex., 1958. Asst. prof., Tex. A. & M. Coll., 1956-60; asst. prof., U. of Nev., 1960-63; assoc. prof., Wis. State Coll., 1963-66; ASSOC. PROF., HISTORY, SAM HOUSTON STATE COLLEGE, 1966- . Buenos Aires Convention grant (Nicaragua), 1955; U. of Tex. graduate fellow, 1955-56. Membership: Conference on Latin American History; Pacific Coast Council on Latin American Studies. Research: Central America; inter-American agreements and relations. Author: Colonel Henry L Stimson's Peace Mission to Nicaragua (Journal of the West, Jan. 1963); Augusto César Sandino: Good Devil or Perverse God? (Journal of the West, Jan. 1964). Language: Spanish 4,3,3,3; French 3,2,2,2. Office: Dept. of History, Sam Houston State Coll., Huntsville, Tex. 77341.

FREEMAN, CORINNE KEEN, b. Philadelphia, Pa., Dec. 10, 1936. HISTORY. B.A., Radcliffe Coll., 1958; M.A., U. of Calif., Berkeley, 1963. RESEARCH ASSISTANT, INTER-AMERICAN DEVELOPMENT BANK, 1963- . National Defense Foreign Language fellow in Spanish, U. of Calif., Berkeley, and Yale U. Summer Language Institute, 1962-63. Membership: Inter-American Association for Democracy and Freedom. Research: 19th and 20th century Latin American history; urban planning; the Alliance for Progress. Language: Spanish 4,4,4,3; Portuguese 2,3,1,1; French 3,2,2,1. Home: 1731 New Hampshire Ave., NW., Washington, D.C. Office: Inter-American Development Bank, 808 17th St., NW., Washington, 20577.

FRUGÉ, AUGUST. Office: Director, U. of Calif. Press, Berkeley, Calif. 94720.

GAGLIANO, JOSEPH ANTHONY, b. Milwaukee, Wis., Apr. 15, 1930. HISTORY. B.S., Marquette U., 1954; M.A., 1956; Ph.D., Georgetown U., 1960. Instr., Aquinas Coll., 1959-62; ASST. PROF., HISTORY, LOYOLA U. (ILL.), 1962- . Membership: American Association of University Professors; American Historical Association; Catholic Historical Association; Hispanic American Historical Association. Research: the Andean republics. Author: The Coca Debate in Colonial Peru (The Americas, July 1963); The Identity of Gerónimo de Vivar (The Newberry Library Bulletin, Mar. 1964). Language: Spanish 3,3,3,3; Portuguese 2,1,1,1; French 3,1,1,1. Home: 1134 Pratt Blvd., Chicago, Ill. 60611. Office: Dept. of History,

Loyola U., 820 North Michigan Ave., Chicago, 60626.

GALE, THOMAS MARTIN, b. Green Bay, Wis., May 16, 1926. HISTORY. B.A., U. of Calif., Berkeley, 1949; M.A., 1950; Ph.D., U. of Pa., 1958. Instr.-asst. prof., U. of Kans., 1954-62; ASSOC. PROF., HISTORY, ASST. DEAN, COLL. OF ARTS & SCIENCES, U. OF KANS., 1963- ; dir., Junior Year Program in Costa Rica, 1961; dir., U.S. Peace Corps Project (Costa Rica), U. of Kans. contract, 1963-64. Social Science Research Council fellow (Peru), 1952-53; Social Science Research Council fellow, 1953-54; Huntington Library summer fellow, 1959; Fulbright fellow (Peru), 1960-61. Membership: American Historical Association; Conference on Latin American History. Research: Latin American urbanism; colonial Lima, Peru; a bibliography of Latin American urban studies. Language: Spanish 5,5,5,4; Portuguese 2,1,1,1. Office: Dept. of History, U. of Kans., Lawrence.

GALLAGHER, ANN MIRIAM, SISTER. Office: Coll. Misericordia, Dallas, Pa.

GALVÁN, NOEMÍ, b. Raymondville, Tex., Nov. 9, 1939. LANGUAGE AND SPANISH AMERICAN LITERATURE. B.A., Southern Methodist U., 1961. Asst. instr., Southern Methodist U., 1961-62; searcher, Card Division, Library of Congress, 1962-63; bibliographer, Hispanic Foundation, Library of Congress, 1963-65. Clark scholar, Southern Methodist U., 1957-61; Southern Methodist U. scholar, 1958; Texas Good Neighbor Commission grant (Mexico), 1960; Southern Methodist U. graduate fellow, 1961-62. Membership: Conference on Latin American History; Sigma Delta Pi. Research: Mexican literature; contemporary Spanish literature. Language: Spanish 5,5,5,5; Portuguese 2,2,2,2; French 1,1,1,1; Italian 3,3,3,3. Home: 2317 Pennsylvania Ave., NW., Washington, D.C. 20037.

GALVEZ, ARNALDO. Home: Arlington Towers T 530, Arlington, Va.

GAMBRELL, HERBERT (PICKENS), b. Tyler, Tex., July 15, 1898. HISTORY. B.A., Southern Methodist U., 1921; M.A., 1923; Ph.D., U. of Tex., 1946. Prof., Southern Methodist U., 1923-64; PROF. EMERITUS, 1964- ; CURATOR, DIRECTOR, DALLAS HISTORICAL SOCIETY, 1934- . President, Southwestern Committee on Latin American Culture, 1939; delegate, First Conference of United States-Mexican Historians (Monterrey), 1948, Second Conference of United States-Mexican Historians (Austin), 1958; Danforth Foundation faculty fellow, Graduate Council of Humanities, Southern Methodist U., 1963. Membership: American Historical Association; Conference on Latin American History; Mississippi Valley Historical Association; Society of American Historians. Research: Latin American history; Mexico and the Spanish Southwest; Texas-Mexican relations (1821-1859). Author: A Pictorial History of Texas (1960); Anson

Jones, the Last President of Texas (1948, 1964); Mirabeau Buonaparte Lamar, Troubadour and Southwest Press Crusader (1934). Language: Spanish 3,2,1,1. Home 3543 University Blvd., Dallas, Tex. Office: Dallas Historical Society, Box 26038, Dallas, 75226.

GATELL, FRANK OTTO, b. New York, N.Y., July 28, 1931. HISTORY. B.A., City Coll. (N.Y.), 1956; A.M., Harvard U., 1958; Ph.D., 1960. Vis. lectr., U. of P.R., Summer 1959; ASST. PROF., HISTORY, U. OF MD., 1959- . Membership: American Historical Association; Phi Alpha Theta. Research: Caribbean history, particularly Puerto Rico. Author: Puerto Rico and the Tydings Bill of 1936 (Hispanic American Historical Review, Feb. 1958); Panama Canal Episode in Retrospect (The Americas, July 1960); Muñoz Rivera and the Puerto Rican Jones Bill (The Americas, July 1960). Language: Spanish 5,5,4,4; Portuguese 2,2,1,1; French 3,2,1,1. Home: 8523 Garland Ave., Takoma Park, Md. Office: Dept. of History, U. of Md., College Park.

GAULD, CHARLES ANDERSON, b. Portland, Oreg., Aug. 12, 1911. HISTORY. A.B., Stanford U., 1932; M.A., U. of Wash., 1936; Ph.D., Stanford U., 1964. Instr., Hill Military Academy (Oreg.), 1932-34; junior specialist on Latin American official publications, Library of Congress, 1938-41; editorial writer, Foreign Broadcast Intelligence Service, Federal Communications Commission, 1941-42; writer, Press and Information, Office of Inter-American Affairs, 1942-45; freelance research and writing (Brazil), 1946-54; asst. prof., Inter-American U. (P.R.), 1955-58; lectr., asst. editor, Hispanic American Report, Hispanic American Institute, Stanford U., 1955-58; 1962-64. ASST. PROF., HISTORY, MIAMI-DADE JUNIOR COLL., 1966- . Membership: American Historical Association; American Geographical Society; Conference on Latin American History. Research: industrial and mining history and development; economic history and geography of Brazil and Spanish America. Author: Directory of Americans Interested in Brazil (1950); The Last Titan: Percival Farquhar, American Entrepreneur in Latin America (1964). Language: Spanish 5,5,5,4; Portuguese 5,5,5,4; French 3,2, 2,3. Office: Dept. of History, Miami-Dade Junior Coll., Miami, Fla.

GERASSI, MARYSA, b. Pamplona, Spain, Oct. 12, 1934. HISTORY. B.A., Instituto José Batlle y Ordoñez (Uruguay), 1955; M.A., Columbia U., 1960; Ph.D., 1964. Lectr., Consejo de Enseñanza Secundaria (Uruguay), 1955-58; lectr., Riverdale Country School, 1958-59; lectr., Hunter Coll., 1963-64; lectr., Rutgers U., 1963-64; ASST. PROF., HISTORY, NEWARK STATE COLL., 1964- . Institute of International Education fellow, Douglass Coll., Rutgers U., 1956-57; Organization of American States grant (Argentina), 1961-62; Social Science Research Council grant, 1962-63; consultant, Council of Foreign Relations. Membership: American Historical Association. Research: Argentina. Language: Spanish 5,5,5,5; Portuguese 5,5,4,1; French 5,5,5,5; Italian 5,5,4,1. Home: 789 West End Ave., New York 25, N.Y. Office: Dept. of History, Newark State Coll., Morris Ave., Union, N.J.

GERHARD, PETER, b. Evanston, Ill., Sept. 26, 1920. HISTORY. Accountant, American Smelting & Refining Company (Mexico), 1947-49; industrial relations supervisor, Mene Grande Oil Company (Venezuela), 1949-51, 1953-58, RETIRED, 1958- . Research: ethnohistory and historical geography; Mexico. Author: Lower California Guidebook (1956, 1958, 1962); México en 1742 (1962); El avance español en México y Centroamérica (Historia Mexicana, July-Sept. 1959). Language: Spanish 5,5,5,4; Portuguese 2,2,1,1; French 4,3,3,1; Nahuatl 1,2,2,1. Linguistic studies: Nahuatl. Home: Torre de Atongo, Tepoztlán, Morelos, México.

GIBSON, CHARLES, b. Buffalo, N.Y., Aug. 12, 1920. HISTORY. B.A., Yale U., 1941; M.A., U. of Tex., 1947; Ph.D., Yale U., 1950. Asst. prof.-prof., State U. of Iowa, 1949-65; PROF., HISTORY, U. OF MICH., 1965- . Social Science Research Council fellow, 1948; Guggenheim fellow, 1952-53; Rockefeller Foundation grant, 1960. Membership: American Historical Association; Conference on Latin American History. Research: colonial Latin America; Mexico. Author: Tlaxcala in the Sixteenth Century (1952); Guide to Hispanic American Historical Review (1958). Co-author: The Tovar Calendar (1951). Language: Spanish 4,4,3,3; Portuguese 2,—,—,—; French 4,3,3,3. Linguistic studies: Nahuatl. Home: 2872 Glacier Way, Ann Arbor, Mich. Office: Dept. of History, U. of Mich., Ann Arbor.

GIFFIN, DONALD WARREN, b. Long Beach, Calif., July 7, 1927. HISTORY. B.A., U. of Calif., Santa Barbara, 1950; M.A., Vanderbilt U., 1956; Ph.D., 1962. Teacher, Kamehameha Schools (Hawaii), 1952-54; assoc. dir., Development, Vanderbilt U., 1958-61; asst. prof., Ga. State Coll., 1962-63; ASST. PROF., ASST. CHMN., HISTORY, U. OF MD., 1963- . Membership: American Historical Association; Mississippi Valley Historical Association; Southern Historical Association. Research: Brazil; Brazil-United States relations. Author: The American Navy at Work on the Brazil Station, 1827-1861 (American Neptune, Oct. 1959). Language: Spanish 3,2,2,1; Portuguese 3,2,2,1. Home: Apt. 4, 4605 Calvert Rd., College Park, Md. Office: Dept. of History, U. of Md., College Park.

GILLASPIE, WILLIAM ROSCOE, b. Kansas City, Mo., Feb. 11, 1931. HISTORY. B.A., Westminster Coll., 1952; M.A., U. of Mo., 1954; Ph.D., U. of Fla., 1961. ASSOC. PROF., HISTORY, MEMPHIS STATE U., 1961- . American Philosophical Society grant (Mexico), Summer 1963. Membership: Conference on Latin American History; Mississippi Valley Historical Association. Research: civilian—military relations in Mexico, 1876-1910; inter-American relations. Language: Spanish 4,3,3,4. Home: 3687 Norriswood Ave., Memphis, Tenn. 38111.

Office: P.O. Box 653, Memphis State U., Memphis, 38111.

GILLMOR, FRANCES, b. Buffalo, N.Y., May 21, 1903. ANTHROPOLOGY: FOLKLORE. B.A., U. of Ariz., 1928; M.A., 1931; Litt.D., Universidad Nacional Autónoma de México, 1957. Instr., U. of Ariz., 1931-32; instr., U. of N. Mex., 1932-34; asst. prof., U. of Ariz., 1934-44; assoc. prof., 1944-52; PROF., ENGLISH, U. OF ARIZ., 1952- . Guggenheim fellow (Spain), 1959-60. Membership: American Anthropological Association; American Association of University Professors; American Folklore Society; Authors League of America; Modern Language Association; Phi Beta Kappa; Phi Kappa Phi; Sociedad Folklórica de México; Sociedad de Geografía e Historia de Honduras. Research: folklore and preconquest history of Mexico; comparison of village fiestas and folk drama in Spain, Mexico, and the Southwest. Author: Flute of the Smoking Mirror: A Biography of Nezahualcoyotl (1949); The King Danced in the Market Place: A Biography of Moteczuma Ilhuicamina (1964); Spanish Texts of Three Dance Dramas from Mexican Villages (Humanities Bulletin, U. of Ariz., 1942). Language: Spanish 4,4,4,4; Portuguese 2,1,1,1; French 3,1,2,1. Home: Box 4605, University Station, Tucson, Ariz. 85717. Office: Dept. of English, U. of Ariz., Tucson, 85721.

GILMORE, N(EWTON) RAY, b. Chicago, Ill., Jan. 23, 1924. HISTORY. B.A., U. of Mich., 1948; M.A., 1948; Ph.D., U. of Calif., Berkeley, 1956. Instr., San Francisco State Coll., 1956; instr., U. of Calif., Los Angeles, 1957; instr., San Jose State Coll., 1957-58; INSTR., HISTORY, MONTEREY PENINSULA COLL., 1958- . Buenos Aires Convention exchange fellow (Mexico), 1952-53. Membership: American Association of University Professors; American Historical Association; Conference on Latin American History; Hispanic American Society; Pacific Coast Council on Latin American Studies. Research: Mexican national history. Author: Henry George Ward, British Publicist for Mexican Mines (Pacific Historical Review, Feb. 1963); The Bracero in California (Pacific Historical Review, Aug. 1963); Mexico and the Spanish American War (Hispanic American Historical Review, Nov. 1963). Language: Spanish 4,4,3,3; French 3,2,1,2. Home: 1031 North Hanna, Gilroy, Calif. Office: Dept. of History, Monterey Peninsula Coll., Monterey, Calif.

GILMORE, ROBERT LOUIS, b. Monroe, Iowa, Sept. 8, 1913. HISTORY. B.A., Creighton U., 1935; M.A., 1939; Ph.D., U. of Calif., Berkeley, 1949. Officer, Tri-Metrogon Mapping Program, U.S. Army Air Corps (Brazil and British Guiana), 1943-44, 1945; asst. prof., Vanderbilt U., 1951-55; analyst, Office of Intelligence Research, U.S. Dept. of State, 1956-60; ASSOC. PROF., HISTORY, OHIO U., 1960- . Institute of International Education maintenance fellowship (Colombia), 1942. Membership: American Historical Association; Conference on Latin American History; Ohio Academy of History. Research: late 18th and early 19th centuries in Colombia; Mexico. Author: Caudillism and Militarism in Venezuela, 1810-1910 (1964); Nueva Granada's Socialist Mirage (Hispanic American Historical Review, May 1956); The Imperial Crisis, Rebellion, and the Viceroy: Nueva Granada in 1809 (Hispanic American Historical Review, Feb. 1960). Language: Spanish 5,4,3,3; Portuguese 4,2,2,1; French 4,1,1,1. Home: 18 Grand Park Blvd., Athens, Ohio. 45701. Office: Dept. of History, Ohio U., Athens, 45701.

GLAUERT, EARL THEODORE, b. St. Louis, Mo., Mar. 24, 1928. HISTORY. Ph.D., U. of Pa., 1962. ASST. PROF., HISTORY, U. OF CALIF., LOS ANGELES, 1960- . American Philosophical Society fellow, 1958; Doherty fellow (Argentina), 1958; Foreign Policy Research Institute fellow, 1959; Ford Foundation fellow (Argentina), 1963-64; lectr., U.S. Peace Corps, 1963. Membership: American Historical Association; Pacific Coast Council of Latin American Studies. Research: social and intellectual history; cultural nationalism in Argentina. Author: Ricardo Rojas and the Emergence of Argentine Nationalism (Hispanic American Historical Review, Jan., 1963). Language: Spanish 5,4,3,3; German 3,2,2,2. Home: 2310 Malcolm Ave., Los Angeles, Calif. 90064. Office: Dept. of History, U. of Calif., Los Angeles, 90024.

GLIMM, FRANCIS, REV. Office: I.C. Seminary, Huntington, Long Island, N.Y. 11744.

GOLD, ROBERT LEONARD, b. Ossining, N.Y., Sept. 25, 1932. HISTORY. B.S., Columbia U., 1957; M.A., Bowling Green State U., 1958; Ph.D., U. of Tex., 1964. Teacher, Rockland County Board of Public Instruction (N.Y.), 1958-59; instr., State U. of Iowa, 1959-61; asst. prof., U. of South Fla., 1963-65; ASST. PROF., HISTORY, SOUTHERN ILL. U., 1965- . Membership: American Association of University Professors; American Historical Association; Florida Historical Society. Research: modern Mexico; Spanish borderlands during the colonial period. Author: The Restoration of St. Augustine (Florida Guide, Jan. 1962); Politics and Property during the Transfer of Florida from Spanish to English Control, 1763-65 (Florida Historical Quarterly, July 1963); The Settlement of the East Florida Spaniards in Cuba, 1763-66 (Florida Historical Quarterly, Feb. 1964). Language: Spanish 5,4,3,3; French 3,2,2,1. Office: Dept. of History, Southern Ill. U., Carbondale, Ill.

GOODMAN, EDWARD J., b. Dubuque, Iowa, Nov. 19, 1916. HISTORY. A.B., Loras Coll., 1938; M.A., Columbia U., 1939; Ph.D., 1951. Instr., Notre Dame Coll. (N.Y.), 1940-41; instr., Seton Hall U., Spring 1946; asst. prof., U.S. Naval Academy, 1946-50; PROF., HISTORY, XAVIER U., 1950- ; DIR., HISPANIC STUDIES, 1962- . Roberts fellow, Columbia U., 1938-40. Membership: American Historical Association; American Society of International Law. Research: exploration of South America;

nationalism; Spanish history. Author: Spanish Nationalism in the Struggle Against Napoleon (1958). Editor: The U.S. and Latin America Look at Each Other (1959); Colombia, Ecuador, and Venezuela: Their Peoples and Economics (1962). Language: Spanish 3,3,3,3; Portuguese 3,2,2,1; French 3,1,1,1. Home: 5601 Sunny Woods Lane, Cincinnati, Ohio. 45239. Office: Dept. of History, Xavier U., Cincinnati, 45207.

GOODSELL, JAMES NELSON, b. Evanston, Ill., June 7, 1929. HISTORY AND JOURNALISM. B.A., The Principia Coll., 1951; M.A., Mexico City Coll., 1952. Instr., Mexico City Coll., 1953, 1955; asst. American news editor, The Christian Science Monitor, 1957-63; LATIN AMERICAN EDITOR, NEWS DEPT., THE CHRISTIAN SCIENCE MONITOR, 1964- . Membership: American Historical Association; Conference on Latin American History; Sigma Delta Chi. Research: United States and Latin American news; British Empire; colonial municipal formation in Cartagena, Colombia. Language: Spanish 4,4,4,3; Portuguese 3,3,3,2; French 2,2,1,1; Japanese 1,2,2,1; Korean 3,2,2,2. Home: 184 Village St., Millis, Mass. Office: The Christian Science Monitor, One Norway St., Boston 15, Mass.

GORDON, BARBARA W. Home: 2905 Q St., NW., Washington, D.C. 20007.

GOSLEE, HARVEY R. Office: Ronald Press Co., 15 E. 26th St., New York, N.Y. 10010.

GRAHAM, RICHARD, b. Anápolis, Brazil, Nov. 1, 1934. HISTORY. B.A., Coll. of Wooster, 1956; M.A., U. of Tex., 1957; Ph.D., 1961. Editorial asst., Hispanic American Historical Review, 1958; ASST. PROF., HISTORY, CORNELL U., 1961- . Social Science Research Council fellow (Brazil), 1959-60; American Philosophical Society grant, Summer 1962. Membership: American Historical Association; Conference on Latin American History; Hispanic American Society. Research: Brazilian nineteenth century history. Author: Mauá and Anglo-Brazilian Diplomacy, 1862-1863 (Hispanic American Historical Review, May 1962); A questão Christie, 1861-1863 (Revista de Historia, Jan. 1962). Language: Spanish 5,5,4,3; Portuguese 5,5,5,5; French 3,1,1,1; German 2,1,1,1; Italian 3,2,1,1. Home: R.F.D. 1, Dryden, N.Y. Office: Dept. of History, Cornell U., Ithaca, N.Y.

GRAY, WILLIAM HENRY, b. Greenville, Tex., Sept. 13, 1901. HISTORY. A.B., Trinity Coll. (Tex.), 1922; A.M., U. of Chicago, 1924; Ph.D., 1937. Dean, Instituto Politécnico (P.R.), 1922-23; teacher, Morton High School & Junior Coll. (Ill.), 1924-40; PROF., HISTORY, DIR., INTERNATIONAL STUDENT AFFAIRS, PA. STATE U., 1940- . Chmn., Pa. State Committee on International Understanding. Membership: American Academy of Political and Social Science; American Association of University Professors; American Historical Association; Conference on Latin American History.

Research: diplomatic history; Latin American political and economic history. Author: Exploring American Neighbors (1942-1963); American Diplomacy in Venezuela, 1835-1865 (Hispanic American Historical Review, Nov. 1940); Bolivar's Conquest of Guayaquil (Hispanic American Historical Review, Nov. 1947). Language: Spanish 4,4,4,3; Portuguese 3,2,2,1; French 2,1,1,1; German 1,1,1,1; Italian 1,1,1,1. Home: 31 Orlando Apartments, State College, Pa., 16801. Office: 108 Sparks Bldg., University Park, Pa. 16802.

GREENLEAF, RICHARD EDWARD, b. Hot Springs National Park, Ark., May 6, 1930. HISTORY. B.A., U. of N. Mex., 1952; M.A., 1953; Ph.D., 1956. Part-time instr., U. of N. Mex., 1954-57; ASSOC. PROF., CHMN., HISTORY AND INTERNATIONAL RELATIONS, U. OF THE AMERICAS, 1957- ; assoc. graduate dean, 1957-62; ACADEMIC VICE PRESIDENT, 1962- . Knights Templar research grant (Mexico), 1954; Rotary Foundation research fellow (Mexico), 1955-56; U. of the Americas research fellow (Spain), 1962. Membership: American Historical Association; Conference on Latin American History. Research: Mexico. Author: Victoriano Huerta: A Reappraisal (1960); Zumárraga and the Mexican Inquisition, 1536-1543 (1962); Mexican Inquisition Materials in Spanish Archives (The Americas, Winter 1964). Language: Spanish 5,4,4,4; Portuguese 4,3,3,3; French 4,3,—,3. Home: 405 Hermosa NE., Albuquerque, N. Mex. Office: Dept. of History, U. of the Americas. Km. 16 Carretera México-Toluca, México 10, D.F.

GREER, HAROLD EDWARD, JR., b. Carrollton, Ga., Oct. 6, 1938. HISTORY. A.B., U. of Ala., 1960; M.A., 1963; Ph.D., 1965. National Defense Education Act fellow in Hispanic American History. Membership: Phi Alpha Theta; Phi Beta Kappa; Southern Baptist Historical Society. Research: Latin American history; Southern Baptist mission work in Cuba; Protestants in Cuba. Language: Spanish 3,2,2,2. Home: Box 203, Livingston, Ala. 35470.

GREER, VIRGINIA LEONARD, b. Garnet, Mont., Aug. 1, 1900. HISTORY. Third Year Diploma, Teacher's Coll. (Oreg.), 1923; B.A., U. of Oreg., 1929; M.A., 1935; Ph.D., U. of N. Mex., 1954. Teacher, Oreg. Public Schools, 1920-43; instr., dean, U. of Oreg. and University High School, 1943-53; teacher, U.S. Army I. & E. Program (Japan), 1946-47; teacher, Ventura Union High School District (Calif.), 1954-66; VOLUNTEER, U.S. PEACE CORPS (BOLIVIA), 1966- . Consultant, Oregon Course of Study in the Social Sciences, 1948. Membership: California State Teacher's Association; National Education Association; Pacific Coast Council on Latin American Studies; Phi Lambda Theta. Research: Nicaragua. Author: State Department Policy in Regard to the Nicaraguan Election of 1924 (Hispanic American Historical Review, Nov. 1954). Language: Spanish 3,1,1,1; French 3,3,3,1. Home: c/o

Miss Janice Wylie, R.F.D. 1, Box 300, Turner, Oregon 97392.

GREEVER, JANET GROFF, b. Philadelphia, Pa., Sept. 12, 1921. HISTORY. B.A., Bryn Mawr Coll., 1942; M.A., 1945; M.A., Radcliffe Coll., 1951; Ph.D., 1954. Instr., Bryn Mawr Coll., 1949-50; INDEPENDENT RESEARCH AND STUDY, 1954- ; asst. prof., History, Wash. State Coll., Spring 1963. History fellow, Bryn Mawr Coll., 1944-45; graduate fellow, Radcliffe Coll., 1945-47; American Association of University Women fellow, 1948-49. Membership: American Historical Association; Conference on Latin American History; Hispanic American Society. Research: Bolivia, 19th century; colonial period in Latin America. Coauthor: Idaho (in World Book Encyclopedia, 1960). Language: Spanish 4,2,2,2; Portuguese 2,1,1,1; French 4,2,2,2; German 2,1,1,1; Italian 2,1,1,1. Home: 315 South Hayes St., Moscow, Idaho 83443.

GRIEB, KENNETH J., b. Buffalo, N.Y., Apr. 3, 1939. HISTORY. B.A., U. of Buffalo, 1960; M.A., 1962; Ind. U. ASST. PROF., HISTORY, WIS. STATE U.—OSHKOSH, 1966- . Doherty Foundation fellow (Mexico), 1964-65. Membership: American Historical Association; Conference on Latin American History; Mississippi Valley Historical Association; Phi Alpha Theta. Research: Latin American history; United States relations with Latin America; United States relations with Huerta. Language: Spanish 4,3,2,2; French 4,2,2,2. Office: Dept. of History, Wis. State U., 800 Algoma Blvd., Oshkosh, Wis. 54902.

GRIFFIN, CHARLES CARROLL, b. Tokyo, Japan, May 24, 1902. HISTORY. A.B., Harvard Coll., 1922; M.A., Columbia U., 1933; Ph.D., 1937. Clerk, Cía. Argentina de Cemento Portland, 1923-24; sales representative, Cía. Uruguaya de Cemento Portland, 1925-30; research asst., European Mission (Spain), Library of Congress, 1931-32; instr.-PROF., HISTORY, VASSAR COLL., 1934- ; asst. chief, Div. of Research and Liasion, Office of American Republics Affairs, U.S. Dept. of State, 1943-44; vis. prof., U. of Wis., 1949-50, U. of Chile, 1954, Harvard U., 1959-60. University fellow, Columbia U., 1933-34; Buenos Aires Convention exchange prof. (Venezuela), 1940-41; Advisory Committee, Handbook of Latin American Studies, 1958- ; chmn., Conference on Latin American History, 1960. Membership: Academy of Franciscan History; Academy of History of Venezuela, Chile, and Cuba; American Geographical Society; American Historical Association; Sociedade Capistrano de Abreu (Rio de Janeiro). Research: independence period in Spanish America; archival research. Author: The United States and the Disruption of the Spanish Empire, 1810-1822 (1937); The National Period in the History of the New World (1961); Los temas sociales y económicos en la época de la independencia (1962). Language: Spanish 4,4,4,4; Portuguese 3,2,1,1; French 3,2,2,2; German 2,2,2,1; Italian 2,2,1,1.

Home: 79 Raymond Ave., Poughkeepsie, N.Y. Office: Box 141, Vassar Coll., Poughkeepsie.

GRIFFITH, DAVID GIBBS, b. Columbus, Ohio, Mar. 13, 1939. HISTORY. A.B., Antioch Coll., 1961; M.A., U. of Mo., 1963. STUDENT, HISTORY, U. OF MO. National Defense Education Act fellow. Membership: American Historical Association; Mississippi Valley Historical Association. Research: Latin American history; the Mexican revolution. Language: Spanish 3,3,3,2. Home: 1213 East Walnut St., Columbia, Mo.

GRIFFITH, WILLIAM J., b. Kanopolis, Kans., Dec. 20, 1908. HISTORY. B.A., Southwestern Coll. (Kans.), 1930; M.A., U. of Wichita, 1937; Ph.D., U. of Calif., Berkeley, 1942. Unit head, Div. of Education, Office of Inter-American Affairs, 1942-44; special representative in Guatemala, Inter-American Educational Foundation, Office of Inter-American Affairs, 1944-47; asst. prof., Tulane U., 1947-50; assoc. prof., 1950-55; consultant in Guatemala, Foreign Operations Administration, 1954-55; PROF., HISTORY, TULANE U., 1955- ; vis. prof., U. of Colo., Summer 1961. Board of Editors, Hispanic American Historical Review, 1952-57; Social Science Research Council fellow, 1958. Membership: American Historical Association; Mississippi Valley Historical Association; Sociedad de Geografía e Historia de Guatemala; Southern Historical Association. Research: Central America since independence; Spanish borderlands. Author: The Hasinai Indians of East Texas as seen by Europeans, 1687-1772 (1954); Santo Tomás, anhelado emporio del comercio en el Atlántico (1959); Juan Galindo, Central American Chauvinist (Hispanic American Historical Review, Feb. 1960). Language: Spanish 4,4,4,4; French 3,2,1,1. Home: 360 Audubon St., New Orleans, La. 70118. Office: Dept. of History, Tulane U., New Orleans, 70118.

GSCHAEDLER, ANDRÉ. HISTORY. Ph.D., Columbia U., 1954. Membership: American Historical Association. Research: Pacific history; 16th century Mexico. Author: Documents on Spanish Navigation in the Mitchell Library, Sydney (Australia) (Hispanic American Historical Review, Aug. 1950). Language: Spanish 5,4,4,3; Portuguese 2,—,—,—; French 5,5,-5,5. Home: P.O. Box 144, Salem, W. Va. 26426.

GUEST, FLORIAN FRANCIS O.F.M., b. Alameda, Calif., Aug. 29, 1914. HISTORY. M.A., St. Louis U., 1952; M.A., Catholic U. of America, 1958; Ph.D., U. of Southern Calif., 1961. RESEARCH, HISTORY, FRANCISCAN FATHERS OF CALIFORNIA. Membership: Academy of American Franciscan History; California Historical Society. Research: the four presidios of Spanish California in their relationship with the California missions. Author: The Establishment of Branciforte (California Historical Quarterly, Mar. 1962). Language: Spanish 3,3,3,3. Home and office:

Franciscan Fathers of Calif., Old Mission, Santa Barbara, Calif.

GUICE, C. NORMAN, b. Summit, Miss., Feb. 2, 1911. HISTORY. B.A., Hendrix Coll., 1931; M.A., Duke U., 1937; Ph.D., U. of Calif., Berkeley, 1952. Instr., Stephens Coll., 1942-43; lectr., U. of Mich., 1947; ASSOC. PROF., HISTORY, WAYNE STATE U., 1947- . Mills traveling fellow, U. of Calif. (Mexico), 1941-42; consultant, Committee on the Accreditation of Service Experiences, American Council on Education, 1954, 1956, 1958; Fulbright lectr. (Peru), 1959-60; Rockefeller grant (Peru), Summer 1960; Wayne State U. faculty research fellow (Peru and Chile), Summer 1962. Membership: American Historical Association; Conference on Latin American History; Detroit Historical Society; Michigan Historical Society. Research: Peru during the war of the Pacific. Author: Texas in 1804 (Southwestern Historical Quarterly, July 1955); Trade Goods for Texas (Southwestern Historical Quarterly, Apr. 1957); The Latin American University (Graduate Comment, Wayne State University, Dec. 1960). Language: Spanish 4,4,4,3; Portuguese 1,—,—,—; French 2,2,—,—; German 1,—,—,—. Home: 92 Mapleton Rd., Grosse Point Farms 36, Mich. Office: Dept. of History, Wayne State U., Detroit 2, Mich.

HADDICK, JACK ALLEN, b. Olden, Tex., June 12, 1920. HISTORY. B.A., Tex. Coll. of Arts & Industries, 1949; M.A., U. of Tex., 1950; Ph.D., 1954. Lectr., Mexico City Col., 1954; ASSOC. PROF., HISTORY, U. OF HOUSTON, 1955- . E. D. Farmer International Scholar (Mexico), 1954; chmn., Regional Interviewing Committee, International Education Exchange Program, U.S. Dept. of Health, Education, and Welfare, 1963. Membership: American Historical Association; Texas Gulf Coast Historical Association. Research: independence period in Mexico; Spain. Author: The Deliberative Juntas of 1808: A Crisis in Mexican Democracy (in Essays in Mexican History by C. E. Castañeda and T. Cotner, 1958). Language: Spanish 4,3,3,3. Home: 4395 Harvest Lane, Houston 4, Tex. Office: Dept. of History, U. of Houston, 3801 Cullen Blvd., Houston 4.

HAFFNER, GERALD OTIS, b. Jamestown, Ind., Dec. 9, 1916. HISTORY. B.S., Central Normal Coll., 1940; M.A., Ind. U., 1947; Ph.D., 1952. Instr., American U., 1949-50; instr., Ind. U., Southeastern Campus, 1950-55; ASST. PROF., HISTORY, IND. U., SOUTHEASTERN CAMPUS, 1955- . American Philosophical Society research grant, Summer 1962. Membership: American Historical Association; Conference on Latin American History; Indiana Historical Society; Mississippi Valley Historical Association; Phi Alpha Theta; Western History Association. Research: United States history, especially colonial history and the American Revolution. Author: Colonel Henry Hamilton, a Famous P.O.W. of the American Revolution "Visits" Louisville (The Filson

Club History Quarterly, Oct. 1955); Captain Charles Asgill: An Anglo-American Incident, 1782 (History Today, May 1957); Jeffersonville (Encyclopaedia Britannica, 1962). Language: Spanish 2,—,—,—; German 2,—,—,—. Home: 1621 Brigman Ave., Jeffersonville, Ind. Office: Dept. of History, Ind. U., Southeastern Campus, Jeffersonville, 47130.

HAHNER, JUNE E., b. New York, N.Y., July 8, 1940. HISTORY. B.A., Earlham Coll., 1961; M.A., Cornell U., 1963; Ph.D., 1966. ASST. PROF., HISTORY, STATE U. TECHNOLOGICAL COLL., 1966- . National Defense Education Act fellow, Cornell U., 1962-64; Organization of American States research fellow (Rio de Janeiro), 1963; Foreign Area Studies grant (Brazil), 1965-66. Research: Latin American history; Brazilian history, especially the role of the military. Language: Spanish 4,4,4,4; Portuguese 4,4,4,3; French 2,1,1,1; German 2,1,1,1. Office: Dept. of History, Tex. Technological Coll., Lubbock, Tex.

HAIGH, ROGER MALONE, b. Atkinson, Nebr., Feb. 6, 1937. HISTORY. B.A., Nebr. State Teachers Coll., Peru, 1957; M.A., U. of Fla., 1958; Ph.D., 1963. ASST. PROF., HISTORY, NORTH TEX. STATE U., 1963- . Graduate fellow, U. of Fla., 1961-63. Research: the relationship of informal group solidarities to the independence movement. Language: Spanish 4,2,2,1; Portuguese 2,1,1,1; Danish 3,3,3,3. Home: 1108-11 Palmwood Dr., Denton, Tex. Office: Dept. of History, North Tex. State U., Denton.

HAIGHT, CHARLES HENRY, b. Chicago, Ill., May 27, 1909. HISTORY. B.A., U. of Calif., 1946; M.A., 1947; Ph.D., Stanford U., 1956. Instr., Stanford U., 1955-56; instr., U. of Ariz., 1956-58; INSTR., HISTORY, COLL. OF SAN MATEO, 1958- . Membership: American Historical Association. Research: Mexico, the colonial period and the Mexican Revolution. Language: Spanish 4,4,4,4; French 4,2,2,1. Home: 1247 Shafter St., San Mateo, Calif. Office: Dept. of History, Coll. of San Mateo.

HALE, CHARLES ADAMS, b. Minneapolis, Minn., June 5, 1930. HISTORY. B.A., Amherst Coll., 1951; M.A., U. of Minn., 1952; Diplôme, Université de Strasbourg, 1953; Ph.D., Columbia U., 1957. Instr., U. of N.C., 1956-57; asst. prof., Lehigh U., 1957-62; ASST. PROF., HISTORY, AMHERST COLL., 1963- . Fulbright scholar (France), 1952-53; Doherty fellow (Mexico), 1955-56; American Council of Learned Societies-Social Science Research Council grant (Peru), 1962-63. Membership: American Historical Association; Phi Beta Kappa. Research: Mexico. Author: The War with the United States and the Crisis in Mexican Thought (The Americas, Oct. 1957); Alamán, Antunano, y la continuidad del liberalismo (Historia Mexicana, Oct.-Dec. 1961). Language: Spanish 4,4,4,4; Portuguese 3,2,1,1; French 4,4,4,3. Home: 50 Lincoln Ave., Amherst, Mass. Office: Dept. of History, Amherst Coll., Amherst.

HALL

HALL, MICHAEL McDONALD, b. Houston, Tex., Mar. 4, 1941. HISTORY. A.B., Stanford U., 1963; M.A., Columbia U., 1965. STUDENT, HISTORY, COLUMBIA U. Woodrow Wilson fellow, 1963-64; National Defense Foreign Language fellow in Portuguese, Columbia U., 1964-65; Foreign Area fellow (Brazil), 1965-66. Research: Latin American immigration history, especially Brazilian immigration policy, 1822-1930; modern Brazilian history. Language: Spanish 4,4,3,3; Portuguese 4,4,4,3; French 3,2,2,2; Italian 3,3,2,2. Home: 5630 Wickersham, Houston, Tex.

HAMILL, HUGH MAXWELL, JR., b. Philadelphia, Pa., May 23, 1928. HISTORY. B.A., Amherst Coll., 1951; M.A., Harvard U., 1953; Ph.D., 1956. Group leader, Experiment in International Living (Mexico), Summer 1950; instr., Ohio Wesleyan U., 1957-58; asst. prof., 1958-61; asst. prof., U. of Conn., 1961-63; ASSOC. PROF., HISTORY, U. OF CONN., 1963- . Doherty fellow (Mexico), 1953-54; secretary-treasurer, Conference on Latin American History; dir., Latin American Area Studies, Missionary Personnel Program, National Council of Churches, June 1963. Membership: American Association of University Professors; American Historical Association; Hispanic American Society; Phi Beta Kappa. Research: New Spain in late 18th century to 1821; propaganda and psychological warfare. Author: The Hidalgo Revolt: Prelude to Mexican Independence (1964); Early Psychological Warfare in the Hidalgo Revolt (Hispanic American Historical Review, May 1961). Language: Spanish 5,4,4,4; Portuguese 3,2,2,2; French 4,2,2,2. Home: R.F.D. 1, Box 113, Mansfield Center, Conn. Office: Dept. of History, U. of Conn., Storrs.

HAMILTON, HOLMAN, b. Fort Wayne, Ind., May 30, 1910. HISTORY. A.B., Williams Coll., 1932; Ph.D., U. of Ky., 1954. Editorial writer, Fort Wayne Journal-Gazette (Ind.), 1932-50; asst. prof., U. of Ky., 1954-57; ASSOC. PROF., HISTORY, U. OF KY., 1957- . Guggenheim fellow, 1946; Mississippi Valley Historical Association Pelzer Prize, 1954; guest lectr., U. of Fla., 1958; J. P. Young lectr., Memphis State U., 1961. Membership: American Historical Association; Conference on Latin American History; Mississippi Valley Historical Association; Society of American Historians; Southern Historical Association. Research: United States history; career and influence of Claude G. Bowers, including his years as United States ambassador to Chile. Author: Zachary Taylor (1941, 1951); White House Images and Realities (1958); Prologue to Conflict, the Crisis and Compromise of 1850 (1964). Language: Spanish 3,2,2,2; French 3,3,3,3. Home: 220 Barrow Rd., Lexington, Ky. Office: Dept. of History, U. of Ky., Lexington.

HAMLIN, DON F. Office: Dept. of History, Loyola U., New Orleans, La. 70118.

HAMMOND, GEORGE PETER, b. Hutchinson, Minn., Sept. 19, 1896. HISTORY. A.B., U. of Calif., 1920; M.A., 1921; Ph.D., 1924; LL.D., U. of N. Mex., 1954. Instr., U. of N. Dak., 1923-24; asst. prof., U. of Ariz., 1925-27; assoc. prof., U. of Southern Calif., 1927-35; prof., dean of Graduate School, U. of N. Mex., 1935-46; PROF., HISTORY, DIR., BANCROFT LIBRARY, U. OF CALIF., BERKELEY, 1946- . Native Sons of the Golden West fellow (Spain), 1922-23; U.S. delegation, 4th Assembly of Pan American Institute of Geography and History, Caracas, 1946. Membership: American Historical Association; California Historical Society; Mississippi Valley Historical Association; New Mexico Historical Society; Western History Association. Research: early history of California and New Mexico. Author: Narratives of the Coronado Expedition (1940); The Larkin Papers (1950-64). Co-author: Oñate, Colonizer of New Mexico (1953). Language: Spanish 4,3,3,3; Portuguese 2,2,2,—; French 2,2,2,—; Danish 5,5,5,5; German 3,3, 3,3. Home: 810 Contra Costa Ave., Berkeley 7, Calif. Office: Bancroft Library, U. of Calif., Berkeley 4.

HANKE, LEWIS ULYSSES, b. Oregon City, Oreg., Jan. 2, 1905. HISTORY. B.S., Northwestern U., 1924; M.A., 1925; Ph.D., Harvard U., 1936. Instr., Harvard U., 1934-39; dir., Hispanic Foundation Library of Congress, 1939-51; prof., U. of Tex., 1951-61; PROF., HISTORY, COLUMBIA U., 1961- . Archibald Cary Coolidge fellow, 1933-34; Social Science Research Council fellow (Brazil), 1937-38; Rosenwald fellow, 1950. Membership: American Historical Association. Research: the Villa Imperial de Potosí. Author: The Struggle for Justice in the Spanish Conquest of America (1949); Aristotle and the American Indians (1959). Editor: Historia de la Villa Imperial de Potosí (1964). Language: Spanish 4,4,4,4; Portuguese 4,4,4,4; French 2,2,2,2. Home: Apt. 3-D, 90 Morningside Dr., New York 27, N.Y. Office: Fayerweather Hall 603, Dept. of History, Columbia U., New York 27.

HANN, JOHN HENRY, b. Lowell, Mass., July 2, 1926. HISTORY. B.A., George Washington U., 1962; M.A., U. of Tex., 1964. Missionary teacher, Oblate Fathers (São Paulo), 1952-57; STUDENT, HISTORY, U. OF TEX. National Defense Foreign Language fellow in Portuguese, U. of Tex., 1962-65. Membership: South Central Modern Language Association. Research: Latin American history; Brazilian diplomatic history. Language: Spanish 5,5,4,4; Portuguese 5,5,5,5; French 3,2,1,1; Latin 3,1,- 1,1. Home: 22 Third St., Lowell, Mass.

HANNA, ALFRED JACKSON, b. Tampa, Fla., May 5, 1893. HISTORY. A.B., Rollins Coll., 1917; L.H.D. (honorary), 1945. WEDDELL PROF. OF HISTORY OF THE AMERICAS, DIR., LATIN AMERICAN STUDIES, ROLLINS COLL., 1917- . Social Science Research Council and American Philosophical Society grants (France), 1952; Cross Chevalier, Order Palmes Académiques, Republic of France. Membership: American Historical Association; Southern Historical Association. Research: period of French intervention in Mexico. Author: Diplomatic Missions of the United States to Cuba to Secure the Spanish Archives of Florida (in Hispanic American Essays in Commemoration of James Alexander Robertson, 1942). Coauthor: Confederate Exiles in Venezuela (1960); The Immigration Movement of the Intervention and Empire as seen through the Mexican Press (Hispanic American Historical Review, May 1947). Home: 235 Sterling Ave., Winter Park, Fla. Office: Dept. of History, Rollins Coll., Winter Park.

HANNA, KATHRYN ABBEY. Office: Rollins Coll., Winter Park, Fla. 32791.

HANRAHAN, JAMES S. Home: 1732 Candlestick Lane, Newport Beach, Calif. 92660.

HARDING, TIMOTHY FOX, b. New York, N.Y., Oct. 4, 1934. HISTORY. B.A., Harvard Coll., 1956; U. of Mex., 1957; M.A., Stanford U., 1959; U. of Minas Gerais, 1960-61; Stanford U. Asst. to dir., Hispanic American Studies, Stanford U., 1958-59; instr., Stanford U., 1962; ASST. PROF., HISTORY, CALIF. STATE COLL., LOS ANGELES, 1963- . National Defense Education Act fellow in Portuguese and Brazilian Studies, 1959-60; Fulbright scholar (Brazil), 1960-61; asst. editor, Hispanic American Report, Stanford U., 1958-62. Membership: Hispanic American Society; Pacific Coast Council on Latin American Studies; World Affairs Council. Research: Latin American history and modern politics; Latin American labor movements; Latin American universities and student politics; social aspects of Latin American literature; regional folk music. Author: Mexico (Collier's Encyclopedia Yearbook, 1959, 1960); Implications of Brazil's Third Labor Congress (Hispanic American Report, Oct. 1960); Bolivia (Worldmark Encyclopedia of Nations, 1960, 1964). Language Spanish 5,5,5,4; Portuguese 5,5,4,3; French 3,3,3,2. Home: 1116 Galloway St., Pacific Palisades, Calif. 90272. Office: Dept. of History, California State College, 5151 State College Dr., Los Angeles, Calif. 90032.

HARDY, BLAINE CARMON, b. Vernal, Utah, Dec. 24, 1934. HISTORY. B.A., Wash. State U., 1957; M.A., Brigham Young U., 1957; Ph.D., Wayne State U., 1963. ASST. PROF., EDUCATIONAL HISTORY AND PHILOSOPHY, BRIGHAM YOUNG U., 1961- . Membership: American Historical Association; Mississippi Valley Historical Association. Research: Mormon colonies in Mexico; borderlands. Language: Spanish 3,—,2,1; French 2,—,1,1. Home: F-152 Wyview Village, Provo, Utah. Office: Dept. of History, Brigham Young U., Provo.

HARRELL, WILLIAM ASBURY, b. Americus, Ga., Apr. 21, 1922. HISTORY AND EDUCATION. B.A., Emory U., 1945; B.D., 1948; M.A., Scarritt Coll., 1950; Ph.D., U. of Fla., 1964. Missionary, Granbury Institute (Brazil), Board of Missions of the Methodist Church, 1949-62; SPECIALIST, COMPARATIVE EDUCATION, WESTERN HEMISPHERE, U.S.

OFFICE OF EDUCATION, 1964- . National Defense Foreign Language fellow in Portuguese, 1963-64. Research: the Regency period of Brazilian history; Brazilian literature; sociology. Language: Spanish 4,3,3,3; Portuguese 5,5,5,5. Home: 6312 North 36th St., Arlington, Va. Office: Bureau of International Education, U.S. Office of Education, 400 Maryland Ave. SW., Washington, D.C. 20202.

HARRISON, H. V. Office: Dept. of Government and Politics, U. of Md., College Park, Md. 20749.

HARRISON, JOHN PARKER, b. Sacramento, Calif., May 14, 1917. HISTORY. A.B., U. of Calif., 1938; Ph.D., 1951. Latin American specialist, Exhibits and Publications, U.S. National Archives, 1951-56; assoc. dir., Humanities, Rockefeller Foundation, 1956-62; PROF., HISTORY, DIR., INSTITUTE OF LATIN AMERICAN STUDIES, U. OF TEX., 1962- . Doherty fellow, 1949-50; U.S. Dept. of Education grant, 1949-50. Research: Latin American archives; northern South America; intellectual history of Latin America. Author: Guide to Materials on Latin America in the National Archives (1961); Role of the Intellectual in Fomenting Change: The University (1964); Confrontation with Political University (Annals of the American Academy of Political and Social Science, Mar. 1961). Language: Spanish 4,4,4,3; Portuguese 3,3,3,1; French 3,2,2,3. Home: 3505 Perry Lane, Austin, Tex. Office: Institute of Latin American Studies, P.O. Box 8058, University Station, Austin 12.

HARRISON, SANDAS LORENZO, b. Panama City, Panama, Apr. 5, 1922. HISTORY. B.A., Roosevelt U., 1954; M.A., U. of Chicago, 1955; Ph.D., Ind. U., 1963. Assoc. prof., chmn., Talladega Coll., 1957-60; prof., chmn., 1962-63; ASST. PROF., HISTORY, U. OF WIS., MILWAUKEE, 1963- . Lilly fellow, Ind. U., 1960-61; Doherty fellow and Whitney Foundation fellow (Central America), 1961-62; consultant, Phelps-Stokes Fund Project for the Improvement of Instruction in the High Schools, 1957-59. Membership: American Historical Association; Association for the Study of Negro Life and History; Conference on Latin American History; Mississippi Valley Historical Association. Research: Central American Common Market; Central American union. Language: Spanish 4,4,4,4; French 2,2,1,1. Home: 4303 North 16th St., Milwaukee, Wis. 53209. Office: Dept. of History, U. of Wis., Milwaukee, 3203 North Downer Ave., Milwaukee, 53211.

HAUBERG, CLIFFORD A., b. Fergus Falls, Minn., Jan. 12, 1906. HISTORY. B.S., U. of Minn., 1931; M.A., 1940; Ph.D., 1950. Teacher, principal, Minn. Public Schools, 1931-37; instr., Panama Canal Zone Schools, 1937-47; asst. prof., St. Olaf Coll., 1947-64; vis. prof., U. of Panama, Summer 1955; vis. prof., Eau Clair State Coll., 1955; PROF., HISTORY, ST. OLAF COLL., 1964- . Social Science Research Council grant (Panama), 1952-53; Associated Colleges of the Midwest faculty fellow (Central America and Mexico), Summer 1962. Membership: American Association of University Professors; American Historical Association; Mississippi Valley Historical Association. Research; Panama—economic and social history since 1839. Author: Panama; Pro Mundi Beneficio (Current History, Apr. 1957); Venezuela under Betancourt (Current History, Apr. 1961); Changing Conditions in Guatemala (Current History, Feb. 1963). Language: Spanish 3,3,3,2; French 3,1,—,—. Home: R.F.D. 2, Northfield, Minn. Office: Dept. of History, St. Olaf Coll., Northfield.

HAUCH, CHARLES CHRISTIAN, b. Chicago, Ill., Apr. 26, 1913. EDUCATION. Ph.B., U. of Chicago, 1934; M.A., 1936; Ph.D., 1942. Instr., Ind. U., 1941-43; program officer, Office of Inter American affairs, 1943-44; specialist, Bureau of Inter American Affairs, U.S. Dept. of State, 1944-52; program officer, Institute of Inter American Affairs, 1952-53; asst. chief, Legislative Reference Service, Library of Congress, 1954; editorial asst., American Peoples Encyclopedia, 1954-55, Encyclopaedia Britannica, 1955-57; specialist, comparative education in the Western Hemisphere, U.S. Office of Education, 1957-62; ACTING DIR., COMPARATIVE EDUCATION BRANCH, U.S. OFFICE OF EDUCATION, 1962- . Buenos Aires Convention fellow (Dominican Republic), 1940-41. Membership: American Historical Association; Comparative Education Society; Conference on Latin American History. Research: comparative education; Caribbean; Columbia; Haiti. Author: Foreign Attitudes towards Spanish Reoccupation of the Dominican Republic (Hispanic American Historical Review, May 1947); Educational Trends in the Caribbean: European Affiliated Areas (U.S. Office of Education, Oct. 1960); Current Situation in Latin American Education (U.S. Office of Education, Sept. 1963). Language: Spanish 3,3,3,3; Portuguese 1,1,1,—; French 3,2,2,3. Home: 5418 North 21st St., Arlington, Va. 22205. Office: Comparative Education Branch, Bureau of International Education, U.S. Office of Education, Washington, D.C. 20202.

HAYES, ROBERT C. Home: 5425 Harwood Rd., Bethesda, Md. 20014.

HELGESEN, LEIGH LYNN, b. Janesville, Wis., June 21, 1941. HISTORY. B.A., Drake U., 1963; M.A., U. of Wis., 1965. STUDENT, HISTORY, U. OF WIS. National Defense Foreign Language fellow, U. of Wis. Membership: Phi Beta Kappa. Research: Latin American history; history and anthropology of Brazil. Language: Spanish 4,3,2,3. Home: 3400 Edgewood Dr., Janesville, Wis.

HELGUERA, J. LEON, b. New York, N.Y., Oct. 29, 1926. HISTORY. B.A., Mexico City College, 1948; M.A., U. of N.C., 1951; Ph.D., 1958. Assoc. prof., N.C. State U., 1957-63; vis. prof., Universidad de Buenos Aires, Summer 1958; PROF., HISTORY, VANDERBILT U.,

1963- . Doherty fellow (Colombia), 1953-54; N.C. State U. research grant (Argentina), Summer 1958; Organization of American States fellow (Venezuela), Summer 1962; consultant, Boulton Foundation of Caracas; U.S. consultant, Bolivarian Society of Venezuela, 1963. Membership: American Historical Association; Centro de Historia del Cauca; Colombian Academy of History; Conference on Latin American History; Southeastern Conference on Latin America; Southern Historical Association; Venezuelan National Academy of History. Research; northern South America in the 19th century. Author: El impacto de Bolívar en la consciencia gran-colombiana, 1830-1863 (Revista de la Sociedad Bolivariana de Venezuela, Dec. 1958); The Changing Role of the Military in Colombia (Journal of Inter-American Studies, July 1961); Research Opportunities in Modern Latin America: The Bolivarian Nations (The Americas, Apr. 1962). Language: Spanish 5,5, 5,5; Portuguese 3,4,3,3; French 3,3,2,1; German 3,3,3,2; Russian 2,2,—,2. Home: 2613 Barton Ave., Nashville, Tenn. 37212. Office: Box 1606, Vanderbilt U., Nashville, 37203.

HELLYER, CLEMENT DAVID, b. Glendale, Calif., Aug. 15, 1914. JOURNALISM AND HISTORY. B.A., The Principia, 1936; M.S., Columbia U., 1938; U. of Fla., 1950-52. Asst. prof., San Diego State Coll., 1947-59; dir., Centro Cultural Costarricense-Norteamericano (San José), 1949-50; asst. dir., School of Inter-American Studies, U. of Fla., 1950-52; public relations asst. to Div. manager, General Dynamics Corporation, 1952-53; Latin American news editor (Mexico), The San Diego Union (Calif.), 1953-60; BRAZIL REPRESENTATIVE, FODOR'S MODERN GUIDES, INC., 1962- . U.S. Dept. of State lectr. (Latin America), 1952; participant, The American Assembly Conference on Latin America, 1959; Maria Moors Cabot Award, Columbia U., 1959; Pan American Foundation fellow (São Paulo, Brazil), 1960-62. Membership: American Association of University Professors; Sigma Delta Chi. Research: history of labor movement in Brazil. Author: The Story of the Border Patrol (1963). Co-author: American Air Navigator (1946); La cultura y el periodismo en América (1953). Language: Spanish 4,4,4,4; Portuguese 4,4,4,4. Home and office: P.O. Box 91, Rancho Santa Fe, Calif.

HENDERSON, DONALD C., JR., b. Williamsport, Pa., Oct. 1, 1931. HISTORY AND LANGUAGE. B.A., U. of Vt., 1955; M.A., Johns Hopkins U., 1957; Ph.D., Mich. State U., 1964. Instr., Mich. State U., 1959-62; instr., Pa. State U., 1962-64; ASST. PROF., SPANISH, STATE U. OF N.Y., COLL. AT ONEONTA, 1964- . U. of Vt. and Johns Hopkins U. tuition grants; Middle East Institute grant; Fulbright fellow (Chile, Argentina), 1958-59; National Defense Foreign Language fellow in Persian. Membership: Modern Language Association. Research: Chile; methodology of research in social science area; economics. Language: Spanish 5,5,5,5; Portuguese 1,1,1,1; French 5,3,3,3; Persian 1,2,2,1. Home: 55 University Terr., Burlington, Vt. Office: Dept. of Spanish, State U. of N.Y., Coll. at Oneonta, Oneonta.

HENDRICKS, FRANCES KELLAM, b. Blanco, Tex., Nov. 20, 1900. HISTORY. B.A., U. of Tex., 1922; M.A., 1925; Ph.D., U. of Ill., 1931. Asst. prof., Stephen F. Austin State Coll., 1927-28; prof., U. of San Antonio, 1936-42; PROF., CHMN., HISTORY, TRINITY U., 1942- . Administrative asst. for curriculum revision, Trinity U., 1958-60. Membership: American Association for State and Local Historical Societies; American Historical Association; San Antonio Historical Association; Texas State Historical Association. Research: Chile; Mexico; Texas history. Author: The First Apostolic Mission to Chile (Hispanic American Historical Review, Nov. 1942). Co-translator: Two Novels of the Revolution, by Mariano Azuela (1963). Language: Spanish 3,2,2,2. Home: 130 Stanford Dr., San Antonio 12, Tex. Office: Dept. of History, Trinity U., San Antonio 12.

HENDRICKS, WILLIAM. Home: 614 Dahlia Ave., Corona del Mar, Calif. 92625.

HENDRICKSON, EMBERT JULIUS, b. Minneapolis, Minn., June 22, 1928. HISTORY. B.S., St. Cloud State Coll., 1950; M.A., U. of N. Dak., 1954; Ph.D., U. of Minn., 1964. ASST. PROF., HISTORY, SAN JOSE STATE COLL., 1961- . Research: inter-American relations; relations of the United States and Venezuela, 1904-14. Language: Spanish 3,2,2,1. Home: 210½ South Kendall, Thief River Falls, Minn. 56701. Office: Dept. of History, San Jose State Coll., San Jose, Calif. 95112.

HENLEY, LLEWELLYN. Home: 5816 Temple Hills Rd., Washington, D.C. 20022.

HERR, RICHARD. Office: Dept. of History, U. of Calif., Berkeley, Calif. 94720.

HERRERA, ALFRED CHARLES, b. El Paso, Tex., Apr. 7, 1920. ECONOMICS AND POLITICAL SCIENCE. B.S., U. of Md., 1951; U. of Madrid, 1955; M.A., George Washington U., 1956. Dir., Operations Div., Office of Foreign Liquidation Commission, American Embassy (Brazil), 1946-1948; asst. air attaché, American Embassy (Spain) 1952-55; LIEUTENANT COLONEL, U.S. AIR FORCE, HEADQUARTERS, DEFENSE INTELLIGENCE AGENCY. Membership: Conference on Latin American History. Research: economic structure, culture and customs of Mexico and Spain; history of the Spanish borderlands of the United States. Editor: Historia de la Nueva México (1953). Language: Spanish 4,4,4,3; Portuguese 4,4,4,3. Home: 9404 Rose Hill Dr., Bethesda, Md. 20034. Office: Headquarters, Defense Intelligence Agency, Washington, D.C. 20301.

HERRICK, JANE, b. Chicago, Ill., Sept. 16, 1916. HISTORY. Ph.D., Catholic U. of America, 1955. Asst. editor, Academy of American Franciscan History, 1955-57; asst. editor, The

Americas, 1956-63; PROF., HISTORY, STATE COLL. AT BRIDGEWATER, 1957- . Assoc. editor for Latin American church history, New Catholic Encyclopedia. Research: Spanish America and Brazil. Author: The Reluctant Revolutionist: Hipólito da Costa (The Americas, Oct. 1957). Language: Spanish 4,2,—,—; Portuguese 4,2,—,—; French 4,3,—,—. Home: 100 Pleasant St., Bridgewater, Mass. Office: Dept. of History, State Coll., Bridgewater.

HERRING, HUBERT C., b. Winterset, Iowa, Dec. 29, 1889. HISTORY. A.B., Oberlin Coll., 1911; A.M., Columbia U., 1912; Union Theological Seminary, 1913. Prof., Latin American History, Pomona Coll. and Claremont Graduate School, 1944-58; RETIRED, 1958- . Author: Good Neighbors (1941); History of Latin America (1955). Home: 765 Indian Hill Blvd., Claremont, Calif.

HEWITT, CLYDE EATON, b. Hudson Falls, N.Y., June 24, 1916. HISTORY. B.A., Aurora Coll., 1937; M.A., U. of Chicago, 1939; Ph.D., 1948. PROF., HISTORY, AURORA COLL., 1939- ; REGISTRAR, 1955- . Membership: American Association of Collegiate Registrars and Admissions Officers; American Historical Association. Research: Venezuela; international investment and diplomacy; Mexico. Author: A Study in Opportunity, the Story of the First United States Industrial and Machinery Trade Mission to Mexico (Dec. 1963). Co-author: Cipriano Castro, Man Without a Country (American Historical Review, Oct. 1949). Language: Spanish 3,—,—,—. Home: 231 Calumet Ave., Aurora, Ill. Office: Dept. of History, Aurora Coll., Aurora, 60507.

HICKEY, HAROLD W. Office: Broome Technical Community Coll., Binghamton, N.Y. 13902.

HIGGINS, RUTH L., b. Columbus, Ohio, June 21, 1895. HISTORY AND POLITICAL SCIENCE. B.A., B.S., Ohio State U., 1917; M.A., 1921; Ph.D., 1926; LL.D. (honorary), Beaver Coll., 1953. Instr., Elmira Coll., 1924-25; asst. prof., Earlham Coll., 1925-26; prof., head, Woman's Coll. of Ala., 1926-34; vis. prof., U. of Ala., Summers 1930, 1931; dean, prof., Beaver Coll., 1934-60; chmn., History and Government, 1949-60; RETIRED; PROF. EMERITUS, HISTORY AND GOVERNMENT, BEAVER COLL., 1960- . Ohio State U. fellow, 1921-22, 1923-24. Membership: American Academy of Political and Social Science; American Association of University Professors; American Association of University Women; American Conference on Academic Deans; American Historical Association; Conference on Latin American History; Mississippi Valley Historical Association. Research: United States history and government; higher education; Latin American history. Author: Expansion in New York (1931); Recent Trends in Higher Education (Journal of Higher Education, June 1940); International-Mindedness on the College Campus (The Keystonian, Dec. 1949). Language: Spanish 1,1,1,1; French 3,—,—,—.

Home: 73 Mayfair Blvd., Columbus, Ohio 43213.

HILDNER, ERNEST GOTTHOLD, JR., b. Detroit, Mich.. Nov. 7, 1903. HISTORY. A.B., U. of Mich., 1927; M.A., 1928; Ph.D., 1932. Asst. prof., Fisk U., Summer 1934; asst. prof., Western Ill. State Teachers Coll., 1934-38; prof., dean, Ill. Coll., 1938-58; prof., Mich. State U., Summer 1943; PROF., HISTORY, ILL. COLL., 1958- . Economic history fellow, U. of Mich. (England, Spain), 1930-31; sabbatical, Archives of the Indies (Seville, Spain), 1961. Membership: American Historical Association. Research: the Caribbean area in the mid-18th century. Author: Ensenada and the French Alliance, 1752-56 (1933); Role of the South Sea Company in the Diplomacy Leading to the War of Jenkins' Ear (Hispanic American Historical Review, Aug. 1938). Language: Spanish 4,3,3,2; Portuguese 1,—,—,—; French 1,—,—,—. Home: 1120 West College Ave., Jacksonville, Ill. Office: Dept. of History, Ill. Coll., Jacksonville.

HILL, LAWRENCE F., b. Bivins, Tex., Nov. 19, 1890. HISTORY. B.S., West Tex. State Coll., 1915; A.B., U. of Calif., 1919; M.A., 1921; Ph.D., 1923. Asst. prof.-prof., Ohio State U., 1922-59; RETIRED, 1959- ; summer vis. prof., West Tex. State Coll., 1930, U. of Mich., 1929, 1942, U. of Nev., 1931, Duke U., 1939; vis. prof., Southern Ill. U., 1962-63, U. of Kans., 1963-64. Membership: American Historical Association; Conference on Latin American History; Mississippi Valley Historical Association; Phi Beta Kappa. Research: Brazil. Author: Diplomatic Relations between the United States and Brazil (1947). Language: Spanish 3,—,—,—; Portuguese 3,—,—,—; French 3,—, —,—. Home: 520 Ridgewood Ave., Colorado Springs, Colo.

HILLMON, TOMMIE J., b. Vassar, Kans., Dec. 9, 1924. HISTORY AND GOVERNMENT. B.A., Washburn U., 1949; M.A., Syracuse U., 1951; D.S.S., 1963. Intelligence specialist, Latin American Section, U.S. Dept. of the Army, 1951-53; cartographer, U.S. Navy Hydrographic Office, 1953-56; part-time geographer, asst. engineer, Geonautics, Inc., 1960-63; Hispanic reference specialist, Hispanic Foundation, Library of Congress, 1963-64; ASSOC. PROF., HISTORY, CHMN., SOCIAL SCIENCE, KY. WESLEYAN COLL., 1964- . Membership: American Association of University Professors; American Historical Association; Conference on Latin American History. Research: the role of the military in Latin America. Language: Spanish 3,2,2,1. Home: 3405 Hawthorne Dr., Owensboro, Ky. 42301. Office: Dept. of Social Science, Ky. Wesleyan Coll., Owensboro.

HILTON, RONALD, b. Torquay, England, July 31, 1911. LANGUAGE. B.A., Oxford U., 1933; M.A., 1936; Sorbonne, 1933-34; U. of Madrid, 1934-35; U. of Perugia, 1935-36; Oxford U., 1936-37; U. of Calif., Berkeley, 1937-39. Dir., Comité Hispano Inglés Library (Madrid), 1936; asst. prof., U. of British Columbia, 1939-41; assoc. prof., Stanford U., 1942-49; PROF., ROMANCE LANGUAGES, DIR., INSTITUTE OF HISPANIC AMERICAN AND LUSO-BRAZILIAN STUDIES, STANFORD U., 1949- . Commonwealth Fund fellow, U. of Calif., 1937-39; officer, Cruzeiro do Sul (Brazil); editor; Hispanic American Report. Membership: American Academy of Franciscan History; American Association of Teachers of Spanish; American Association of University Professors; Hispanic Society of America; Modern Language Association. Research: history of Hispanic America; Luso-Brazilian culture. Author: Handbook of Hispanic Source Materials in the United States (1942, 1956). Editor: Who's Who in Latin America (1946); The Life of Joaquim Nabuco (1950). Language: Spanish 5,5,5,5; Portuguese 5,5,5,5; French 5,5,5,5; German 1,1,1,1; Italian 1,1,1,1. Home: 766 Santa Ynez, Stanford, Calif. Office: Bolivar House, Stanford U., Stanford.

HILTON, STANLEY E., b. Hot Springs, Ark., Jan. 1, 1940. HISTORY. B.A., Long Beach State Coll., 1962; M.A., U. of Tex., 1964. STUDENT, HISTORY, U. OF TEX., 1963- . National Defense Foreign Language fellow in Spanish, U. of Tex., 1963-65. Membership: American Historical Association; Mississippi Valley Historical Association. Research: modern Latin America; 20th century Mexico and Brazil. Language: Spanish 5,5,5,4; Portuguese 5,4,3,3; French 5,4,3,3. Home: 3311 Hollywood Ave., Austin, Tex.

HILTY, HIRAM HORACE, b. Donnellson, Iowa. HISTORY AND LANGUAGE. B.A., Bluffton Coll., 1937; B.D., Hartford Theological Seminary, 1940; National U. of Mex., 1953; Duke U. Representative in residence, American Friends Board of Missions (Cuba), 1943-48; PROF., SPANISH, GUILFORD COLL., 1948- . Membership: American Association of Teachers of Spanish and Portuguese; American Association of University Professors. Research: Latin American history; Cuba; Spanish literature. Author: Cuba at Another Crossroad? (Quaker Life, Dec. 1960); Year Two and One-Half in Cuba (Friends Journal, Aug. 1962). Co-author: Understanding Cuba (1960). Language: Spanish 4,4,4,4; Portuguese 3,3,1,1; French 3,3,1,1; German 3,3,2,1. Home: 1509 Nathan Hunt Rd., Greensboro, N.C. Office: Dept. of Spanish, Guilford Coll., Greensboro.

HINDS, HAROLD E., JR. Home: Box 2500, Station B, Vanderbilt U., Nashville, Tenn. 37203.

HOFFMAN, FRITZ LEO, b. New Braunfels, Tex., Jan. 4, 1907. HISTORY. B.A., U. of Tex., 1928; M.A., 1930; Ph.D., 1935. Instr., U. of Tex., 1930-32, Summers 1933, 1934; chmn., Social Sciences, Corpus Christi Junior Coll., 1935-37; instr., U. of Colo., 1937-39; lectr., National U. of Buenos Aires and U. of Paraguay, 1943-44; asst. prof., U. of Colo., 1939-45; assoc. prof., 1945-52; PROF., HISTORY, U. OF COLO., 1952- ; lectr., U.S.

Information Agency (Argentina, Uruguay), 1956. E. D. Farmer International Scholarship, Universidad Nacional Autónoma de Mexico, 1932-34; Laura Spelman Rockefeller fellow, U. of Tex.; Faculty fellow, U. of Colo.; Board of Editors, Hispanic American Historical Review. Membership: American Historical Association; Conference on Latin American History; Rocky Mountain Council on Latin American Studies. Research: Rosas era; River Plate history; Mexico archival research. Author: The Diary of the Alarcón Expedition into Texas (1935); The Financing of San Martín's Expeditions (Hispanic American Historical Review, Nov. 1952); El movimiento de Mayo en los periódicos de los Estados Unidos (Trabajos y Communicaciones, Universidad Nacional de la Plata, Nov. 9, 1960). Language: Spanish 5,5,5,5; Portuguese 3,2,1,1; French 1,1,1,1; German 5,5,4,4. Home: 1360 Bluebell, Boulder, Colo. 80302. Office: Dept. of History, U. of Colo., Boulder, 80304.

HOLASEK, JANET EVELYN, b. Minneapolis, Minn., Dec. 16, 1940. HISTORY. B.A., Hamline U., 1964. STUDENT, HISTORY, IND. U., 1964- . Ind. U. fellow, 1964-65. Research: Latin American history; the 1962 presidential election in Peru; Latin America's role in the United Nations. Language: Spanish 4,3,3,4. Home: 6233 Baker Rd., Hopkins, Minn. 55343.

HOLLERAN, MARY PATRICIA, b. Norfolk, Conn., May 21, 1905. HISTORY. B.A., Mt. St. Vincent-on-the-Hudson, 1928; M.A., Columbia U., 1929; Ph.D., 1948. Teacher, New Haven High School (Conn.), 1931-38; prof., Catholic U. of America, Summer 1942; chmn., History, dir. of public relations, St. Joseph Coll., 1938-52; academic dean, Hampton Institute, 1952-56; PROF., CHMN., HISTORY, STATE COLL. AT WESTFIELD, 1956- . Inter-American Advisory Committee, State of Connecticut Development Commission, 1945; U.S. delegate, Inter-American Cultural Council meeting (Peru), 1956. Membership: American Association of University Professors; American Association of University Women; Delta Kappa Gamma. Research: Guatemala. Author: Church and State in Guatemala (1949); Who Should Go to College? (Journal of Higher Education, Oct. 1947); Function of a College (Journal of Higher Education, Oct. 1956). Language: Spanish 4,—,—,—; Portuguese 2,—,—,—; French 2,—,—,—. Home: 81 Broad St., Westfield, Mass. Office: Dept. of History, State Coll., Westfield.

HOLLIS, HELEN. Home: 1817 Monroe, Little Rock, Ark. 72204.

HOLMES, JACK D. L., b. Asbury Park, N.J., July 4, 1930. HISTORY. B.A., Fla. State U., 1952; M.A., U. of Fla., 1953; Universidad Nacional Autónoma de México, 1954-55; Ph.D., U. of Tex., 1959. Editorial asst., Hispanic American Historical Review, U. of Tex., 1955-56; instr., Memphis State U., 1956-58; asst. prof., McNeese State Coll., 1959-61; researcher, San Juan National Park (P.R.), U.S. National

Park Service, 1962-63; ASSOC. PROF., HISTORY, U. OF ALA., BIRMINGHAM CENTER, 1963- . Mexican Government grant, 1954-55; Charles W. Hackett fellow in Latin American Studies, U. of Tex., 1959; Fulbright grant (Spain and Portugal), 1961-62. Membership: Louisiana Historical Association; Southern Historical Association. Research: Spanish Louisiana; Spanish borderlands. Author: Documentos inéditos para la historia de Louisiana (1963); Some Economic Problems of Spanish Governors in Louisiana (Hispanic American Historical Review, Nov. 1962); The Spanish-American Rivalry over the Chickasaw Bluffs, 1780-1795 (East Tennessee Historical Society Publications, 1962). Language: Spanish 5,5,5,5; Portuguese 4,4,4,4; French 4,3,-3,4; German 2,2,2,2; Italian 3,3,2,2. Home: 505 Poinciana Dr., Birmingham 9, Ala. Office: Dept. of History, U. of Ala.-Birmingham Center, 720 South 20th St., Birmingham.

HOLMES, VERA BROWN, b. Frederictown, New Brunswick, Canada, Sept. 21, 1890. HISTORY. B.A., McGill U., 1912; M.A., 1913; Ph.D., Bryn Mawr Coll., 1922; D. Litt. (honorary), Smith Coll., 1960. Sessional lectr., McGill U., 1916-20; prof., Wilson Coll. (Pa.), 1922-23; prof., Smith Coll., 1924-58; vis. prof., Mount Holyoke Coll., 1930-31, 1951-52; vis. prof., U. of N. Mex., Summer 1948; vis. prof., San Diego State Coll., Fall 1959; RETIRED, 1960- . Mary Cary Thomas European fellow (England), 1920-21; Cecil and Helena Rubel Foundation fellow (England, Spain), 1923-24; John Simon Guggenheim-Latin American fellow (Spain, England), 1930-31. Membership: American Association of University Professors; American Historical Association; Conference on Latin American History. Research: Latin American history; relations of England and Spain as colonial powers; inter-American relations; imperialism. Author: History of the Americas: From Discovery to Nationhood (1950); History of the Americas: From Nationhood to World Status (1964); Anglo-Spanish Relations in America in the Closing Years of the Colonial Era (Hispanic American Historical Review, Aug. 1922). Language: Spanish 3,—,—,—. Home: 5870 E. 14th St., Tucson, Ariz.

HOOVER, JOHN PAGE, b. Burlingame, Calif., Nov. 7, 1910. HISTORY. A.B., Stanford U., 1931; M.A., 1932; Yale U.; Universidad de la Habana Law School (Cuba), 1938-40; Graduate School of Business Administration, Harvard U., 1958; American U. Asst. commercial attaché, vice consul (Guatemala, Cuba), U.S. Dept. of State and U.S. Dept. of Commerce, 1936-42; asst. commercial attaché (Caracas), U.S. Dept. of State, 1942-48; commercial attaché (Montevideo), 1948-50; international affairs officer, 1950-52; consul general (Rhodesia, Nyasaland), 1952-54 (Havana), 1954-56; dir., U.S. Operations Mission, counselor of embassy (Haiti); prof., Foreign Service Institute, U.S. Dept. of State, 1958-60; special asst., Bureau of Inter-American Affairs, U.S. Dept. of State, 1960-62; SPECIAL ADVISER, ORGANIZA-

TION OF AMERICAN STATES, 1962- . Membership: American Historical Association; American Political Science Association. Research: Latin American history; political science; economic development and international relations; Antonio José de Sucre. Language: Spanish 5,5,5,4; Portuguese 4,4,1,1; French 4,4,3,3. Home: 6105 Cromwell Dr., Washington 16, D.C. 20016.

HOSKINS, LEWIS M., b. McMinnville, Oreg., Feb. 23, 1916. HISTORY. A.B., Pacific Coll., 1938; M.A., Haverford Coll., 1939; Ph.D., U. of Mich., 1946. Prof., dean of faculty, Pacific Coll., 1943-45; chmn. of administration, Friends Ambulance Unit, 1945-48; personnel secretary, American Friends Service Committee, 1949-50; executive secretary, 1950-59; PROF., CHMN., HISTORY, EARLHAM COLL., 1959- . Part-time administrator of foreign study operations and AID contract in Kenya, 1964. Research: class structure in Mexico in 17th century. Language: Spanish 2,2,2,1; Chinese —,1,1,—; German 2,2,2,1. Home: 842 National Rd. West, Richmond, Ind., 47375. Office: Dept. of History, Earlham Coll., Richmond, 47375.

HOUSEMAN, PHILIP JOSEPH, b. Grand Rapids, Mich., Apr. 3, 1922. HISTORY. A.B., Wayne State U., 1949; M.A., Stanford U., 1951; Ph.D., 1961. Teacher, Instituto Chileno-Norte-americano de cultura, 1954-55; Sacramento City Unified School District (Calif.), 1958-60; CHMN., HISTORY, VICTOR VALLEY COLL., 1960- . Stanford U. grant, 1954; Buenos Aires Convention fellow (Chile), 1954-55. Membership: American Historical Association; Bolivarian Society; Conference on Latin American History; Hispanic American Historical Association; Latin American Studies Council; Phi Delta Kappa; Sigma Delta Pi. Research: Chilean nationalism, 1920-52. Language: Spanish 5,5,4,4; Portuguese 2,2,2,1; French 2,1,1,1; Italian 2,1,1,1. Home: 16222 Tejon St., Victorville, Calif. Office: P.O. Box 725, Victor Valley Coll., Victorville.

HUCK, EUGENE ROGER, b. Jan. 24, 1928. HISTORY. A.B., Temple U., 1952; M.A., U. of Ala., 1954; Ph.D., 1963. Part-time instr., Jacksonville State Teacher's Coll., 1956; historian, Public Information Office, U.S. Air Force, 1954-56; instr., U. of Ala., Huntsville Center, Summer 1958; teacher, Centro Colombo-Americano (Colombia), 1959; ASSOC. PROF., HISTORY, WEST GA. COLL., 1959- . Graduate fellow, U. of Ala., 1952-53, 1956-58; Buenos Aires Convention fellow (Colombia), 1958-59; Regent's Committee on Graduate Work and Research, West Ga. Coll. Membership: American Association of University Professors; Southeastern Conference on Latin American Studies; Southern Historical Association. Research: history, sociology and economics of Latin America; international relations concerning Panama. Language: Spanish 4,3,3,3; Portuguese 1,1,1,1; French 2,2,1,2. Home: 151 Howell Rd., Carrollton, Ga. 30117. Office: Div. of Social Science, West Ga. Coll., Carrollton.

HUDDLESTON, LEE ELDRIDGE, b. Seagraves, Tex., Oct. 19, 1935. HISTORY. B.A., Tex. Technological Coll., 1959; U. of Tex. Vis. instr., Kansas State U., Summer 1964; STUDENT, HISTORY, U. OF TEX. Woodrow Wilson fellow, U. of Tex., 1959-60; U. of Tex. fellow, 1960-62. Membership: Mississippi Valley Historical Association. Research: Latin American history; Argentine dictatorships; the origins and antiquity of the American Indians; Indian-Spanish relations on the frontiers. Author: Spaniard and Chiriguano in the Viceroyalty of Peru, 1569-1581 (The Historian of the University of Texas, 1963). Language: Spanish 4,3,—,—; Portuguese 3,—,—,—; French 3,—,—,—. Home: Box 7601, U. T. Station, Austin, Tex. 78712.

HULL, ANTHONY HARDINGE, b. London, England, Oct. 10, 1923. HISTORY. M.A., Magdalen Coll., Oxford U., 1951; U. of Ala. Company representative, Glaso Labs (Cuba), 1950-51; asst. dir., Alianza Anglo-Mexicana (Mexico City), 1951-54; teacher-trainee, foreign language specialist, British Ministry of Education and Iraqi Ministry of Education, 1954-56; foreign language specialist and vocational training consultant, International Labour Office (Geneva), 1956-58; prof., English and Linguistics, U. of Ala., 1958-61; prof., Russian, American U., 1961-63; Hispanic manuscript research specialist, Hispanic Foundation, Library of Congress, 1964; ASST. PROF., RUSSIAN, RHODE ISLAND COLL., 1964- . Tapon scholar in history. Membership: American Association for the Advancement of Slavic Studies; American Association of Teachers of Slavic and East European Languages; American Association of University Professors; American Historical Association; Modern Language Association. Research: Latin American history; Russian-Latin American relations. Author: From a Foreign Shore (1956); T.V. Guide for the Russian Language (1960). Language: Spanish 5,4,4,4; Portuguese 2,1,1,1; French 4,3,3,3; Russian 4,4,4,4. Home: 132 Pinehill Ave., Centredale 11, R.I. Office: Rhode Island Coll., Providence 8.

HUNDLEY, NORRIS CECIL, JR., b. Houston, Tex., Oct 26, 1935. HISTORY. B.A., Whittier Coll., 1958; Ph.D., U. of Calif., Los Angeles, 1963. Editorial asst., Pacific Historical Review, Summer 1961; acting instr., U. of Calif., Los Angeles, 1962-63; instr., U. of Houston, 1963-64; ASST. PROF., HISTORY, U. OF CALIF., LOS ANGELES, 1964- . U. of Calif., Los Angeles, fellow, 1960-62; American Philosophical Society fellow, 1963. Membership: American Historical Association; American West Historical Association; Mississippi Valley Historical Association. Research: history of American West; U.S. diplomatic history; economic development of northern Mexico's arid border region; Mexican-American controversies over the waters of the Colorado, Tijuana, and Rio Grande Rivers. Author: Colorado Waters Dispute (Foreign Affairs, Apr. 1964). Language: Spanish 3,2,2,3; French 3,2,2,3; German 3,1,1,3.

Home: 11337 Burnham St., Los Angeles, Calif., 90049. Office: Dept. of History, U. of Calif., Los Angeles, 90024.

HUNT, LESTER C., b. Lander, Wyo., Sept. 5, 1927. HISTORY. B.A., Swarthmore Coll., 1949; U. of Chicago. Instr., Ruston Academy (Cuba), 1949; instr., American School (Mexico City), 1950; asst. producer, Educational Radio Program, U. of Chicago Radio Office, 1954-55; organizer of Puerto Rican and Mexican-American programs, Catholic Charities of the Archdiocese of Chicago, 1955-57; field representative, Industrial Areas Foundation, 1957-60; executive asst., Bishops' Committee for Migrant Workers (Chicago), 1960-62; ASST. PROF., DIV. OF THE SCIENCE OF SOCIETY, MONTEITH COLL., WAYNE STATE U., 1963- . National Association of Educational Broadcasters grant; National Defense Foreign Language fellow in Spanish, U. of Chicago, 1962-63. Membership: American Historical Association; Midwest Council of the Association for Latin American Studies. Research: intellectual history; community organization and development. Co-author: The Meanings of Democracy: Puerto Rican Organizations in Chicago (Etc., Spring 1956). Language: Spanish 4,4,4,4; Portuguese 1,1,1,1; French 3,3,2,2. Home: 247 California, Highland Park 3, Mich. Office: Div. of the Science of Society, Monteith Coll., Wayne State U., Detroit 2, Mich.

HUTCHINS, J(ENNINGS) RANDOLPH, b. Cananea, Sonora, Mexico, July 26, 1906. HISTORY AND LANGUAGE. B.A., U. of Calif., Los Angeles, 1928; M.A., U. of Southern Calif., 1947. Assoc. prof., Pacific Coll., 1942-43; assoc. prof., Lewis and Clark Coll., 1943-47; instr., College of the Sequoias, 1948-49; instr., Pasadena, Calif., Junior Colleges, 1949-51; assoc. prof., U. of Redlands, 1953-54; assoc. prof., U. of the Pacific, 1954-64; PROF., HISTORY, U. OF THE PACIFIC, 1964- . Danforth grant. Membership: American Historical Association; Instituto Internacional de Literatura Iberoamericana. Research: European and Latin American history; Spanish language and literature; Quaker social thought and action in Southern California. Language: Spanish 5,5,5,5; Portuguese 3,3,3,2; French 3,3,3,2; Italian 3,2,2,2; German 3,2,2,2. Home: 5922 Mitchler Ave., Stockton 7, Calif. Office: Dept. of History, U. of the Pacific, Stadium Drive at Pacific Ave., Stockton 4.

HUTCHINSON, CECIL ALAN, b. Lowestoft, England, Mar. 13, 1914. HISTORY. B.A., Cambridge U., 1937; M.A., 1941; Ph.D., U. of Tex., 1948. Instr., Dartmouth Coll., 1938-40; editor, translator, Committee on Cultural Relations with Latin America, Inc. (Conn.), 1944-45; ASSOC. PROF., HISTORY, U. OF VA., 1948- . U. of Va. grants (Mexico), 1952-53, 1955 (South America), 1960. Membership: American Historical Association; Conference on Latin American History. Research: Mexico from independence to 1860, especially social and intellectual history. Author: Mexican Federalists in New Orleans and the Texas Revolu-

tion (Louisiana Historical Review, Jan. 1956); Valentín Gómez Farías and the Secret Pact of New Orleans (Hispanic American Historical Review, Nov. 1956); Asiatic Cholera Epidemic of 1833 in Mexico (Bulletin of Historical Medicine, Jan.-Feb. 1958). Language: Spanish 4,4,4,4; Portuguese 3,3,2,2; French 4,4,3,3. Home: 216 High View Lane, R.F.D. 4, Charlottesville, Va. Office: Dept. of History, U. of Va., Charlottesville.

ICE, ORVA LEE, b. Elkhart, Ind., Mar. 10, 1920. HISTORY AND EDUCATION. B.A., U. of Pittsburgh, 1942; M.A., U. of Chicago, 1948; Ed.M., Wayne State U., 1956. Instr., U. of Pittsburgh, 1941-43; superviser of social work, State of Ind., 1948-52; export manager, John C. Jensen Company (Chicago), 1952-56; teacher, East Detroit Public Schools, 1956-60; part-time instr., South Macomb Community Coll., 1957-60; INSTR., HISTORY, REGISTRAR, MACOMB COUNTY COMMUNITY COLL., 1960- . Membership: American Association of College Registrars and Admissions Officers; Conference on Latin American History; Hispanic American Historical Association; Michigan Association for Higher Education; National Education Association; Phi Alpha Theta. Research: United States history; Latin American history; comparative education; investments in Brazil and Mexico. Language: Spanish 3,2,2,3; Portuguese 3,1,1,2; French 3,3,2,3. Home: 3812 Garrick, Warren, Mich. 48091. Office: Macomb County Community Coll., 22240 Federal St., Warren, 48089.

INNES, JOHN S., b. Warrensburg, Mo., May 19, 1938. HISTORY. B.A., Oberlin Coll., 1960; M.A., Vanderbilt U., 1963; U. of Tex. STUDENT, HISTORY, U. OF TEX. National Defense Education Act fellow in Latin American Studies, 1961-62. Membership: Conference on Latin American History. Research: recent economic history of Brazil. Language: Spanish 5,5,4,3; Portuguese 5,5,4,3. Home: R.F.D. 5, Warrensburg, Mo. 64093.

JACKSON, GABRIEL, b. Mount Vernon, N.Y., Mar. 10, 1921. HISTORY. A.B., Harvard U., 1942; M.A., Stanford U., 1950; Doctorat d'université, U. of Toulouse (France), 1952. Instr., Putney School (Vt.), 1946-49; instr., Goddard Coll., 1952-55; asst. prof., Wellesley Coll., 1955-60; assoc. prof., Knox Coll., 1962-65; ASSOC. PROF., HISTORY, U. OF CALIF., SAN DIEGO, 1965- . Sheldon traveling fellow (Mexico), 1942; Fulbright research fellow (Spain), 1960-61; Social Science Research Council fellow (Europe), 1960-61, 1961-62; consultant, Wesleyan U. Press, American Historical Association Guide to Historical Literature, and Encyclopedia Americana. Membership: American Historical Association; American Association of University Professors; Conference on Latin American History; Phi Beta Kappa. Research: 19th and 20th century Spanish history. Author: The Origins of Spanish Anarchism (Southwestern Social Science Quarterly, Sept.

1955); The Azaña Regime in Perspective (American Historical Review, Jan. 1959); Reflections on Two Loyalty Purges (Centennial Review of the Arts and Sciences, Apr. 1960). Language: Spanish 5,4,4,3; French 5,4,4,4; Catalan 3,1,1,1; German 4,2,2,2. Office: Dept. of History, U. of Calif., San Diego, Calif.

JACKSON, WILLIAM V. Home: 196 W. Kathleen Dr., Park Ridge, Ill. 60068.

JACOBSEN, JEROME V., S.J. Office: Loyola U., 6525 Sheridan Rd., Chicago, Ill. 60626.

JAKUBCZYK, ZIGMUND S., b. Ashley, Pa., July 5, 1906. HISTORY. A.B., U. of Scranton, 1933; M.A., Bucknell U., 1938; U. of Pa., 1945-46. HEAD OF DEPT., HISTORY, ASHLEY-SUGAR NOTCH JOINT SCHOOLS (PA.), 1934- . Membership: American Historical Association; Pennsylvania Historical Association; Wyoming Valley Historical and Geological Society. Research: Latin American and United States history; Conservative party in Colombia. Language: Spanish 3,3,3,3; French 4,3,3,3; Polish 4,4,4,3. Home: 94 West Hartford St., Ashley, Pa. Office: Dept. of History, Ashley-Sugar Notch Joint Public High School, Ashley.

JAMISON, EDWARD A., b. Pontiac, Ill., July 10, 1909. HISTORY. B.S., Northwestern U., 1931; M.A., Tufts Coll., 1933; Fletcher School of Law & Diplomacy, 1933-34; Ph.D., Harvard U., 1943. Inter-American Regional Affairs, Foreign Service, U.S. Dept. of State, 1947-55; deputy chief of mission, Embassy (Costa Rica), 1956-59, (Guatemala), 1959-60; alternate representative, Organization of American States Council, 1960-63; dir., Office of Inter-American Regional Political Affairs, 1960-63; POLITICAL ADVISER TO COMMANDER IN CHIEF, ATLANTIC, 1963- . Research: inter-American organizations; Organization of American States; inter-American political-military relationships; Central American governments and economics. Author: Keeping Peace in the Caribbean (The Department of State Bulletin, July 1950). Language: Spanish 4,4,4,2; Portuguese 2,2,—,—; French 2,1,1,1. Home: 503 Battery Rd., Virginia Beach, Va. Office: SAC-LANT Headquarters, Box 30, Norfolk, Va. 23511.

JEFFREY, WILLIAM H., b. Burlington, Vt., Jan. 24, 1921. HISTORY. B.A., Drew U., 1942; M.A., U. of Mich., 1944; Ph.D., U. of Colo., 1950. Instr., Union Coll. (Ky.), 1945-46; PROF., HISTORY, U. OF MAINE, 1946- . American Philosophical Society grant (Argentina), 1954. Membership: American Historical Association; Conference on Latin American History; Hispanic American Society; Northeast Council on Latin American Studies; Northern New England Historians Conference. Research: 19th century Argentina; Mexico. Author: Mitre and Argentina (1952); Mitre and Urquiza (Drew University Studies, Sept. 1952). Language: Spanish 3,—,—,—; German 2,2,2,2. Home: 12 Spencer St., Orono, Maine. Office 130 Stevens Hall, U. of Maine, Orono.

JOHNSON, DONALD D., b. Hartford, Conn., Jan. 10, 1917. HISTORY. A.B., U. of Calif., Los Angeles, 1938; M.A., U. of Southern Calif., 1941; Ph.D., 1946. Lectr., U. of Southern Calif., 1944-46; instr.-asst. prof., Wash. State U., 1946-49; asst. prof.-prof., U. of Hawaii, 1949-60; PROF., CHMN., HISTORY, U. OF HAWAII, 1960- ; professorial lectr., Pentagon War College programs, George Washington U., U. of Md., 1962-63. Community Foundation fellow, Honolulu, 1955; Fulbright senior lectr. (Australia), 1956. Membership: American Association of University Professors; American Historical Association; Conference on Latin American History; Hawaiian Historical Society. Research: United States diplomatic history with special reference to the Pacific basin, including the west coast of Latin America. Author: The U.S. in the Pacific: A Syllabus (1957). Language: Spanish 3,2,2,2; Portuguese 1,1,1,1; French 3,2,2,2; Italian 2,1,1,1. Home: 672 Lawelawe St., Honolulu 16, Hawaii. Office: Dept. of History, U. of Hawaii, Honolulu, 96822.

JOHNSON, JOHN J., b. White Swan, Wash., Mar. 26, 1912. HISTORY. B.A., Central Wash. Coll., 1939; M.A., U. of Calif., Berkeley, 1943; Ph.D., 1947. PROF., HISTORY, STANFORD U., 1946- ; acting chief, Research Div., American Republics, U.S. Dept. of State, 1952-53. Mills traveling fellow, 1943-44, 1945-46, (Chile). Membership: American Historical Association; Conference on Latin American History; Pacific Coast Council on Latin American Studies. Research: the role of the military in politics and society in Latin America. Author: Political Change in Latin America (1958); The Military and Society in Latin America (1964). Editor: The Role of the Military in Underdeveloped Countries (1962). Language: Spanish 5,4,4,3; Portuguese, 5,4,3,3. Office: Dept. of History, Stanford U., Stanford Calif.

JOHNSON, PHILIP BRIAN, b. Lee, Ill., Feb. 7, 1941. HISTORY. B.A., U. of Minn., 1963; Tulane U. STUDENT, HISTORY, TULANE U. National Defense Education Act fellow. Membership: Phi Alpha Theta; Phi Eta Sigma. Research: Latin American history; Brazilian history; inter-American diplomatic relations; Peruvian guano trade. Language: Spanish 3,3,3,—; Portuguese 3,2,2,—; French 3,1,1,—. Home: 3653 Arden, Brookfield, Ill.

JOHNSON, RICHARD A., b. Moline, Ill., Apr. 17, 1910. HISTORY. B.A., Augustana Coll., 1932; M.A., U. of Tex., 1933; Ph.D., 1938. Commercial attaché, Embassy (Bolivia), U.S. Dept. of State, 1948-50; officer-in-charge, Consulate (Guadalajara, Mexico), 1950-52; deputy chief of mission, Embassy (Dominican Republic), 1952-54; political counselor, Embassy (Spain), 1955-57; CONSUL GENERAL, CONSULATE (MONTERREY, MEXICO), U.S. DEPT. OF STATE, 1962- . Advanced University fellow, U. of Tex., 1937-38. Membership: American Foreign Service Association; American Historical Association; Conference on Latin American History; International Good

Neighbor Council. Research: inter-American diplomacy. Author: The Mexican Revolution of Ayutla (1939). Language: Spanish 5,5,4,4; Portuguese 4,2,1,1; French 3,2,2,1; German 1,1,1,1; Italian 2,2,2,1. Home: American Consulate General, AP 152, Monterrey, Nuevo León, México. Office: Foreign Service, U.S. Dept. of State, Washington 25, D.C.

JONES, OAKAH L., JR., b. Providence, R.I., June 20, 1930. HISTORY. B.S., U.S. Naval Academy, 1953; M.A., U. of Okla., 1960. Instr.-ASSOC. PROF., HISTORY, U.S. AIR FORCE ACADEMY, 1960- ; CHMN., LATIN AMERICAN HISTORY, 1964- . Membership: Conference on Latin American History; Historical Society of New Mexico; Western History Association. Research: colonial Latin American history; Spanish borderlands. Author: Pueblo Indian Auxiliaries in New Mexico, 1763-1821 (New Mexico Historical Review, Apr. 1962); Pueblo Indian Auxiliaries and the Reconquest of New Mexico, 1692-1704 (Journal of the West, July 1963). Language: Spanish 4,3,3,4; Portuguese 2,1,1,1; French 3,2,2,2. Home: Box 8223, Station C, Albuquerque, N. Mex. Office: Dept. of History, U.S. Air Force Academy, Colo.

JONES, ROBERT CUBA, b. Gibara, Cuba, May 12, 1902. SOCIAL WELFARE. A.B., Earlham Coll., 1923; U. of Chicago. Researcher, chief, Div. of Labor and Social Affairs, Pan American Union, 1942-51; senior officer, Technical Assistance Administration, United Nations, 1949-53; social science analyst, Presidential Commission on Migratory Labor, Executive Office of the President, 1950-51; technical consultant, Mexican Social Security Institute, 1953-54; FOUNDER AND DIR., VILLA JONES INTERNATIONAL CULTURAL CENTER, 1954- . Consultant on immigration, United Nations, 1949-50; consultant, Mexican Institute of Economic Research. Membership: American Anthropological Association; American Economic Association; American Sociological Association; Mexican Anthropological Society; Mexican Society of Geography and Statistics; Mexican Sociological Society. Research: labor; social work programs; community development. Author: Mexican War Workers in the U.S. (1942); Low Cost Housing in Latin America (1943); Immigration Possibilities in Venezuela (1950). Language: Spanish 5,5,5,4; Portuguese 3,3,—,—; French 2,2,1,1; German 2,2,1,1. Home and office: 23 Chilpancingo, México, D.F., Mexico.

JONES, TOM BARD, b. Dunkirk, N.Y., June 21, 1909. HISTORY. A.B., U. of Mich., 1931; M.A., 1932; Ph.D., 1934. PROF., HISTORY, U. OF MICH., 1935- . Membership: American Oriental Society; Archeological Institute of America. Research: ancient history. Author: Introduction to Hispanic American History (1939; revised edition, 1950); South America Rediscovered (1949); Bibliography of South American Economic History (1955). Language: Spanish 4,3,1,1; Portuguese 4,2,1,1; French 4,4,1,1; Greek 4,2,1,1. Linguistic Studies:

Abbadian, Hebrew, Italian, Latin. Home: 3911 East 50th St., Minneapolis, Minn. 55417. Office: Dept. of History, U. of Minn., Minneapolis 14.

JONES, WILBUR DEVEREUX, b. Youngstown, Ohio, Sept. 28, 1916. HISTORY. A.B., Youngstown Coll., 1940; A.M., Western Reserve U., 1947; Ph.D., 1949. Instr., Western Reserve U., 1948-49; instr., U. of Ga., 1949-51; asst. prof., 1951-57; assoc. prof., 1957-62; PROF., HISTORY, U. OF GA., 1962- . Membership: Conference on British Studies. Research: Anglo-Latin American relations; Argentina and Brazil; Jamaica. Author: Lord Derby & Victorian Conservatism (1956); Lord Aberdeen and the Americas (1959); Civilization through the Centuries (1960). Language: Spanish 2,2,2,—; German 3,3,3,—. Home: 420 South Milledge Ave., Athens, Ga. Office: Dept. of History, U. of Ga., Athens.

JUAREZ, JOE ROBERT, b. Laredo, Tex., Dec. 18, 1934. HISTORY. B.A., St. Edward's U., 1957; M.A., U. of Tex., 1959. ASST. PROF., HISTORY, ST. EDWARD'S U., 1959- . Woodrow Wilson fellow, 1957-58; U. of Tex. fellow, 1958-59; John Hay Whitney Opportunity fellow, 1961-62; U. of Tex. fellow, 1961-62. Membership: American Association of University Professors; Hispanic American Historical Association. Research: Latin American history; Spanish borderlands; United States foreign policy in the Caribbean; Mexican church-state relations; La Reforma in Mexico. Author: La lucha por el poder a la caída de Santa Anna (Historia Mexicana, July-Sept. 1960); United States' Withdrawal from Santo Domingo (Hispanic American Historical Review, May 1962); Argentine Neutrality, Mediation and Asylum during the Spanish Civil War (The Americas, Apr. 1963). Language: Spanish 5,5,5,5; Portuguese 3,2,1,1; French 2,1,1,1. Home: 1108 Fieldcrest Dr., Austin 4, Tex. Office: Dept. of Social Science, St. Edward's U., Austin 4.

KAHLER, MARY ELLIS, b. Santiago, Chile, Aug. 2, 1919. LIBRARY SCIENCE. A.B., Swarthmore Coll., 1940; B.L.S., Drexel Institute of Technology, 1949; M.A., George Washington U., 1953. Library asst., Fort Dix Post Library, 1944-48; head, Bibliographic Unit, and bibliographer, Order Div., Library of Congress, 1949-51; classifier, Personnel Div., 1951-52; editor of publications, Union Catalog Div., 1952-53; asst. chief, Serial Record Div., 1953-57; CHIEF, SERIAL RECORD DIV., LIBRARY OF CONGRESS, 1957- . Membership: American Historical Association; American Library Association; Conference on Latin American History; Society of American Archivists; Special Libraries Association. Research: Latin American history. Language: Spanish 3,3,3,—; Portuguese 5,4,4,—; French 4,4,3,4; German 2,2,2,—. Home: 712 Lakeview Dr., Falls Church, Va. 22041. Office: Serial Record Div., Library of Congress, Washington, D.C. 20540.

KAISER, CHESTER CARL, b. Garland, Kans., Sept. 16, 1908. HISTORY. B.S., Kans. State Teachers Coll., 1932; M.S., 1936; M.A., U. of Southern Calif., 1940; Ph.D., American U., 1954. Instr., secondary schools, 1936-43; asst. prof., Colo. State U., 1943-45; instr., U. of Minn., 1945-46; ASSOC. PROF., HISTORY, WILLAMETTE U., 1946- ; teacher, Mexico City Coll., Summer 1956. American U. research grant, 1951-53. Membership: American Association for State and Local History; American Historical Association; Mississippi Valley Historical Association. Research: United States-Mexican relations; Mexico since 1876. Author: J. W. Foster y el desarrollo económico de México (Historia Mexicana, July-Sept. 1957); México en la Primera Conferencia Panamericana (Historia Mexicana, July-Sept. 1961). Language: Spanish 3,3,3,3; French 1,1,1,1. Home: 1175 Court St. NE., Salem, Oreg. Office: Dept. of History, Willamette U., Salem.

KARNES, THOMAS L., b. Kenosha, Wis., Aug. 21, 1914. HISTORY. A.B., Colo. U., 1940; M.A., Stanford U., 1949; Ph.D., 1953. Instr., Stanford U., 1951-54; assoc. prof., Tulane U., 1954-64; PROF., HISTORY, TULANE U., 1964- . Inter-American exchange fellow (Costa Rica), 1950-51; American Philosophical Society fellow (Guatemala), 1955; assoc., Middle American Research Institute. Membership: Conference on Latin American History; Mississippi Valley Historical Association; Phi Beta Kappa; Southwestern Social Science Association; Western History Association. Research: United States-Latin American relations; Central American history. Author: The Failure of Union: Central America, 1824-1960 (1961); The Origins of Costa Rican Federalism (The Americas, Jan. 1959); Hacia la federación centroamericana (Las Américas, May 1962). Language: Spanish 4,3,4,3; French 2,1,1,1. Home: 1301 Waltham St., Metairie, La. Office: Dept. of History, Tulane U., New Orleans, La. 70118.

KEEN, BENJAMIN, b. Bethlehem, Pa., Apr. 25, 1913. HISTORY. A.B., Muhlenburg Coll., 1936; M.A., Lehigh U., 1939; Ph.D., Yale U., 1941. Research assoc., Strategic Index of Latin America, Yale U., 1941-43; instr., 1943-45; asst. prof., Amherst Coll., 1945-46; prof., W. Va. U., 1946-56; editor, G. and C. Merriam Co., 1956-59; prof., Jersey City State Coll., 1959-65; PROF., HISTORY, NORTHERN ILL., U., 1965- . Bulkeley fellow, Yale, 1940-41; chmn., Prize Committee, Conference on Latin American History, 1964. Membership: Conference on Latin American History. Research: Mexico; revolutionary Latin American history. Author: David C. DeForest and the Revolution of Buenos Aires (1947); Readings in Latin American Civilization (1955). Translator: The Life of the Admiral Christopher Columbus, by his Son Ferdinand (1959). Language: Spanish 4,4,4,4; French 4,3,3,3. Office: Dept. of History, Northern Ill. U., De Kalb, Ill.

KEITH, HENRY HUNT, b. Shreveport, La., Dec. 22, 1926. HISTORY. B.A., La. State U., 1948; M.A., U. of Va., 1950; U. of Calif.,

Berkeley. Dir. of courses, U.S.-Brazilian Institute, U.S. Information Agency (Rio de Janeiro), 1950-55; international account executive, McCann-Erickson, Inc. (N.Y.), 1955-58; asst. manager, San Francisco Chamber of Commerce, 1958-60; STUDENT, HISTORY, U. OF CALIF., BERKELEY. Rotary Foundation fellow, Graduate Institute of International Studies (Geneva, Switzerland), 1949-50; National Defense Foreign Language fellow (Brazil), 1963-64. Membership: American Historical Association; American Political Science Association. Research: Latin American history and political science; role of the Brazilian armed forces in politics; the Brazilian tenente revolts, 1920-1930. Language: Spanish 4,4,4,3; Portuguese 4,4,4,3; French 4,4,4,3; Italian 2,2,2,2. Home: 6206 Claremont Ave., Oakland 18, Calif.

KENYON, ROBERT GORDON B., b. Peace Dale, R.I., Mar. 19, 1914. HISTORY. U. of R.I., 1934-35; B.A., Pa. Military Coll., 1948; M.A., U. of N. Mex., 1949; Ph.D., 1952. Vis. instr., Beloit Coll., 1953; assoc. prof., Nebr. State Teachers Coll., Peru, 1953-58; head, Social Science, Ark. State Coll., 1958-60; CHMN., DIV. OF HISTORY AND SOCIAL SCIENCE, SOUTHERN COLO. STATE COLL., 1960- . Membership: American Association of University Professors; American Historical Association; Conference on Latin American History. Research: Central America, Mexico, and Brazil. Author: Gabino Gainza and Central America's Independence from Spain (The Americas, Jan. 1957); The Sugar-Cane Cycle of José Lins do Rego (The Americas, Jan. 1958); Mexican Influence in Central America, 1821-1823 (Hispanic American Historical Review, May 1961). Language: Spanish 3,3,2,2; Portuguese 4,3,3,3; French 4,4,4,3. Home: 325 Henry Ave., Pueblo, Colo. Office: Div. of History and Social Science, Southern Colo. State Coll., Pueblo.

KIDDER, FREDERICK ELWYN, b. White Bear Lake, Minn., Sept. 22, 1919. LIBRARY SCIENCE. A.B., U. of Calif., Berkeley, 1940; B.L.S., 1950; M.A., 1952. Principal asst., Bancroft Library, U. of Calif., Berkeley, 1949-50; asst. librarian and lectr., Inter American U. (P.R.), 1955-56; asst. dir., School of Inter American Studies, U. of Fla., 1956-57; lectr., Inter American U., 1957-59; Latin American bibliographer, U. of Fla., 1959-60; librarian, P.R. Nuclear Center (Mayagüez), 1961-62; LECTR., SOCIAL SCIENCES, U. OF P.R., 1962- . U. of Fla.-Rockefeller Foundation grant, 1961-62; Southern Fellowships Fund grant, 1962. Membership: American Association of Teachers of Spanish and Portuguese; American Association of University Professors; American Library Association; American Political Science Association; Conference on Latin American History; Inter-American Bibliographical and Library Association; Political Science Association of Puerto Rico; Sociedad de Bibliotecarios de Puerto Rico; Southeastern Conference on Latin American Studies. Research: political Puerto Rico; acquisition of Latin American library materials. Author: Survey of Investigations in Progress in the

Field of Latin American Studies (1956); Latin America and UNESCO: The First Five Years (1960); Theses on Pan American Topics (1962). Language: Spanish 5,5,4,4; Portuguese 3,3,1,1; French 3,2,2,1; German 2,1,1,1; Russian 1,1,1,1. Home: Apartado 3294, Mayagüez, P.R. 00709. Office: Dept. of Social Sciences, U. of P.R., Mayagüez, 00709.

KIEMEN, MATHIAS CHARLES, O.F.M., b. Chippewa Falls, Wis., Jan. 10, 1917. HISTORY. B.A., Our Lady of Angels Seminary, 1940; M.A., Catholic U., 1946; Ph.D., 1954. Editor, The Americas, 1953-63; VIS. ASSOC. PROF., HISTORY, GEORGETOWN U., 1954- ; RESIDENT MEMBER, DIR., ACADEMY OF AMERICAN FRANCISCAN HISTORY, 1963- ; vis. assoc. prof., Catholic U., 1963-64. Instituto para Alta Cultura (Portugal) fellow, 1950-51; Brazilian Dept. of State fellow, 1953; U.S. specialist in Brazil, U.S. Dept. of State, 1957; Organization of American States grant (Brazil), 1963. Membership: American Historical Association; Catholic Historical Association; Centro de Estudos Históricos Ultramarinos (Lisbon); Conference on Latin American History. Research: Brazil; colonial church history; the Indian policy of Portugal in Brazil during the colonial period. Author: The Indian Policy of Portugal in the Amazon Region, 1614-1693 (1954); The Indian Policy of Portugal in Maranhão (The Americas, Oct. 1948, Apr. 1949); Status of Brazilian Indian since 1820 (The Americas, Spring 1964). Language: Spanish 4,3,3,3; Portuguese 4,4,4,3; French 3,2,1,1; German 3,3,2,1; Italian 2,2,1,1. Home and office: Academy of American Franciscan History, Box 5850, Washington, D.C. 20014.

KILLIAN, BARBARA GUANTT. Home: 623 Mass. Ave., NE., Washington, D.C. 20002.

KING, JAMES EDWIN, b. Maryville, Tenn., July 14, 1938. HISTORY. A.B., Duke U., 1960; A.M., U. of Colo., 1964; U. of Fla. STUDENT, HISTORY, U. OF FLA., 1964- . National Defense Foreign Language fellow, U. of Fla., 1964-65. Research: United States-Latin American diplomatic relations; Poinsett and Butler's diplomatic careers in Mexico, 1825-1835; Chilean society and history. Language: Spanish 2,2,2,3. Home: 1507 Robin Rd., Maryville, Tenn. 37801.

KING, JAMES F., b. Spokane, Wash., Feb. 16, 1913. HISTORY. B.A., U. of Minn., 1934; M.A., U. of Calif., Berkeley, 1935; Ph.D., 1939. Assoc. divisional asst., Div. of American Republics, U.S. Dept. of State, 1940-41; instr.-asst. prof., Northwestern U., 1941-44; asst. prof.-PROF., HISTORY, U. OF CALIF., BERKELEY, 1944- ; chmn., 1953-56; chmn., Center for Latin American Studies, 1956-60; assoc. dean, Graduate Div., 1960- . Rockefeller Foundation traveling fellow (Brazil, Venezuela, Colombia), 1937-38; managing editor, Hispanic American Historical Review, 1945-49; Rockefeller Foundation grant (Spain, Great Britain), 1950-51; chmn., Conference on

Latin American History, 1962. Membership: American Historical Association; Pacific Coast Council of Latin American Studies; Phi Beta Kappa. Research: history of the period, 1750-1890; Spain and Spanish American independence; the Negro in Spanish America. Author: Evolution of the Free Slave Trade Principle in Spanish Colonial Administration (Hispanic American Historical Review, Feb. 1942); The Latin American Republics and the Suppression of the Slave Trade (Hispanic American Historical Review, Aug. 1944); The Colored Caste and American Representation in the Cortes of Cadiz (Hispanic American Historical Review, Feb. 1953). Language: Spanish 5,5,5,5; Portuguese 4,4,4,4; French 3,2,2,2; German 3,2,2,2; Italian 2,2,2,2. Home: 715 Santa Barbara Rd., Berkeley 7, Calif. Office: Dept. of History, U. of Calif., Berkeley 4.

KITCHENS, JOHN W., b. Roanoke, Ala., Dec. 31, 1934. HISTORY. U. of Paris, 1960; A.B., U. of Ala., 1961; M.A., Vanderbilt U., 1963. STUDENT, HISTORY, VANDERBILT U., 1961- . National Defense Education Act fellow in Latin American Studies, Vanderbilt U., 1961-64. Membership: Conference on Latin American History; Southeastern Conference on Latin American Studies; Southern Historical Association. Research: the Rurales of Porfirian Mexico; northern South America. Language: Spanish 4,4,3,3; Portuguese 2,1,1,1; French 4,4,3,3. Office: Box 2508, Dept. of History, East Tenn. State U., Johnson City, Tenn. 37602.

KLEIN, HERBERT SANFORD, b. New York, N.Y., Jan. 6, 1936. HISTORY. A.B., U. of Chicago, 1957; M.A., 1959; Ph.D., 1963. Instr., U. of Chicago, 1962-63; ASST. PROF., HISTORY, U. OF CHICAGO, 1963- . Doherty fellow (Bolivia), 1960-61; Fulbright travel grant (Bolivia), Summer 1963. Membership: Conference on Latin American History. Research: Latin American colonial history; ethnohistory of the Maya; Bolivian history since 1900. Author: The War of the Castes in Chiapas, Mexico (Anthropology Tomorrow, Dec. 1960). Language: Spanish 5,4,4,3; Portuguese 3,1,1,1. Home: 5530 South Kimbark Ave., Chicago 37, Ill. Office: Dept. of History, U. of Chicago, Chicago 37.

KNAPP, FRANK AVERILL, JR., b. Wellington, Kans., Sept. 24, 1922. HISTORY AND POLITICAL SCIENCE. B.A., U. of Okla., 1943; M.A., U. of Tex., 1949; Ph.D., 1950. Research asst., Institute of Latin American Studies, U. of Tex., 1950; prof., U. of Tex., 1950-51; staff officer, U.S. Army, 1951-52; U.S. GOVERNMENT 1952- . Research: contemporary Latin America; 19th century Mexico; economic development and economic trends in Latin America. Author: The Life of Sebastian Lerdo de Tejada (1951; Spanish edition, 1962); Precursors of American Investment in Mexican Railroads (Pacific Historical Review, Feb. 1952); Mexican Fear of Manifest Destiny in California (in Essays in Mexican History, 1958). Language: Spanish 4,4,4,4; Portuguese

KNOWLTON

2,—,—,—; French 3,2,2,2. Home: Apt. 515, 825 New Hampshire Ave., NW., Washington, D.C. 20037.

KNOWLTON, ROBERT, b. Akron, Ohio, Jan. 16, 1931. HISTORY. B.A., Miami U., 1953; M.A., Western Reserve U., 1959; Ph.D., State U. of Iowa, 1963. U.S. Army (Panama), 1955-56; ASST. PROF., HISTORY, WIS. STATE COLL., 1962- . University fellow, State U. of Iowa 1961-62. Membership: American Historical Association; Midwest Council of the Association for Latin American Studies. Research: Mexico since Independence; the Mexican Reform. Language: Spanish 3,3,3,3; German 2,2,-2,2. Home: 1217 College Ave., Stevens Point, Wis. Office: Dept. of History, Wis. State Coll., Stevens Point.

KNOX, A. J. GRAHAM, b. Thames, New Zealand, Oct. 10, 1931. HISTORY. B.A., U. of New Zealand, 1955; M.A., U. of S.C., 1957; Ph.D., U. of Fla., 1962. Catedrático auxiliar, Universidad de P.R., 1959-62; ASST. PROF., HISTORY, HOWARD U., 1962- . Membership: Institute of Race Relations (London); Inter-American Council (Washington, D.C.); Phi Beta Kappa. Research: Antillian area; race relations in Jamaica, 1838-1962; social development in Latin America. Author: Problems of Establishing a Free Society in Jamaica, 1838-1865 (Caribbean Studies, Jan. 1963). Language: Spanish 4,4,4,4; Portuguese 2,2,1,1; Hindustani 1,2,2,1. Home: Apt. 2, 2940 Southern Ave., SE., Washington 20, D.C. Office: Dept. of History, Howard U., Washington, D.C.

KOLINSKI, CHARLES JAMES, b. Milwaukee, Wis., July 17, 1916. HISTORY. B.A., George Washington U., 1941; M.A., U. of Fla., 1961; Ph.D., 1963. Officer-in-charge, Consulate (Cape Verde Islands), Foreign Service, U.S. Dept. of State, 1940-43; asst. attaché, economic officer (Portugal), 1948-53 (Brazil), 1953-54; consul, economic officer (Guayaquil, Ecuador), 1957-59; second secretary, economic and political officer (Paraguay), 1959-60; asst. prof., Rollins Coll., 1963-64; ASSOC. PROF., HISTORY, FLA. ATLANTIC U., 1964- . Lake Forest Coll. scholarship, 1934-35; student asst., Hispanic American Historical Review, 1961-62; National Defense Foreign Language fellow in Spanish, U. of Fla., 1962-63. Membership: Phi Alpha Theta; Phi Kappa Phi; Pi Gamma Mu. Research: history and peoples of Brazil and the La Plata area. Author: Independence or Death: The Story of the Paraguayan War (1964); The Death of Francisco Solano (The Historian, Nov. 1963). Language: Spanish 5,5,-5,5; Portuguese 5,5,5,5; French 3,3,3,2; German 2,2,2,2; Italian 3,3,3,2. Office: Dept. of History, Fla. Atlantic U., Boca Raton.

KORN, PEGGY A., b. Philadelphia, Pa., Oct. 3, 1927. HISTORY. B.A., Beaver Coll., 1961; M.A., U. of Pa., 1962. STUDENT, HISTORY, U. OF PA. Seminar in Latin American Nationalism fellow, U. of Pa., 1963-64. Research: Latin American history; Miguel Hidalgo and the beginnings of Mexican nationalism. Lan-

guage: Spanish 4,3,3,3; Portuguese 2,—,—,—; French 3,—,—,—. Home: 1446 Rydal Rd., Rydal, Pa.

KORTH, EUGENE HENRY, S.J., b. Mankato, Minn., Nov. 23, 1917. HISTORY. B.A., St. Louis U., 1941; Ph.L., 1943; M.A., 1945; S.T.L., 1950; Ph.D., U. of Tex., 1956. Instr., St. Louis U. High School, 1943-46; ASSOC. PROF., HISTORY, MARQUETTE U., 1956- ; chmn., 1958-60; DEAN, COLL. OF LIBERAL ARTS, 1960- . Doherty fellow (Chile), 1953-54. Membership: American Historical Association; Catholic Historical Association; Conference on Latin American History; Jesuit Educational Association; Jesuit Historical Association; Wisconsin State Historical Society. Research: colonial and national periods; Mexico; Chile; church-state relations; education. Author: Modern European History (1946); Pre-Registration and Registration Procedures (1961); Economic Aspects of German Intervention in the Spanish Civil War, 1936-1939 (Mid-America, July 1960). Language: Spanish 4,4,3,2; Portuguese 2,2,1,1; French 3,2,1,1; German 3,3,2,1. Office: Coll. of Liberal Arts, Marquette U., 1131 West Wisconsin Ave., Milwaukee, Wis. 53233.

KRIEGHOFF, CLAUDIO, b. Púa, Chile, Mar. 17, 1913. HISTORY. Ph.D., George Washington U., 1965. Superintendent of schools, Central Argentine Conference, 1934-39; bursar, Southeastern U., 1955-61; LECTR., HISTORY, GEORGE WASHINGTON U., 1961- . Membership: American Historical Association; Hispanic American Historical Association; National Education Association. Research: Latin American history. Contributor: Other Lands, Other People (1961). Language: Spanish 5,5,-5,5; Portuguese 5,5,5,5; French 5,5,5,5; German 5,5,5,5; Greek 4,—,—,4; Latin 4,—,—,4. Home: Apt. 702, 7611 Maple Ave., Takoma Park, Md. 20012.

KROEBER, CLIFTON BROWN, b. Berkeley, Calif., Sept. 7, 1921. HISTORY. A.B., U. of Calif., Berkeley, 1943; M.A., 1947; Ph.D., 1951. Lectr., U. of Calif. Extension Div., Berkeley, 1950-51; asst. prof., U. of Wis., 1951-55; ASSOC. PROF., HISTORY, OCCIDENTAL COLL., 1955- ; assoc. prof., Guadalajara Summer School (Mexico), Summers 1960, 1963. Heller traveling fellow (Argentina), 1949-50; Area Research fellow, Social Science Research Council, 1949-50; Haynes Foundation summer fellow, 1959. Membership: American Association of University Professors; American Historical Association; Conference on Latin American History; Pacific Coast Council on Latin American Studies; Western History Association. Research: Mexico and the Río de la Plata region. Author: The Growth of the Shipping Industry in the Río de la Plata Region, 1794-1860 (1957); The Mobilization of Philip II's Revenue in Peru, 1590-1596 (The Economic History Review, Apr. 1958); El Consulado de Buenos Aires en el Proceso de la Revolución de Mayo, 1794-1810 (Trabajos y Comunicaciones, Universidad Nacional de la Plata, No.

9, 1960). Language: Spanish 4,4,4,4; French 2,2,1,1; German 2,2,1,1. Home: 1701 Linda Rosa Ave., Los Angeles, Calif. 90041. Office: Dept. of History, Occidental Coll., Los Angeles, 90041.

KROUSEL, HILDA SANCHEZ, b. Tampa, Fla., Oct. 8, 1927. HISTORY. M.A., Fla. State U., 1951. Research: Latin American history and political science; José Antonio Paez; comparative study of town government in Lima, Peru, and Boston, Massachusetts. Language: Spanish 5,5,5,5; Portuguese 1,1,1,1; French 2,2,2,2. Home: 3646 South Lakeshore, Baton Rouge, La.

KUETHE, ALLAN JAMES, b. Waverly, Iowa, Feb. 1, 1940. HISTORY. B.A., U. of Iowa, 1962; M.A., U. of Fla., 1963. STUDENT, HISTORY, U. OF FLA. Woodrow Wilson fellow; National Defense Foreign Language fellow in Spanish. Research: Latin American history; 18th century militia of New Granada. Language: Spanish 4,4,3,3; French 2,1,1,2. Home: 234-S Flavet III, Gainesville, Fla.

KUHN, GARY GLEN, b. St. Paul, Minn., July 22, 1937. HISTORY. B.A., U. of Minn., 1959; M.A., 1961; Ph.D., 1965. Membership: Phi Beta Kappa. Research: Latin American history; civil aviation in Latin America. Author: American Aircraft in Uruguayan Colors (American Aviation Historical Society Journal, Summer 1960); Aviones civiles venezolanas (Aeronaves, 1962-63). Language: Spanish 3,2,-2,3; Portuguese 2,2,2,2. Home: 643 15th Ave. North, South St. Paul, Minn.

LAMB, URSULA SCHAEFER, b. Essen, Germany, Jan. 15, 1914. HISTORY. U. of Berlin (Germany), 1932-35; Smith Coll., 1935-36; M.A., U. of Calif., Berkeley, 1937; Ph.D., 1949. Lectr., Barnard Coll., 1943-49; assoc., 1949-51; tutor, Spanish, Brasenose Coll. (England), 1960; RESEARCH ASSOC., LECTR., HISTORY, YALE U., 1963- . Exchange student, Smith Coll., 1935-36; Walter Loewy scholar, U. of Calif., 1936-39; American Council of Learned Societies grant, 1943; Columbia U.-Social Science Research Council grant (Spain), 1947. Membership: American Historical Association; Conference on Latin American History; Society of the History of Discoveries. Research: Latin American colonial history; use of 16th century sources. Author: Frey Nicolás de Ovando, Gobernador de las Indias, 1501-1509 (1956); Religious Conflicts in the Conquest of Mexico (Journal of the History of Ideas, Oct. 1956). Language: Spanish 5,5,3,3; Portuguese 4,2,1,1; French 5,5,3,2; German 5,5,5,5. Home: 166 Linden St., New Haven, Conn. Office: Dept. of History, Yale U., New Haven.

LANE, GEORGE B., JR., b. San Antonio, Tex., Nov. 18, 1930. POLITICAL SCIENCE. B.A., Trinity U., 1951; Ph.D., American U., 1962. Intelligence officer, U.S. Air Force, 1953-58; research asst., Special Operations Research Office, American U., Summer 1959; Latin American affairs analyst, U.S. Dept. of Health, Education, and Welfare, 1962-64; EDUCATION RESEARCH AND PROGRAM SPECIALIST, LANGUAGE AND AREA CENTERS SECTION, U.S. OFFICE OF EDUCATION, 1964- . Massey Foundation fellow, American U., 1959-60; National Defense Foreign Language fellow in Portuguese, U. of Tex., Summer 1963. Membership: American Academy of Political and Social Science; American Political Science Association; Pi Gamma Mu; Pi Sigma Alpha. Research: Latin American foreign affairs; socio-political development; Brazilian social change; Peruvian education. Language: Spanish 3,3,3,3; Portuguese 3,3,2,2; French 1,—,—,—; Mandarin Chinese 1,2,2,1. Home: 9624 Brunett Ave., Silver Spring, Md. Office: U.S. Office of Education, Dept. of Health, Education, and Welfare, Washington, D.C.

LANNING, JOHN TATE, b. Linwood, N.C., Sept. 13, 1902. HISTORY. A.B., Trinity Coll. (Duke), 1924; A.M., U. of Calif., Berkeley, 1925; Ph.D., 1928. Instr.-prof., Duke U., 1927-61; JAMES B. DUKE PROF. OF HISTORY, DUKE U., 1961- ; lectr., U. of Chile and U. of Córdoba, 1931; lectr., George Washington U., 1935; Trumbull lectr., Yale U., 1943. Guggenheim Latin American exchange fellow, 1930-31; American Council of Learned Societies grant, 1932; assoc. managing editor, Hispanic American Historical Review, 1935-39; managing editor, 1939-45; Duke U. research grants (Mexico), 1936, 1942, (Guatemala), 1938, (Spain), 1949; Social Science Research Council grant, 1941; Committee on Inter-American Cultural and Artistic Relations, 1942; Carnegie Revolving Fund Prize, 1955; Bolton Prize, 1956; Serra Award, Academy of American Franciscan History, 1958; Medal of Merit, U. of Ariz., 1960; Board of Advisory Editors, Hispanic American Historical Review, The Americas, and Latin American Review; chmn., Council on Research, Duke U. Membership: American Historical Association; Conference on Latin American History; Phi Beta Kappa; Sociedad Cubana de Estudios Históricos e Internacionales; Sociedad de Geografía e Historia de Guatemala. Research: academic, intellectual, and cultural history of the Spanish Empire. Author: Academic Culture in the Spanish Colonies (1940); The University in the Kingdom of Guatemala (1955); The Eighteenth Century Enlightenment in the University of San Carlos de Guatemala (1956). Language: Spanish 5,5,4,4; Portuguese 4,4,4,4; French 4,4,4,4; German 4,4,4,4; Greek 4,4,4,4; Latin 4,4,4,4. Home: 3007 Surrey Rd., Hope Valley, Durham, N.C. Office: 120 Allen Bldg., Duke U., Durham.

LaPIERRE, LAURIER L. Office: Dept. of History, McGill U., Montreal, Canada.

LATHAM, FRED C. Home: 5942 23rd Pl., SE., Washington, D.C. 20021.

LAUERHASS, LUDWIG, JR., b. Asheville, N.C., Jan. 6, 1935. HISTORY. B.A., U. of N.C., 1957; M.A., U. of Calif., Los Angeles, 1959. ACTING ASST. PROF., HISTORY, U. OF

CALIF., RIVERSIDE, 1964- . John Randolph and Dora Haines fellow, 1957-58; National Defense Foreign Language fellow in Portuguese, 1961-62; Ford Foundation Foreign Area fellow, 1962-64. Membership: American Historical Association. Research: Latin American history; Brazilian nationalism in the 1930's; post-war communism in Latin America. Author: Communism in Latin America: A Bibliography. The Post-War Years, 1945-1960 (1962). Language: Spanish 4,3,2,3; Portuguese 4,3,2,3; French 3,2,1,2; German 2,2,1,2. Home: 1405 Barry Ave., Los Angeles, Calif. 90025.

LEONARD, IRVING ALBERT, b. New Haven, Conn., Dec. 1, 1896. HISTORY AND SPANISH AMERICAN LITERATURE. Ph.B., Yale U., 1918; M.A., U. of Calif., Berkeley, 1925; Ph.D., 1928. Prof., U. of the Philippines, 1921-22; teacher, Petaluma High School (Calif.), 1922-23; asst. dir., Humanities, Rockefeller Foundation, 1937-40; prof., Brown U., 1940-42; prof., U. of Mich., 1942-65; RETIRED, 1965- . American Council of Learned Societies fellow (Spain), 1930-31, (Mexico), 1932; Guggenheim fellow, 1935; Fulbright prof., Oxford U., 1952. Membership: American Association of Teachers of Spanish and Portuguese; Hispanic Society of America. Research: cultural history of Spain and Spanish America. Author: Don Carlos de Sigüenza, Mexican Savant (1929); Books of the Brave (1949); Baroque Times in Old Mexico (1959). Language: Spanish 5,5,4,4; Portuguese 4,3,1,1; French 3,2,1,1. Home: Box 278, Goldenrod, Fla.

LEVETT, ELLA PETTIT, b. Elizabeth, N.J., Sept. 19, 1905. HISTORY. M.A., U. of S.C., 1934; Ph.D., U. of Chicago, 1941; M.A., Middlebury Coll., 1950; Ph.D., U. of Salamanca (Spain), 1961. Teacher, North Charleston High School (S.C.), 1928-37; asst. in Latin American History, U. of Chicago, 1941-42; prof., Hunter Coll., 1944-45; PROF., LATIN AMERICAN HISTORY, SPANISH, CHMN., FOREIGN LANGUAGES, HARDIN-SIMMONS U., 1945- . University fellow, U. of Chicago; Buenos Aires Convention fellow (Colombia); Spanish Government grant. Membership: American Historical Association; American Association of University Women; Modern Language Association; Pi Gamma Mu; Sigma Delta Pi; South Central Modern Language Association; West Texas Historical Association. Research: United States-Latin American relations; Spanish philology; John Steinbeck and the Hispanic World. Author: Loyalism in the American Colonies (Proceedings, South Carolina Historical Association, 1936); Negotiations for Release from the Inter-oceanic Obligations of the Clayton-Bulwer Treaty (1945). Language: Spanish 4,4,-4,4; Portuguese 2,2,1,1; French 2,2,1,1; German 3,2,1,1. Home: 1801 University, Abilene, Tex. Office: Dept. of Spanish, Hardin-Simmons U., Abilene.

LEVINE, ROBERT M., b. New York, N.Y., Mar. 26, 1941. HISTORY. A.B., Colgate U., 1962; Princeton U. INSTR., HISTORY, STATE

UNIV. OF N.Y., COLL. AT STONY BROOK, 1966- . Carnegie Corporation European Summer Research Program, 1961; National Education Act fellow; Ford Foundation Latin American fellow, 1962-64; Doherty fellow (Brazil), 1964-65. Membership: American Historical Association; Hispanic American Historical Association; Mississippi Valley Historical Association; Phi Beta Kappa. Research: Latin American radicalism; Brazilian communism. Language: Spanish 4,4,3,3. Office: Dept. of History, State Univ. of N.Y., Coll. at Stony Brook, Stony Brook, N.Y.

LEVY, JAMES ROBERT, b. Newark, N.J., Sept. 3, 1937. HISTORY. B.A., Columbia Coll., 1959; M.A., Columbia U., 1961; Ph.D., U. of Pa., 1964. Instr., U. of Pa., 1962-63; INSTR., HISTORY, POMONA COLL., 1963- . U. of Pa. and Rockefeller Foundation fellow (Argentina), 1962. Membership: American Historical Association; Conference on Latin American History. Research: social and intellectual developments in Latin American history; 19th century nationalism and liberalism in Argentina. Language: Spanish 4,3,3,2; Portuguese 2,2,1,1; French 2,1,1,1. Home: Norton Hall, Pomona Coll., Claremont, Calif. Office: Pearsons 109, Pomona Coll., Claremont.

LIETZ, PAUL STANTON, b. México, D.F., May 3, 1906. HISTORY. A.B., Loyola U. (Ill.), 1929; A.M., 1935; Ph.D., 1940. Teacher, Loyola Academy (Chicago), 1931-40; PROF., HISTORY, LOYOLA U. (ILL.), 1940- ; summer vis. prof., U. of Havana, 1947, U. of San Marcos and Catholic U. (Peru), 1950. U.S. Dept. of State grants (Cuba, Peru), Summers 1947, 1950; Newberry Library fellow in Philippine Studies, 1953-55; Editorial Staff, Mid-America; Bolton Prize Committee, 1964. Membership: American Catholic Historical Association; American Historical Association; Conference on Latin American History. Research: Spanish colonial history; history of the Philippines; Mexico. Author: Calendar of Philippine Documents in the Ayer Collection of the Newberry Library (1956); Alzina's Historia de Visayas (Bibliographical Society of the Philippines, Occasional Papers, 1962). Language: Spanish 5,4,3,3; Portuguese 3,3,2,1; French 4,3,2,1; Latin 3,—,—,—. Home: 1233 Arthur Ave., Chicago 26, Ill. Office: Dept. of History, Loyola U., Chicago 26.

LIEUWEN, EDWIN, b. Harrison, S. Dak., Feb. 8, 1923. HISTORY. A.B., U. of Calif., Berkeley, 1947; M.A., 1948; Ph.D., 1951. Vis. instr., U. of Calif., Los Angeles, 1951-52; chief, Latin American Branch, Intelligence, U.S. Government, 1952-53; vis. asst. prof., U. of Calif., Berkeley, 1954-55; chief, Latin American Section, Intelligence, U.S. Government, 1955-57; PROF., CHMN., HISTORY, U. OF N. MEX., 1957- . Doherty fellow (Venezuela), 1950-51; Fulbright lectr., U. of Utrecht (Netherlands), 1953-54; Carnegie fellow, Council on Foreign Relations, 1957-58; Rockefeller research fellow (Mexico), 1963-64. Membership: American Historical Association; Conference on Latin

American History; Council on Foreign Relations. Research: Mexico; petroleum industry in Venezuela; Latin American politics. Author: Petroleum in Venezuela: A History (1954, 1955); Arms and Politics in Latin America (1959, 1961); Venezuela (1961, 1964). Language: Spanish 5,4,3,3; Portuguese 3,2,1,1; French 3,2,1,1. Home: 309 Dartmouth, NE., Albuquerque, N. Mex. Office: Dept. of History, U. of N. Mex., Albuquerque.

LISS, SHELDON B., b. Nov. 3, 1936. HISTORY. B.A., American U., 1958; M.A., Duquesne U., 1962; Ph.D., American U., 1964. Executive-administrator, Public Relations, private corporation in Mexico and U.S., 1958-62; asst. prof., Ind. State Coll., 1964-66; VIS. PROF., HISTORY, U. OF NOTRE DAME, 1966- . Membership: American Historical Association; American Political Science Association; Hispanic American Society; Phi Alpha Theta. Research: the Chamizal conflict between Mexico and the United States; Cuba. Language: Spanish 5,4, 4,4; Portuguese 3,2,1,1; French 3,2,2,3; German 1,3,1,1; Rumanian 3,3,1,1. Office: Dept. of History, U. of Notre Dame, Notre Dame, Ind.

LOBO, EULALIA MARIA LAHMEYER, b. Rio de Janeiro, Brazil, July 17, 1924. HISTORY. Doutor, Universidade do Brasil, 1953; Docente Livre, 1958. Political adviser for Latin American affairs, Indonesian Embassy (Rio de Janeiro), 1955-56; prof., Colégio D. Pedro II (Rio de Janeiro), 1957-60; vis. prof., U. of Tex., 1960-61; vis. prof., Occidental Coll., 1961; regente de history of the Americas, Faculdade Nacional de Filosofia, Universidade do Brasil, 1963. Fulbright travel grant (United States); John Hay Whitney vis. prof., U. of Tex., 1960-61; Committee for the Cultural Agreement between Brazil and Portugal research grant (Portugal, Spain). Membership: American Studies Association; Conference on Latin American History; PEN Club do Brasil. Research: Latin American history; Spanish and Portuguese colonial commercial policy. Author: Administração colonial luso-espanhola nas Américas (1952); Caminho de chiquitos ás missões guaranis, 1690 a 1718 (1957); Aspectos da influência dos homens de negócio na política comercial ibero-americana (1963). Language: Spanish 4,5,4,3; Portuguese 5,5,5,5; French 4,5,4,3; German 4,3,2,2. Home: Rua Senador Simonsen, 42, Apt. 401, Jardim Botânico, ZC. 20, Rio de Janeiro, Guanabara, Brasil.

LOGAN, RAYFORD W., b. Washington, D.C., Jan. 7, 1897. HISTORY. A.B., Williams Coll., 1917; A.M., Harvard U., 1932; Ph.D., 1936. Prof., chmn., Va. Union U., 1925-30; prof., chmn., Atlanta U., 1933-38; PROF., HISTORY, HOWARD U., 1938- ; chmn., 1942-64. Advisory Committee, Coordinator of Inter-American Affairs, 1941-42; Fulbright fellow (France), 1951-52; Advisory Committee on Latin America, Institute of International Education, 1962- . Membership: American Historical Association; Conference on Latin American History; Inter-American Council (Washington, D.C.); International Institute of Arts

and Letters; Phi Beta Kappa. Research: colonial administration; race relations in the Caribbean; diplomatic history of Haiti. Author: Diplomatic relations of the United States with Haiti, 1776-1891 (1941). Language: Spanish 1,2,2,2; Portuguese 3,—,—,—; French 1,1,1,1. Home: 1519 Jackson St. N.E., Washington, D.C. Office: Dept. of History, Howard U., Washington.

LOHR DE IRIZARRY, MILDRED TUCKER, b. Brandy, Va., Dec. 10, 1905. HISTORY. London School of Economics; M.A., Columbia U., 1933. Teacher (Orange County, Va.), 1924-25; teacher (Madison, Va.), 1927-28; teacher (San German, P.R.), 1928-38; ASSOC. PROF., HISTORY, INTER AMERICAN U., 1938- . Fulbright scholar (Netherlands), 1952. Membership: American Forestry Association; American Historical Association; American Political Science Association; Association of American Geographers. Research: Latin American history and political science; economic and human geography. Language: Spanish 2,3,4,—. Office: Box 413, Inter American U., San German, P.R. 00753.

LOMBARDI, JOHN V. Home: 3847 Ingraham St., Los Angeles, Calif. 90005.

LORETTA CLARE, SISTER. Office: Coll. of Mt. St. Joseph, St. Joseph, Ohio 45051.

LOU, DENNIS WINGSOU, b. Canton, China, Oct. 6, 1924. HISTORY. B.A., Phillips U., 1953; M.A., Tex. Christian U., 1956; Ph.D., Ind. U., 1963. Chmn., Talladega Coll., 1961-62; ASSOC. PROF., SOCIAL SCIENCE, STATE U. OF N.Y., COLL. AT ONEONTA, 1963- . Tex. Christian U. fellow, 1954-56; Asian History and Latin American History fellow, Ind. U., 1959-61; senior faculty fellow, University Committee of Oriental Studies, Columbia U., 1962-63. Membership: American Academy of Social and Political Sciences; American Historical Association; Asian Studies Association; Pacific Institute, Far East Prehistory Association; Pan American Union Latin American Conference. Research: China's cultural relations with Latin America; the possible early relationship between the Chinese civilization and the high culture of America. Author: Folklore of Si-chow (Chi Heng School Journal, Hong Kong, 1941); Rain Worship among the Ancient Chinese and the Nahua-Maya Indians: A Comparative Study of Cultural Similarities (Academia Sinica, 1957). Language: Spanish 4,3,2,2; Portuguese 1,—,—,—; French 3,3,2,2; Chinese 5,5,5,5; Japanese 3,3,3,2. Home: 107 Spruce St., Oneonta, N.Y. Office: Dept. of History, State U. of N.Y., Coll. at Oneonta, Oneonta.

LOVE, JOSEPH L., JR., b. Austin, Tex., Feb. 28, 1938. HISTORY. B.A., Harvard Coll., 1960; M.A., Stanford U., 1963; Columbia U. Latin American Asst., U.S. National Student Association, 1961-62; ASST. PROF., HISTORY, U. OF ILL., 1966- . Woodrow Wilson fellow; Foreign Area fellow. Research: Latin American history; 20th century Brazil; Rio Grande do Sul in the latter half of the First Republic, 1909-1932. Language: Spanish 5,5,4,4; Portuguese 5,5,5,4; French 5,5,4,4; Italian 3,2,2,2. Office: Dept. of History, U. of Ill., Urbana, Ill.

LOWENTHAL, DAVID, b. New York, N.Y., Apr. 26, 1923. GEOGRAPHY AND HISTORY. B.S., Harvard Coll., 1943; M.A., U. of Calif., Berkeley, 1950; Ph.D., U. of Wis., 1953. Asst. prof., chmn., Geography, Vassar Coll., 1952-56; RESEARCH ASSOC., AMERICAN GEO-GRAPHICAL SOCIETY, 1957- . Fulbright research fellow, U. of the West Indies (Jamaica), 1956-57; consultant, U. Coll. of the West Indies, 1959- ; commission from Institute of Race Relations (London), 1961-65; Humid Tropics Commission, International Geographical Union. Membership: American Anthropological Association; American Historical Association; Association of American Geographers; Society for the History of Discoveries. Research: historical geography of the Guianas; the Caribbean; population; race relations in the Caribbean. Author: The West Indies Federation (1961); Physical Resources of the British Caribbean (in The Economy of the West Indies, 1960); Levels of West Indian Government (Social and Economic Studies, 1962). Language: Spanish 2,1,1,1; French 4,4,4,4; Dutch 2,2,1,1; German 3,3,3,3. Home: 75 Riverside Dr., New York 24, N.Y. Office: American Geographical Society, Broadway at 156th St., New York 32.

LOWERY, MARTIN JOSEPH, b. Chicago, Ill., Dec. 23, 1919. HISTORY. B.Ed., Chicago Teachers Coll., 1940; M.A., Loyola U. (Chicago), 1947; Ph.D., 1951. Special agent, Federal Bureau of Investigation, 1941-44; PROF., CHMN., HISTORY, ASSOC. DEAN, DE PAUL U., 1950- . Membership: American Catholic Historical Association; American Historical Association; Conference on Latin American History; Mississippi Valley Historical Association. Research: Latin American history, especially that of colonial Argentina. Author: The Inland Customshouse at Cordoba (Mid-America, Jan. 1953). Language: Spanish 3,2,-2,2. Home: 1345 West 98th St., Chicago, Ill. 60643. Office: Dept. of History, De Paul U., 25 East Jackson Blvd., Chicago, 60604.

LOY, JANE MEYER, b. Indianapolis, Ind., Dec. 12, 1940. HISTORY. B.A., DePauw U., 1962; M.A., U. of Wis., 1964. Teacher, Western Hills High School (Cincinnati), 1962-63; STUDENT, HISTORY, U. OF WIS. Knapp fellow; Ibero-American fellow (Colombia). Research: Latin American history and politics; the role of the freed Negro in colonial Spanish America; Colombian education. Language: Spanish 5,4,4,3. Home: 501 North Sherman Ave., Madison, Wis.

LUX, WILLIAM ROBERT, b. Pomona, Calif., July 17, 1938. HISTORY AND SPANISH AMERICAN LITERATURE. B.A., U. of N. Mex., 1962; M.A., U. of Southern Calif., 1963; M.A., Stanford U., 1964; U. of Southern Calif. STUDENT, HISTORY, U. OF SOUTH-ERN CALIF. Grunsfeld fellow; Ford Foundation M-3 Program fellow; National Defense Foreign Language fellow. Membership: Phi Alpha Theta; Pi Sigma Alpha; Sigma Delta Pi. Research: Latin American history and literature; the development of the Cuban sugar industry, 1511-1895. Language: Spanish 4,5,4,4; Portuguese 3,3,2,3. Home: 1736 Van Court, SW., Albuquerque, N. Mex.

McALISTER, LYLE NELSON, b. Twisp, Wash., Feb. 14, 1916. HISTORY. B.S., State Coll. of Wash., 1938; M.A., U. of Calif., Berkeley, 1947; Ph.D., 1950. Instr., assoc. prof., U. of Fla., 1950-59; prof., chmn., 1959-63; PROF., HISTORY, DIR., CENTER FOR LATIN AMERICAN STUDIES, U. OF FLA., 1963- . Doherty fellow (Mexico), 1949-50; American Philosophic Society grant, 1953, 1955; chmn., Robertson Prize Committee, Conference on Latin American History, 1957; Rockefeller Foundation grant, 1962. Membership: American Association of University Professors; American Historical Association; Association for Latin American Studies. Research: New Spain; civil-military relations in Latin America; social organization in colonial Latin America. Author: The Fuero Militar in New Spain (1957); The Reorganization of the Army of New Spain, 1763-1767 (Hispanic American Historical Review, Feb. 1953); Social Structure and Social Change in New Spain (Hispanic American Historical Review, Aug. 1963). Language: Spanish 5,4,4,4; Portuguese 3,3,3,2; French 3,1,1,1. Home: 2712 SW. 5th Pl., Gainesville, Fla. Office: Center for Latin American Studies, Library 450, U. of Fla., Gainesville.

MACAULAY, NEILL WEBSTER, JR., b. Columbia, S.C., Apr. 1, 1935. HISTORY. A.B., The Citadel, 1956; M.A., U. of S.C., 1962; Ph.D., U. of Tex., 1965. First lieutenant, Movimiento 26 de Julio (Cuba), 1958-59; planter, exporter (Cuba), 1959-60; free lance journalist (Miami, Fla.; Columbia, S.C.), 1960-61; U. OF FLA. POST-DOCTORAL FELLOW (BRAZIL), 1965-66. U. of Tex. fellow, 1962-64. Membership: American Historical Association. Research: guerrilla warfare; Nicaragua, Venezuela, Mexico and Cuba. Author: Castro's Threat to the Hemisphere (Marine Corps Gazette, Mar. 1961); The Strategy of Guerrilla Conquest (National Guardsman, Sept. 1961); Counter-insurgency Series (Marine Corps Gazette, Apr.-July 1963). Language: Spanish 5,4,4,4; Portuguese 4,3,2,2; French 4,3,2,2. Home: 12 Clement Rd., Columbia, S.C.

McCANN, FRANK DANIEL, JR., b. Lackawanna, N.Y., Dec. 15, 1938. HISTORY. A.B., Niagara U., 1960; M.A., Kent State U., 1962; Ind. U. Teacher, Lincoln Junior High School (Lackawanna, N.Y.), 1961-62; STUDENT, HISTORY, INDIANA U., 1962- . Consultant, Brazil Study, Special Operations Research Office, American U., 1965; Fulbright grant (Brazil), 1965-66. Membership: American Historical Association; Mississippi Valley Historical

56

Association; Western History Association. Research: Latin American history; Brazilian-United States relations, 1937-1945; Brazilian foreign policy. Language: Spanish 2,2,2,1; Portuguese 4,4,4,3; French 2,1,1,1. Home: Apt. 2, 43 Maple Grove, Lackawanna, N.Y.

McCARRAN, MARGARET-PATRICIA, S.N.-J.M., b. Reno, Nev., July 22, 1904. HISTORY. Mus.B., Mt. St. Mary's Coll. (Calif), 1931; M.A., Catholic U. of America, 1946; Ph.D., 1952. ASSOC. PROF., SOCIAL SCIENCES, COLL. OF THE HOLY NAMES, 1952- . Membership: Academy of Political Science; Pi Gamma Mu. Language: Spanish 3,—,—,2; French —,2,—,2; Latin —,3,—,2. Home and office: Coll. of the Holy Names, 3500 Mountain Blvd., Oakland 19, Calif.

McCARTY, KIERAN, O.F.M., b. Tama, Iowa, June 19, 1925. HISTORY. B.A., San Luis Rey Coll., 1946; M.A., Catholic U. of America, 1960. RESIDENT MEMBER, ACADEMY OF AMERICAN FRANCISCAN HISTORY, 1958- ; technical consultant, Instituto Nacional de Antropología e Historia, 1960-61; EDITOR, THE AMERICAS, 1963- ; INSTR., HISTORY, CATHOLIC U. OF AMERICA, 1964- . Organization of American States fellow (Mexico), 1961. Research: archival studies in Mexico; colonial church history. Author: Los Franciscanos en la Frontera Chichimeca (1962); Apostolic Colleges of the Propagation of the Faith: Old and New World Background (The Americas, July 1962). Language: Spanish 4,4,-4,4; Portuguese 3,3,3,3; French 2,2,2,2; German 2,2,2,2; Italian 2,2,2,2. Home and office: Academy of American Franciscan History, 9800 Kentsdale Dr., Box 5850, Washington, D.C. 20014.

McCLOSKEY, MICHAEL B., O.F.M. Office: Siena Coll., Loudonville, N.Y. 12211.

McGANN, THOMAS FRANCIS, b. Cambridge, Mass., Mar. 25, 1920. HISTORY. B.A., Harvard U., 1941; M.A., 1949; Ph.D., 1952. U.S. naval attaché in Latin America, 1942-46; teaching fellow, instr., asst. prof., Harvard U., 1950-58; assoc. prof.-PROF., LATIN AMERICAN HISTORY, U. OF TEX., 1958- ; vis. prof., Stanford U., 1962-63. Lowery fellow, Milton fellow, Harvard U.; U. of Texas research fellow. Membership: American Historical Association; Conference on Latin American History. Research: Argentina; colonial Peru; inter-American relations; Spain. Author: Argentina, the United States, and the Inter-American System, 1880-1914 (1957). Editor: Portrait of Spain (1963). Translator: A History of Argentine Political Thought, by José Luis Romero (1963). Language: Spanish 5,5,4,3; Portuguese 3,2,1,1; French 3,2,2,1. Home: 4615 Crestway Dr., Austin, Tex. Office: Dept. of History, U. of Tex., Austin, 78712.

McGARRY, DANIEL D., b. Los Angeles, Calif., Oct. 10, 1907. HISTORY. M.A., U. of Calif., Los Angeles, 1938; Ph.D., 1940. Instr., Mt. St. Joseph's Coll., 1940-43; asst. prof., Ind. U.,

1946-50; PROF., MEDIEVAL HISTORY, SAINT LOUIS U., 1950- . U. of Calif., Los Angeles, and American Philosophical Society fellowships. Membership: American Historical Association; Catholic Historical Association; Conference on Latin American History; Medieval Academy. Research: medieval history; history of education; medieval Europe. Author: Metalogicon of John of Salisbury (1955); Sources of Western Civilization (1962); Educational Methods of the Franciscans in Spanish California (The Americas, Jan. 1950). Language: Spanish 4,4,3,2; French 3,3,3,2. Home: 20 Parkland, Glendale 22, Mo. Office: Dept. of History, Saint Louis U., St. Louis 3, Mo.

MACHADO, MANUEL ANTHONY, JR., b. Nogales, Ariz., June 4, 1939. HISTORY. B.A., U. of Calif., Santa Barbara, 1961; M.A., 1962; Ph.D., 1964. ASST. PROF., SOCIAL SCIENCES, STATE U. OF N.Y., COLL. AT PLATTSBURGH, 1964- . John Hay Whitney Foundation opportunity fellow, 1962-63; Organization of American States summer research fellow (Mexico), Summer 1963. Membership: Pacific Coast Council of Latin American Studies. Research: modern Latin American history; Mexican-United States cooperation in control of foot and mouth disease. Language: Spanish 5,5,5,5; Portuguese 4,2,1,1; French 2,1,1,1. Office: Div. of Social Sciences, State U. of N.Y., Coll. at Plattsburgh, Plattsburgh, N.Y.

MACÍAS, ANNA, b. Sewaren, N.J., May 20, 1930. HISTORY. B.A., Hunter Coll., 1952; M.A., Smith Coll., 1954; Ph.D., Columbia U., 1965. Instr., Dana Hall School (Wellesley, Mass.), 1954-56; instr., Smith Coll., 1962-63; INSTR., HISTORY, OHIO WESLEYAN U., 1963- . Buenos Aires Convention fellow (Mexico), 1956-57; President's fellow, Columbia U., 1960-61. Membership: American Association of University Professors; American Historical Association. Research: Latin American history; the Mexican Apatzingán Constitution of 1814. Language: Spanish 5,5,4,4; Portuguese 4,4,3,3; French 4,3,3,3; Italian 4,3,3,3. Home: 78½ West Lincoln Ave., Delaware, Ohio. Office: Dept. of History, Ohio Wesleyan U., Delaware.

MACLEOD, MURDO JOHN, b. Imtarfa, Malta, Apr. 22, 1935. HISTORY. M.A., U. of Glasgow (Scotland), 1959; U. of Guatemala, Summer 1959; M.A., U. of Fla., 1961; Ph.D., 1962. Asst. dir., Inter-American Studies, U. of Fla., 1961-62; ASST. PROF., LATIN AMERICAN HISTORY, U. OF PITTSBURGH, 1962- . Xiralt travel fellow, U. of Glasgow, 1957; assistant de langue anglaise, French Government, 1957-58; U. of Fla. fellow, 1959-63; Pan American Foundation travel grant (Guatemala), 1959; U.S. Agency for International Development—U. of Pittsburgh Program (Ecuador), 1963-65. Membership: American Academy of Social and Political Sciences; American Historical Association; Conference on Latin American History; Phi Alpha Theta; Phi Beta Kappa. Research: history and analysis of social protest with emphasis on the Indo-Andean Republics; political novelists in Latin American politics in 19th and 20th centuries. Author: Colonial Central America (in The Caribbean: The Central American Area, edited by A. Curtis Wilgus, 1961); The Haitian Novel of Social Protest (Journal of Inter-American Studies, Apr. 1962). Language: Spanish 4,5,4,4; Portuguese 2,2,2,1; French 4,5,4,4; Gaelic 3,5,5,1; German 2,2,1,1. Office: Dept. of History, U. of Pittsburgh, Pittsburgh 13, Pa.

McMAHON, DOROTHY ELIZABETH, b. Troy, N.Y., Dec. 2, 1912. SPANISH AMERICAN LITERATURE. A.B., U. of Ariz., 1935; A.M., 1938; Ph.D., U. of Southern Calif., 1947. PROF., HEAD, SPANISH, U. OF SOUTHERN CALIF., 1944- . Del Amo fellow (Spain), 1948-49. Membership: American Association of Teachers of Spanish and Portuguese; American Association of University Professors; Conference on Latin American History; Modern Language Association; Pacific Coast Council for Latin American Studies; Phi Beta Kappa; Philological Association of the Pacific Coast. Research: contemporary Hispanic literature; Spanish American colonial history. Author: Variations in the Text of Zaraté's Historia del descubrimiento y conquista del Perú (Hispanic American Historical Review, Nov. 1953); Zaraté's Historia del descubrimiento y conquista del Perú (Papers of the Bibliographic Society of America, Apr. 1955); Indian in Romantic Literature of the Argentine (Modern Philology, Aug. 1958). Language; Spanish 5,5,4,4; Portuguese 3,2,—,1; French 4,3,3,3; German 1,3,1,1. Home: 6577 4th Ave., Los Angeles 43, Calif. Office: Dept. of Spanish, U. of Southern Calif., Los Angeles 7.

MacMICHAEL, DAVID CHARLES, b. Albany, N.Y., June 5, 1928. HISTORY. B.A., Hampden-Sydney Coll., 1952; M.A., U. of Oreg., 1961; Ph.D., 1964. INSTR., HISTORY, DOMINICAN COLL. OF SAN RAFAEL, 1962- . National Defense fellow, U. of Oreg., 1959-62. Research: American relations with the Dominican Republic, 1871-1940. Language: Spanish 2,—,—,—. Home: 645 Cedarberry Lane, San Rafael, Calif. 94903. Office: Dominican Coll. of San Rafael, San Rafael, 94905.

McNEELY, JOHN HAMILTON, b. Evansville, Ind., Mar. 2, 1917. HISTORY. B.A., American U., 1938; M.A., George Washington U., 1939; Ph.D., U. of Tex., 1958. ASSOC. PROF., HISTORY, TEX. WESTERN COLL., 1946- . Membership: Texas State Historical Association. Research: Central America; land reform in Mexico. Language: Spanish 3,3,3,—. Home: 1828 Cliff Dr., El Paso, Tex. Office: Dept. of History, Tex. Western Coll., El Paso.

McNICOLL, ROBERT EDWARDS, b. St. Louis, Mo., Feb. 4, 1907. HISTORY. A.B., U. of Miami, 1931; M.A., Duke U., 1936; Ph.D., 1938. Prof., co-dir., Hispanic American Institute, U. of Miami, 1933-55; vis. prof., U. of Havana, 1940-41, Summers 1940-55; divisional asst., Cultural Relations, U.S. Dept. of State, 1943-45; prof., Southern Ill. U., 1945-46; divisional asst., Intelligence Resources, U.S. Dept.

of State, 1946-47; editor, Journal of Inter-American Studies, Pan American Foundation, 1952-64; DIR., BI-NATIONAL CULTURAL CENTER (CUZCO, PERU), U.S. INFORMATION AGENCY, 1964- . Pan American Foundation grant (Chile), 1956-58; consultant, Duke U. Hispanic Program, Ford Foundation. Membership: Asociación de Artistas y Escritores Americanos (Cuba); Conference on Latin American History; El Ateneo (El Salvador). Research: contemporary relations in Latin America; intellectual history. Author: Educación interamericana (1942); Intellectual Origins of Aprismo (Hispanic American Historical Review, Aug. 1943). Translator: Bolivar and the Political Thought of the Spanish-American Revolutions, by V. A. Belaúnde (1938). Language: Spanish 5,5,4,4; Portuguese 3,3,2,3; French 3,2,2,2. Office: Journal of Inter-American Studies, Box 13625, Gainesville, Fla.

MAGNER, JAMES A., RT. REV., b. Wilmington, Ill., Oct. 23, 1901. HISTORY AND PHILOSOPHY. B.A., St. Mary of the Lake Seminary, 1923; M.A., 1924; S.T.D., Urban U. (Rome), 1928; Ph.D., Academy of St. Thomas (Rome), 1929. Instr., Quigley Preparatory Seminary, 1929-40; PROCURATOR AND ASST. TREASURER, BUSINESS AND FISCAL OFFICE, CATHOLIC U. OF AMERICA, 1940- ; DIR., CATHOLIC U. PRESS, 1941- . Membership: American Catholic Historical Association; Catholic Association for International Peace; Institute of Ibero-American Studies, Catholic U. of America. Research: Mexican history; social ethics. Author: Men of Mexico (1942); The Latin American Pattern (1943); Mental Health in a Mad World (1953). Language: Spanish 3,4,3,3; Portuguese 2,2,1,1; French 3,3,2,2; German 2,2,2,1; Greek 1,1,1,1; Latin 3,3,2,2. Office: The Catholic U. of America, 620 Michigan Ave., NE., Washington, D.C. 20017.

MAINGOT, ANTHONY PETER, b. Port of Spain, Trinidad, West Indies, Oct. 19, 1937. HISTORY. B.A., U. of Fla., 1960. STUDENT, HISTORY, U. OF FLA. Organization of American States fellow in Social Sciences, U. of P.R., 1960-62; West Indies Study Program fellow, U. of Calif., Los Angeles, 1962. Research: Latin American history; the Caribbean area; socio-political behavior of Latin American elites; French Creole of Trinidad. Language: Spanish 5,5,5,5; Portuguese 3,2,2,2; French 3,3,3,3; Dutch 4,4,4,4; Papiamento 5,5,5,5. Home: 932 SW. 8th Lane, Gainesville, Fla.

MALAGÓN BARCELÓ, JAVIER, b. Toledo, Spain, May 24, 1911. HISTORY AND LAW. Bachiller, Instituto de San Isidro, 1927; Maestro de Primera Enseñanza, Escuela Normal de Maestros, 1929; LL.D., Universidad de Madrid, 1934. Asst., Universidad de Madrid, 1932-34, 1935-36; librarian, Sala de Lectura Francisco Giner, 1931-35; librarian, Museo Laboratorio Jurídico Ureña, 1935-39; asst. prof., 1936-39; catedrático, Universidad de Santo Domingo, 1940-46; member, Centro de Estudios Históricos, El Colegio de México, 1946; vis. prof.,

Universidad de P.R., Summers 1947, 1949; prof., El Colegio de México, 1947; catedrático, Universidad Nacional Autónoma de México, 1948-49; vis. prof., American U., Summers 1956, 1960-61, 1963-64; TECHNICAL SECRETARY, FELLOWSHIP AND PROFESSORSHIP PROGRAM, ORGANIZATION OF AMERICAN STATES, 1958- ; lectr., Catholic U. of America, 1964. Ministerio de Educación (Spain) scholarship, 1932; Universidad de Madrid grants (Germany), 1934, 1935-36; Universidad de Santo Domingo research grant to Archivo Nacional de Cuba, 1941; secretary, Revista de Historia de América and Boletín Bibliográfico de Antropología Americana (Mexico), 1947-55; Rockefeller Foundation grant, 1950, 1952-53; dir., Inter-American Review of Bibliography, Pan American Union, 1955-61; Advisory Board, Handbook of Latin American Studies, 1955-63; consultant, Miembro Nacional de la Comisión de Historia de México, 1955, U.S. Dept. of Justice, 1955-56; Biblioteca Nacional de México, 1957; Committee on International Exchange of Persons, 1958; advisory editor, The Americas, 1955; assoc. editor, Hispanic American Historical Review, 1956-60; Serra Award of the Americas, 1962. Membership: Academia Nacional de Historia y Geografía (Mexico); American Historical Association; Conference on Latin American History; Instituto de Estudios Afro-americanos (Mexico); Pan American Institute of Geography and History; Sociedad Mexicana de Historia. Research: history of Spanish law, metropolitan and colonial. Author: Programa de historia del derecho español en Indias (1941); La literatura jurídica española del Siglo de Oro en la Nueva España (1959); Toledo and the New World in the XVI Century (1963). Language: Spanish 5,5,5,5; Portuguese 4,4,1,1; French 4,4,3,2; German 3,3,3,1; Latin 3,—,—,1. Home: 4840 43rd Pl., NW., Washington, D.C. Office: Organization of American States, 1725 I St., NW., Washington 6.

MANCHESTER, ALAN K., b. Camden, N.J., July 2, 1897. HISTORY. A.B., Vanderbilt U., 1920; M.A., Columbia U., 1922; Ph.D., Duke U., 1930. School administrator, Methodist Church (Brazil), 1922-27; Instr.-PROF., HISTORY, DUKE U., 1929- ; asst. dean-DEAN, 1934- ; cultural attaché, Embassy (Brazil), U.S. Dept. of State, 1951-52. Assoc. managing editor, Hispanic American Historical Review, 1939-44; specialist, International Educational Exchange Program, U.S. Dept. of State, 1954, 1955; consultant, U.S. Dept. of State, 1956, 1958; member-at-large, U.S. National Commission for UNESCO, 1958-62; consultant, Brazilian Institute, N.Y.U., 1958; U.S. representative, Inter-American Cultural Council, Organization of American States, 1959- . Research: Brazilian history, particularly the 19th century; the Portuguese Empire. Author: British Pre-eminence in Brazil (1933); Constitutional Dictatorship in Brazil (in Studies in Hispanic American Affairs: South American Dictators During the First Century of Independence, 1937); Dom Pedro Segundo, the Democratic Emperor (in Brazil, 1947). Language: Spanish 3,3,2,1; Portuguese 4,4,4,2. Home: 406

Swift Ave., Durham, N.C. 27705. Office: Dept. of History, Duke U., Durham.

MANLEY, VAUGHN PORTER, b. Sioux City, Iowa, Aug. 24, 1930. GEOGRAPHY. A.B., Stanford U., 1952; M.A., San Diego State Coll., 1954; D.S.S., Syracuse U., 1958. Asst. prof., Wis. State Coll., 1958-59; asst. prof., Drake U., 1959-62; ASST. PROF., ECONOMICS, IOWA STATE U., 1962- . National Science Foundation grants, Summers 1961, 1962, 1963. Membership: Association of American Geographers; Farm Economic Association; Phi Alpha Theta. Research: regional economic patterns of farming; Chilean resources. Language: Spanish 4,4,4,4. Home: 6429 University Ave., Des Moines, Iowa 50311. Office: Dept. of Economics, Iowa State U., Ames.

MANTON, JUDY. Home: 6321 King Louis Dr., Alexandria, Va. 22312.

MANNO, FRANCIS J., b. Clermont, Pa., Dec. 24, 1914. HISTORY. B.A., B.S., Georgetown U., 1941; Ph.D., 1954. Prof., St. Mary's Coll. (Kans.), 1955-57; prof., Villanova U., 1957-63; PROF., HISTORY, STATE OF N.Y., COLL. AT BROCKPORT, 1963- . Vis. fellow, Ohio State U., Summer 1957. Membership: American Academy of Social and Political Science; American Association of University Professors; American Historical Association; Conference on Latin American History; Phi Alpha Theta. Research: diplomatic history of the United States and Mexico. Author: Yucatán en la guerra entre México y los Estados Unidos (Revista de la Universidad de Yucatán, July-Aug. 1963). Language: Spanish 3,3,3,3; French 3,3,3,3; Italian 5,5,5,5. Office: Dept. of History, State U. of N.Y., Coll. at Brockport, Brockport.

MARCUS, HOWARD, b. Jersey City, N.J., Oct. 19, 1940. HISTORY. B.A., Brandeis U., 1962; M.A., U. of Wis., 1964; Yale U. STUDENT, HISTORY, YALE U. National Defense Foreign Langauge fellow in Spanish, U. of Wis., 1962-64; Helena P. Bulkley fellow in American History, Yale U., 1964-65. Research: Latin American history; Brazil; history of Portuguese Africa. Language: Spanish 4,4,4,3; Portuguese 3,3,3,2; French 2,2,2,1. Home: 411 Gorge Rd., Cliffside Park, N.J.

MARIA RENATA, SISTER. Office: St. Mary's Coll., Notre Dame, Ind. 46556.

MARIE LEONORE, SISTER. Office: Coll. of Mt. St. Vincent, Bronx, N.Y. 10471.

MARKMAN, SIDNEY DAVID, b. Brooklyn, N.Y., Oct. 10, 1911. ART AND ARCHITECTURE. A.B., Union Coll., 1934; M.A., Columbia U., 1936; Ph.D., 1943. Prof., Universidad Nacional de Panamá, 1941-45; ASST. PROF., ART, DUKE U., 1947- . Chmn., Junta de Conservación y Restauración de Monumentos Históricos de Panamá, 1942-45; Duke U. Research Council grants (Central America), 1949-62; Philosophical Society grant (Spain), 1959; Fulbright research scholar (Spain), 1961-62. Membership Archaeological Institute of America; Society of Architectural Historians. Research: architecture of colonial Central America, especially Guatemala. Author: San Cristobal de las Casas y su arquitectura (1963); Colonial Architecture of Antigua, Guatemala (1965); Santa Cruz, Antigua, Guatemala, and the Spanish Colonial Architecture of Central America (Journal, Society of Architectural Historians, Mar. 1956). Language: Spanish 5,5,5,4; Portuguese 2,1,1,1; French 5,2,2,1; German 4,4,2,1. Home: 919 Urban Ave., Durham, N.C. Office: Dept. of Art, Duke U., Durham.

MARTIN, NORMAN FRANCIS, S.J., b. Half Moon Bay, Calif., July 8, 1914. HISTORY. U. of Santa Clara, 1933-35; A.B., Gonzaga U. (Wash.), 1941; M.A., 1942; S.T.L., Colegio Máximo San Miguel (Argentina), 1948; M.A., Mexico City Coll., 1950; Ph.D., Universidad Nacional Autónoma de México, 1957. Instr. U. of Santa Clara, 1942-43; Colegio Centro América (Nicaragua), 1943-45; Colegio de San Bartolomé (Colombia), 1944-45; prof., U. of Santa Clara, 1958-62; WRITER, JESUIT INSTITUTE OF HISTORY (ROME), 1963- . Guggenheim fellow (Europe), 1962-63. Membership: American Catholic Historical Association; American Historical Association; Conference on Latin American History; Pacific Coast Council on Latin American Studies. Research: social and economic aspects of Mexican colonial history; Jesuit achievements in Baja, California in the 17th and 18th centuries. Author: Los Vagabundos de la Nueva España, Siglo XVI (1957); Instrucción del Virrey Marqués de Croix que deja a su sucesor Antonio María Bucareli (1960). Language: Spanish 5,5,5,5; Portuguese 4,4,3,3; French 4,3,3,3; Italian 4,3,3,3. Linguistic studies: Greek, Hebrew, Italian, Latin. Home: Faculty Residence, U. of Santa Clara, Santa Clara, Calif. Office: Jesuit Institute of History, Via dei Penitenzieri 20, Rome 6, Italy.

MARTINEZ, JOHN R., b. Midvale, Utah, Jan. 31, 1927. HISTORY. B.A., Brigham Young U., 1950; M.A., U. of Calif., Berkeley, 1953; Ph.D., 1957. Asst. Prof., Brigham Young U., 1956-57; ASSOC. PROF., HISTORY, ARIZ. STATE U., 1957- . John Hay Whitney fellow (Mexico). Membership: Pacific Coast Council for Latin American Studies; Rocky Mountain Council on Latin America. Research: intellectual and cultural history; current political and diplomatic problems; Mexican emigration to the United States, 1848-1930. Author: Sarmiento and Rodó on Democracy (1960); The Changing Role of the Military (Bureau of Government Research, Ariz. State U., 1962); Three Cases of Communism: Cuba, Brazil, and Mexico (1964). Language: Spanish 5,5,5,5; Portuguese 3,3,3,3; French 3,3,3,3; German 2,2,2,2. Home: 607 West 19th St., Tempe, Ariz. Office: Dept of History, Ariz. State U., Tempe.

MARTÍNEZ, MANUEL GUILLERMO, b. México, D.F., July 13, 1897. HISTORY AND SPANISH AMERICAN LITERATURE. B.S., Georgetown U., 1928; Ph.D., Georgetown U., 1932; M.A., Catholic U. of America, 1936;

Ph.D., 1947. Research asst., Inter-American High Commission, 1919-25; clerk, Chancery, Embassy of Mexico (Washington, D.C.), 1925-30; PROF., SPANISH AND HISPANIC AMERICAN CIVILIZATION, INSTITUTE OF LANGUAGES AND LINGUISTICS, GEORGETOWN U., 1930- . Staff member, U.S. Secretary of State Colby's delegation to South America, 1920; Pan American Highway Commission, 1923; Georgetown U. representative, Fourth Pan American Commercial Congress, 1932. Membership: American Association of Teachers of Spanish and Portuguese; American Association of University Professors; Hispanic American Academy of Arts and Sciences; Instituto de las Españas; Pi Gamma Mu. Research: Mexican historiography. Author: Don Joaquín Garcia Icazbalceta—His Place in Mexican Historiography (1947; Spanish edition, 1950); Don Joaquín García Icazbalceta (Review of Inter-American Bibliography, Apr.-June 1951). Language: Spanish 5,5,5,5; Portuguese 3,3,2,2; French 3,3,2,2. Home: 7111 Beechwood Dr., Chevy Chase, Md. 20015. Office: Institute of Languages and Linguistics, Georgetown U., Washington, D.C. 20007.

MARTÍNEZ, RODOLFO, b. Corpus Christi, Tex., Oct. 17, 1927. POLITICAL SCIENCE AND HISTORY. B.S., U. of Utah, 1954; M.A., U. of Tex., 1955; U. of Utah. Instr., acting chmn., Social Science, Navarro Jr. Coll., 1955-59; instr., chmn., Social Science, Casper Coll., 1959-61; INSTR., HISTORY AND POLITICAL SCIENCE, BRIGHAM YOUNG U., 1965- . Membership: American Association of University Professors; American Political Science Association; American Society for Public Administration; Conference on Latin American History; Phi Alpha Theta; Pi Sigma Alpha; Rocky Mountain Social Science Association. Research: historical development of Costa Rica, Guatemala, and Nicaragua; history of efforts to create a Central American confederation; United States history and government. Author: Short Research Papers for History Classes (American Junior College Journal, Sept. 1960); A Layman Looks at Wyoming Judicial Selection (Wyoming Law Journal, Fall 1960). Language: Spanish 4,5,5,4. Home: 2233 Nogales, Corpus Christi, Tex. Office: Dept. of Political Science, Brigham Young U., Provo, Utah.

MARY CONSUELA, I.H.M. Home and office: Immaculata Coll., Immaculata, Pa. 19345.

MARY GRACE, C.S.C. Office: St. Mary's Coll., Notre Dame, Ind. 46556.

MASUR, GERHARD S., b. Berlin, Germany, Sept. 17, 1901. HISTORY. U. of Marburg (Germany), 1921; Ph.D., U. of Berlin, 1925. Privatdozent, U. of Berlin, 1930-35; prof., Escuela Normal Superior (Colombia), 1936-45; PROF., HISTORY, SWEET BRIAR COLL., 1947- ; vis. prof., U. of Va., 1949-51, U. of N. Mex., 1953, Free U. of Berlin, 1960, U. of Calif., Berkeley, 1963-64. Rockefeller grant, 1945-47, 1954-55; Guggenheim fellow, 1955;

Fulbright lectr., 1960. Membership: American Historical Association; Conference on Latin American History; Conference on Central European History. Research: Latin American independence period; history of ideas. Author: Simon Bolivar (1948). Language: Spanish 5,5,4,4; Portuguese 3,2,—,—; French 5,4,3,2; German 5,5,5,5. Office: Dept. of History, Sweet Briar Coll., Sweet Briar, Va.

MATAMOROS, RAMUNTCHO, b. Westborough, Mass., Nov. 21, 1906. HISTORY. B.A., U. of Southern Calif., 1949; M.A., Tulane U., 1955; U. of Southern Calif. Principal, Anglo-American School (Oruro, Bolivia), 1954; teacher, New Orleans Public Schools (1954-57); teacher (Downey, Calif.), 1957-59; TEACHER, FREMONT HIGH SCHOOL (LOS ANGELES), 1959- . Civil Liberties Foundation of Los Angeles fellow, U. of Calif., Santa Barbara, Summer 1963. Membership: American Federation of Teachers; American Historical Association; National Education Association; Phi Alpha Theta; Phi Delta Kappa. Research: Latin American history; the Mexican Constitution of 1917; Woodrow Wilson's Mexican Policy. Language: Spanish 4,3,3,3; Portuguese 2,2,2,1; French 3,4,2,2; German 4,2,2,1. Home: Apt. 12-A, 401 Union Dr., Los Angeles, Calif. 90017. Office: Fremont High School, 7676 San Pedro St., Los Angeles.

MATHES, WILLIAM MICHAEL, b. Los Angeles, Calif., Apr. 15, 1936. HISTORY. B.S., Loyola U. (Calif.), 1957; M.A., U. of Southern Calif., 1962; U. of N. Mex. Editorial asst., Calif. Historical Society, 1961-62; lectr., U.S. Information Service (Madrid), 1962-63; special collections dir., Coronado Room, U. of N. Mex. Library, 1963-65; STUDENT, HISTORY, U. OF N. MEX. Fulbright grant (Spain), 1962-63; correspondent, Servicio Histórico Militar (Madrid). Membership: American Historical Association; California Historical Society; Phi Alpha Theta; Western History Association. Research: Sebastian Vizcaíno and Spanish commercial expansion in the Pacific, 1585-1616. Author: Derrotero de Sebastian Rodríguez Cermeño (1963); Documentos para la demarcación comercial de California (1964); Judicial Transformation in California (Los Angeles Bar Association Journal, Sept. 1960). Language: Spanish 5,5,5,5; Portuguese 4,4,4,3; French 3,3,1,1; Russian 3,3,3,3. Home: 1012 Bryn Mawr, NE., Albuquerque, N. Mex.

MATHEWS, THOMAS GEORGE, b. Bloomington, Ind., Oct. 31, 1925. HISTORY. B.A., Oberlin Coll., 1949; M.A., Columbia U., 1953; Ph.D., 1957. Vis. lectr., U. of P.R., Mayagüez, 1950-53; asst. prof., 1953-57; vis. lectr., Mexico City Coll., 1954; consultant, Hispanic Foundation, Library of Congress, 1956; assoc. prof., chmn., U. of P.R., Mayagüez, 1957-61; Latin American specialist, Embassy (Cuba), U.S. Dept. of State, 1960; DIR., INSTITUTE OF CARIBBEAN STUDIES, U. OF P.R., 1961- . Membership: American Historical Association; Conference on Latin American History. Research: politics in Puerto Rico; confederation in the Caribbean. Author: Puerto Rican Politics and the New Deal (1960); Rafael Altamira: An Appreciation (Hispanic American Historical Review, Aug. 1952); Plans for a Confederation of the Greater Antilles (Caribbean Historical Review, Dec. 1954). Language: Spanish 4,4,4,4; Portuguese 2,3,2,—; French 2,2,1,—. Home: Ruta Rural 2, Buzón 39, Beverly Hills, P.R. Office: Institute of Caribbean Studies, U. of P.R., Río Piedras.

MAUGHAN, SCOTT JARVIS, b. Wilmar, Calif., Sept. 22, 1929. HISTORY. B.A., Brigham Young U., 1957; M.A., U. of Utah, 1959. Missionary (Argentina), Church of the Latter Day Saints, 1950-52; instr., Eastern Montana Coll., 1961-63. Research: Latin American history, politics and social development; explorations of Francisco Garcés, a Franciscan missionary in Arizona in the 18th century. Language: Spanish 4,4,4,4; Portuguese 2,2,1,1; French 2,2,1,1; German 3,1,1,1. Home: 5431 North Delta, San Gabriel, Calif. Office: Dept. of Social Sciences, Calif. State Polytechnic Coll., San Luis Obispo, Calif.

MAYFIELD, MILTON RAY, b. Cullman, Ala., Jan. 14, 1935. HISTORY AND LANGUAGE. A.B., Birmingham-Southern Coll., 1960; M.A., U. of Ala., 1963. INSTR., SPANISH, ALA. COLL., 1963- . National Defense Education Act fellow in Hispanic History, U. of Ala., 1960-63. Membership: Alabama Education Association; Association of Teachers of Spanish and Portuguese (Ala.); Phi Alpha Theta. Research: Latin American history and literature; American investments in Cuba, 1895-1906; Spanish language. Language: Spanish 5,5,5,5; Portuguese 3,3,3,3. Home: 805 Alden Ave., Fairfield Highlands, Ala. 35064. Office: Ala. Coll., Montevallo, Ala.

MECUM, KENT B. Office: Dept. of Spanish and Portuguese, Ballantine Hall, Ind. U., Bloomington, Ind. 47405.

MEIER, MATT S., b. Covington, Ky., June 4, 1917. HISTORY. B.A., U. of Miami, 1948; M.A., Mexico City Coll., 1949; Ph.D., U. of Calif., Berkeley, 1954. Research asst., Documents Div., Bancroft Library, lectr., Extension Div., U. of Calif., Berkeley, 1953-54; vis. lectr., San Francisco State Coll., Summers 1953, 1954, 1955; asst. prof., Bakersfield Coll., 1955-63; asst. prof., Fresno State Coll., Spring 1963; assoc. prof., Long Beach State Coll., Summer 1963; ASST. PROF., HISTORY, U. OF SANTA CLARA, 1963- . Fulbright lectr. (Argentina), 1958-59. Membership: American Association of University Professors; American Historical Association. Research: the Díaz period in Mexico, especially the economic aspect. Editor: Folsom Letter (Sacramento County Historical Society Golden Notes, Apr.-May 1955). Language: Spanish 5,4,4,4; Portuguese 3,3,2,1; French 3,2,2,1; German 3,3,2,2; Italian 3,2,2,1. Home: 591 Remington Ave., Sunnyvale, Calif. Office: Dept. of History, U. of Santa Clara, Santa Clara, Calif.

MEIKLEJOHN, NORMAN ARTHUR, REVEREND, b. Somersworth, N.H., May 18, 1928. HISTORY. S.T.L., Angelicum U. (Rome), 1955; M.A., Georgetown U., 1963; Columbia U. Instr., Assumption Coll., 1955-58; dean of men, 1956-60; registrar, 1958-60; STUDENT, HISTORY, COLUMBIA U. National Defense Foreign Language fellow, 1963-64; Fulbright-Hays research grant (Bogotá), 1965. Membership: American Historical Association. Research: Latin American history; Negro slavery in colonial Spanish America. Language: Spanish 3,3,3,3; Portuguese 3,1,1,1. Home: Assumption Coll., 500 Salisbury St., Worcester 9, Mass.

MÉNDEZ, J. IGNACIO, b. Santa Marta, Colombia, June 28, 1929. HISTORY. B.A., U. of Fla., 1954; U. of Pa.; U. of Ill.; M.A., U. of Chicago, 1959; U. of Calif., Berkeley. ASST. PROF., HISTORY, STATE U. OF N.Y., COLL. AT NEW PALTZ, 1961- . U. of Fla. scholar, 1950-54; Foreign Policy research scholar, 1955-56; Organization of American States fellow (Colombia, Panama), Summer 1963. Membership: American Historical Association; Conference on Latin American History. Research: Latin American history, especially 19th century and diplomatic history; socio-economic factors in Panamanian history, 1825-1855. Language: Spanish 5,5,5,5; Portuguese 3,2,2,—; French 4,3,3,3. Home: 14 Prospect St., New Platz, N.Y. Office: Dept. of Social Science, State U. of N.Y., Coll. at New Paltz.

MERSCHEL, CARL W. Office: Div. of Science of Society, Monteith Coll., Detroit, Mich. 48202.

MEYER, MICHAEL CARL, b. Albuquerque, N. Mex., Sept. 6, 1935. HISTORY. B.A., U. of N. Mex., 1957; U. of Wis., 1957-58; Mexico City Coll., 1958-59; M.A., U. of N. Mex., 1961; Ph.D., 1963. Vis. asst. prof., U. of N. Mex., Summer, 1963; ASST. PROF., HISTORY, U. OF NEBR., 1963- . National Defense Education Act fellow, 1962-63; U. of Nebr. faculty research grant, 1964; consultant, U.S. Peace Corps Training Programs, U. of N. Mex., U. of Nebr., and Los Angeles City Coll.; Latin American Studies Committee, U. of Nebr. Membership: American Historical Association; Mississippi Valley Historical Association. Research: modern Mexico; General Pascual Orozco, Jr., in the Mexican Revolution. Author: Albert Bacon Fall's Mexican Papers (New Mexico Historical Review, Jan. 1965). Language: Spanish 5,5,4,4; Portuguese 4,4,3,2; French 3,2,1,1. Home: 643 Eastridge Dr., Lincoln, Nebr. Office: Dept. of History, U. of Nebr., Lincoln.

MICHAELS, ALBERT LOUIS, b. Buffalo, N.Y., June 20, 1937. HISTORY. M.A., U. of Pa., 1962. STUDENT, HISTORY, U. OF PA. Fellow in Argentine nationalism, U. of Pa., 1963-64; Doherty fellow (Latin America), 1964-65. Research: Latin American history; nationalism; military history; land reform; United States and Bolivia, 1952-1956; politics in Mexico, 1934-1940. Language: Spanish 4,3,2,—; French 4,—,—,—. Home: 25 LeBrun Circle, Eggertsville, N.Y.

MILLER, DAVID LYNN, b. Royal Oak, Mich., Nov. 1, 1922. HISTORY AND EDUCATION. B.A., Wesleyan U., 1947; M.A., Mexico City Coll., 1948; Ph.D., U. of Mich., 1960. Vis. prof., Mexico City Coll., Summer 1951; asst. manager, Migration Center (Mexico), Farm Placement Service, U.S. Dept. of Labor, 1951-53; instr., Mexico City Coll., 1952; supervisor of employee communication, Chrysler Corporation, 1953-57; COORDINATOR OF EXTENSION, EDUCATIONAL SERVICE, LOS ANGELES STATE COLL., 1958- . Boston Globe Memorial fellow (Mexico), 1947-48; Orla B. Taylor fellow, U. of Mich., 1949-50; teaching fellow, U. of Mich., 1951. Membership: American Association of University Professors; American Society of Training Directors; Personnel Managers Committee, Los Angeles Chamber of Commerce. Research: Mexico, administration of educational programs. Language: Spanish 4,3,3,3; French 2,2,2,2. Home: 2504 Baltusrol Dr., Alhambra, Calif. 91803. Office: Los Angeles State Coll., 5151 College Dr., Los Angeles, Calif. 90032.

MILLER, GLENN E., JR., b. Youngstown, Ohio, Sept. 21, 1920. HISTORY. B.A., Swarthmore Coll., 1941; M.A., U. of Pa., 1942. Instr.-asst. prof., Franklin and Marshall Coll., 1950-62; ASSOC. PROF., HISTORY, FRANKLIN AND MARSHALL COLL., 1962- . Membership: American Historical Association; Association for Latin American Studies; Conference on Latin American History; Pennsylvania Historical Association. Research: Latin American history; diplomatic history of the United States; Francisco de Paula Santander. Language: Spanish 4,4,3,3. Home: 52 Northview Dr., Lancaster, Pa. Office: Dept. of History, Franklin and Marshall Coll., Lancaster.

MILLER, HUBERT JOHN, b. Hays, Kans., Dec. 9, 1927. HISTORY. B.A., U. of Dayton, 1951; M.A., St. Louis U., 1954; Ph.D., Loyola U. (Ill.), 1964. Teacher, Academy of the Sacred Heart (Mo.), 1951-53; St. Johns High School (St. Louis, Mo.), 1953-54; Escuela Americana (El Salvador), 1955-56; dir., Instituto de Inglés (El Salvador), 1956; ASST. PROF., HISTORY, ST. MARY'S U. OF TEX., 1960- . Fellowship lectr., Loyola U. (Ill.), 1956-59; Smith-Mundt grant (Guatemala), 1959-60. Membership: American Historical Association; Hispanic American Historical Association; Pi Gamma Mu. Research: church and state question in Guatemala during the national period. Language: Spanish 5,3,3,3; German 3,4,4,3. Home: 5803 Angie Pl., San Antonio, Tex. 78240. Office: Dept. of History, St. Mary's U., San Antonio, 78228.

MILLER, ROBERT RYAL, b. Lake Andes, S. Dak., Oct. 3, 1923. HISTORY. B.A., U. of Calif., Berkeley, 1948; M.A., 1951; Ph.D., 1960. Asst. prof., U. of Southwestern La., 1959-60; asst. prof., N. Mex. State U., 1960-66; DIR., INDIANA U. JUNIOR YEAR IN PERU PROGRAM (LIMA, PERU), 1966- . Coordinator, U.S. Peace Corps Training Program, 1962- . Membership: American Historical Association; Conference on Latin American History; Mississippi Valley Historical Association; Sigma Xi; Western History Conference. Research: Mexico and Spain, especially the 19th century. Author: The American Legion of Honor in Mexico (Pacific Historical Review, Aug. 1961); Plácido Vega: A Mexican Secret Agent in the United States (The Americas, Oct. 1962); Lew Wallace and the French Intervention in Mexico (Indiana Magazine of History, Mar. 1963). Language: Spanish 4,4,4,4; Portuguese 2,2,1,1; French 2,1,1,1. Office: Junior Year in Peru Program, Indiana U., Bloomington, Ind.

MILLER, RUSSELL E. Office: Tufts U., Medford, Mass. 02155.

MILLETT, RICHARD L. Office: Dept. of History, Southern Ill. U., Edwardsville, Ill.

MILLS, VIRGINIA NEEL, b. Hillsboro, W. Va., June 26, 1911. POLITICAL SCIENCE. A.B., Emory and Henry Coll., 1931; Ph.D., American U., 1951. Teacher (Brazil), 1937-45; National Education Association, 1934-36, 1947-53, 1956-57; dean of women, West Liberty State Coll., 1957-60; PROF., POLITICAL SCIENCE, FROSTBURG STATE COLL., 1960- . Chmn., International Relations Comm., National Council of Administrative Women in Education; chmn., Comm. for Rural Life and Education. Membership: American Association of University Professors; American Association of University Women; American Historical Association; American Political Science Association; International Studies Association; Southern Political Science Association. Research: Brazilian participation in international organizations and administration, 1889-1949. Language: Spanish 4,2,2,2; Portuguese 5,5,4,3; French 3,2,1,1. Home: 311 Maryland Ave., Cumberland, Md. Office: Frostburg State Coll., Frostburg, Md.

MINER, WILLIAM D., b. Table Grove, Ill., June 26, 1914. HISTORY. A.B., Knox Coll., 1936; M.A., Ind. U., 1948; Ph.D., 1950. Lectr., Southern Ill. U. High School, 1950; PROF., HISTORY, ASST. DEAN OF STUDENTS, EASTERN ILL. U., 1950- . Membership: Conference on Latin American History; Mississippi Valley Historical Association; National Education Association. Research: Spanish borderlands; American West. Language: Spanish 2,—,—,—. Home: Lincoln Highway Rd., Charleston, Ill. 61920. Office: Dept. of History, Eastern Ill. U., Charleston.

MINGER, RALPH ELDIN, b. Gregory, S. Dak., Oct. 19, 1925. HISTORY. B.A., U. of Southern Calif., 1949; Ph.D., 1958. Instr., Immaculate Heart Coll., 1957-59; lectr.-assoc. prof., San Fernando Valley State Coll., 1958-66; PROF., HISTORY, U. OF MAINE, 1966- . lectr., U. of Md., Summers 1962-63; vis. asst. prof., 1962-63. Editorial Board, Southern California Quarterly. Membership: American Association of University Professors; American Historical Association; American Studies Asso-

ciation; Mississippi Valley Historical Association; Phi Alpha Theta; Pi Sigma Alpha; Los Angeles World Affairs Council. Research: United States diplomatic relations in the Caribbean, Central America and Mexico. Author: William H. Taft and the United States Intervention in Cuba in 1906 (Hispanic American Historical Review, Feb. 1961); Panama, the Canal Zone, and Titular Sovereignty (Western Political Quarterly, June 1961). Language: Spanish 3,3,3,3; Portuguese 1,1,1,1; French 1,1,1,1. Office: East Annex 104, U. of Maine, Orono, Maine.

MITCHELL, FREDERICK CLEVELAND, b. Erie, Pa., Feb. 2, 1933. HISTORY. B.A., Yale U., 1955; M.A., Middlebury Coll., 1960; U. of Calif., Berkeley. STUDENT, HISTORY, U. OF CALIF., BERKELEY. National Defense Foreign Language fellow, U. of Calif., Berkeley, 1962-63; Bancroft Library fellow, 1963-64. Membership: American Historical Association. Research: colonial Latin American history; Spanish relations with the Indian nobility in 16th century New Spain. Language: Spanish 5,5,4,3; Portuguese 4,3,2,1; French 4,3,2,2. Home: 1705 La Loma Ave., Berkeley, Calif. 94709.

MOONEY, JOSEPH P. Office: La Salle Coll., Philadelphia, Pa.

MOORE, JAMES MAXWELL, b. Bogota, N.J., Oct. 21, 1914. HISTORY. A.B., U. of Calif., Berkeley, 1936; M.A., 1938; Ph.D., 1943. Asst. prof., Xavier U. (Cincinnati), 1947-49; prof., Rocky Mountain Coll., 1949-50; prof., chmn., Social Science, Boise District Coll., 1950-57; prof., Lake Erie Coll., 1957-60; PROF., HISTORY, NORWICH U., 1960- . Membership: American Association of University Professors; American Committee for Irish Studies; American Historical Association. Research: Latin American population growth; modern European history. Author: The Roots of French Republicanism (1962); Population Increase and Economic Potential in Latin America (1963). Language: Spanish 5,3,3,3; French 5,3,3,3; Gaelic 5,3,3,3; German 5,3,3,3; Russian 3,3,3,3. Home: 57 Central St., Northfield, Vt. Office: Dept. of Social Science, Norwich U., Northfield.

MOORE, JOHN PRESTON, b. Lexington, Va., Nov. 1, 1906. HISTORY. B.A., Washington & Lee U., 1927; M.A., Harvard U., 1930; Ph.D., Northwestern U., 1942. Instr., U. of Ark., 1934-36; asst. prof., The Citadel, 1938-42; PROF., HISTORY, LA. STATE U., 1946- Howard Houston fellow, Washington & Lee U.; Rumford scholarship, Harvard U.; Guggenheim fellow (Spain), 1960-61. Membership: Phi Beta Kappa. Research: Spanish colonial history; Peru and Ecuador in the 18th century. Author: The Cabildo in Peru Under the Hapsburgs (1954). Language: Spanish 5,4,4,3; Portuguese 2,1,1,1; French 5,4,3,3. Home: 4888 Sweetbriar Pl., Baton Rouge, La. Office: Dept. of History, La. State U., Baton Rouge.

MOORHEAD, MAX LEON, b. Grand Junction, Colo., Dec. 28, 1914. HISTORY. B.A., U. of Okla., 1937; M.A., 1938; Ph.D., U. of Calif., Berkeley, 1942. Asst. prof., U. of Okla., 1945-51; assoc. prof., 1951-56; PROF., HISTORY, U. OF OKLA., 1956- ; vis. prof., U. of Tex., 1962-63. American Philosophical Society research grant (Mexico), 1950; contributor, Encyclopaedia Britannica and Britannica Book of the Year, 1938-42, 1945-50, 1962. Membership: Conference on Latin American History; Mississippi Valley Historical Association; Phi Alpha Theta; Phi Beta Kappa; Western History Association. Research: 18th century Mexico; archival research; history of trade and transportation in Mexico. Author: New Mexico's Royal Road: Trade and Travel on the Chihuahua Trail (1958); The Private Contract System of Presidio Supply in Northern New Spain (Hispanic American Historical Review, Feb. 1961). Editor: Commerce of the Prairies, by Josiah Gregg (1953). Language: Spanish 4,3,3,3; Portuguese 2,1,1,1; French 2,1,1,1; German 2,1,1,1. Home: 1228 Caddell, Norman, Okla. Office: Dept. of History, U. of Okla., Norman.

MORALES-CARRION, ARTURO, b. Havana, Cuba, Nov. 16, 1913. HISTORY AND INTERNATIONAL RELATIONS. B.A., U. of P.R., 1935; M.A., U. of Tex., 1936; Ph.D., Columbia U., 1950. Prof., U. of Miami, 1939-40; div. asst., U.S. Dept. of State, 1940-43; chmn., U. of P.R., 1945, 1951-52; consultant, Hispanic Foundation, Library of Congress, 1946-47; vis. lectr., Columbia U., 1947-49; vice president, Committee on Teaching World History, United Nations Educational, Scientific, and Cultural Organization, 1950-51; undersecretary, Dept. of State, Commonwealth of P.R., 1953-61; deputy asst. secretary, Inter-American Affairs, U.S. Dept. of State, 1961-64; SPECIAL ADVISOR TO SECRETARY GENERAL, ORGANIZATION OF AMERICAN STATES, 1964- . Membership: Academia Colombiana de la Historia; Cultural Institute of Puerto Rico; Inter-American Academy; Pan American Institute of Geography and History; Sociedad Peruana de Historia. Research: Latin America and international organizations of the regional system. Author: Puerto Rico and the Non-Hispanic Caribbean: A Study in the Decline of Spanish Exclusivism (1952). Co-author: Introducción a la historia de Europa en el siglo XIX (1940); La enseñanza de la historia en Puerto Rico (1953). Language: Spanish 5,5,5,5; Portuguese 3,—,4,—; French 3,3,3,—; German 1,1,1,—; Italian 2,2,1,—. Home: 5520 Westbard Ave., Westwood, Bethesda, Md. Office: Organization of American States, Pan American Union, 17th and Constitution Ave., NW., Washington, D.C.

MORENO, LAUDELINO, b. Burgos, Spain, Nov. 19, 1901. HISTORY, GEOGRAPHY, LITERATURE, AND INTERNATIONAL LAW. Ph.D. (history), U. of Madrid, 1923; LL.D., 1925; Ph.D. (natural science), 1926; Ph.D. (economics), 1928. Prof., Universidad Central (Spain), 1922-39; vis. prof., Universidad Central (Ecuador), 1929, Universidad Nacional Autónoma de México, 1932; prof., Universidad de Santo Domingo (Dominican Republic), 1939-41; prof., Universidad de Guatemala, 1941-47; prof., Universidad Central de Venezuela, 1947-50; ASSOC. PROF., SPANISH, U. OF SOUTHERN CALIF., 1950- ; vis. prof., U. of Colo., 1963. Delegate, League of Nations; attaché, Spanish Embassy (Mexico), 1932-33. Membership: American Association of University Professors; International Association for Instruction of History; Pan American Institute of Geography and History; Sociedad de Geografía e Historia de Guatemala; Sociedad de Geografía e Historia de Honduras. Author: Historia de las relaciones interestatuales de Centroamérica (1928); Filosofía del derecho (1944); Derecho consular guatemalteco (1946). Language: Spanish 5,5,5,5; French 5,5,4,4; Italian 4,4,4,3; Tagalog 4,4,4,3. Home: 735 West 47th St., Los Angeles, Calif. 90037. Office: Dept. of Spanish, U. of Southern Calif., Los Angeles 7.

MÖRNER, CARL MAGNUS BIRGERSSON, b. Mellösa, Södermanland, Sweden, Mar. 31, 1924. HISTORY AND ECONOMICS. Filosofie kandidat, U. of Stockholm, 1947; Filosofie Licentiat, 1950; Filosofie doktor, 1954. Dir., Institute of Ibero-American Studies, Stockholm School of Economics, 1953- ; docent, U. of Stockholm, 1962-63; vis. prof., U. of Calif., Los Angeles, 1963-64; vis. prof., Cornell U., 1964-65; vis. prof., Columbia U., 1965-66; VIS. PROF., HISTORY, QUEENS COLL., CITY U. OF N.Y., 1966- . Rockefeller fellow (Latin America), 1958; contributing editor, Handbook of Latin American studies; corresponding member, Academia Nacional de la Historia (Buenos Aires), Academia de Letras (Montevideo), Instituto Histórico y Geográfico del Uruguay. Membership: Conference on Latin American History. Research: Latin American history, especially social history of colonial period; political and economic history of the Jesuits in South America. Author: El mestizaje en la historia de Ibero-América (1962); Os Jesuítas espanhois, as suas Missões Guarani e a rivalidade luso-espanhola pela Banda Oriental, 1715-1737 (Revista Portuguesa de História, 1960). Editor: The Expulsion of the Jesuits from Latin America (1965). Language: Spanish 5,4,4,4; Portuguese 4,3,2,1; French 4,3,3,2; German 4,4,3,3; Swedish 5,5,5,5. Home: Askrikevägen 17, Lidingö 1, Sweden. Office: Institute of Ibero-American Studies, Stockholm School of Economics, Stockholm, Sweden.

MORRIS, JAMES OLIVER, b. Akron, Ohio, Feb. 8, 1923. HISTORY AND LABOR RELATIONS. A.B., Hiram Coll., 1948; M.S., U. of Mich., 1951; Ph.D., 1954. PROF., N.Y. STATE SCHOOL OF INDUSTRIAL AND LABOR RELATIONS, CORNELL U., 1955- ; chief of party, U.S. Agency for International Development-Cornell U. contract (Chile), 1959-62. Fulbright research grant (Chile), 1958-59. Research: labor relations in the Western Hemisphere; labor relations system in Chile; labor unions in the United States. Author: Conflict within the American Federation of Labor (1958). Co-author: Afiliación y finanzas sindicales en Chile, 1932-1959 (1962). Language: Spanish 4,4,4,4. Home: 7 Winthrop Pl., Ithaca, N.Y. Office: N.Y. State School of Industrial and Labor Relations, Cornell U., Ithaca, 14850.

MORRISEY, RICHARD JOHN, b. Pierre, S. Dak., Apr. 21, 1918. HISTORY. B.A., San Francisco State Coll., 1940; M.A., U. of Calif., Berkeley, 1941; Ph.D., 1949. Lectr., U. of Calif., Davis, 1948-51; assoc. prof., Air Force Academy, 1956-60; MAJOR, U.S. AIR FORCE. Research: Latin American history and geography. Author: Significance of Two Frontiers (Americas, Jan. 1951). Language: Spanish 2,—,—,—; French 1,—,—,—. Home: 1256 Batson Dr., Charleston Air Force Base, S.C.

MORSE, RICHARD McGEE, b. Summit, N.J., June 26, 1922. HISTORY. B.A., Princeton U., 1943; M.A., Columbia U., 1947; Ph.D., 1952. Lectr.-asst. prof., Columbia U., 1949-58; dir., Institute of Caribbean Studies, U. of P.R., 1958-61; vis. lectr., Harvard U., 1960; prof., chmn., State U. of N.Y., Coll. at Long Island, 1961-62; vis. lectr., Brooklyn Coll., 1962; assoc. prof., Yale U., 1962-63; PROF., HISTORY, YALE U., 1963- . Woodrow Wilson fellow, 1946-47; U.S. Dept. of State grant (Brazil), 1947-48; consultant, Economics Faculty, U. of Nuevo León, 1958-60; consultant, Ford Foundation, 1958- ; Albert J. Beveridge Award Committee, 1963- . Membership: Conference on Latin American History; Phi Beta Kappa. Research: Brazilian history; comparative history of the Americas. Author: From Community to Metropolis: A Biography of São Paulo, Brazil (1958); Toward a Theory of Spanish American Government (Journal of the History of Ideas, Jan. 1954); Some Characteristics of Latin American Urban History (American Historical Review, Jan. 1962). Language: Spanish 4,4,4,4; Portuguese 4,4,4,4; French 4,4,4,4. Home: Sunbrook Rd., Woodbridge, Conn. Office: Dept. of History, Yale U., New Haven, Conn.

MORTENSEN, MELVYN LEONARD, b. Monterey Park, Calif., May 6, 1942. HISTORY. B.A., U. of Calif., Santa Barbara, 1963; M.A., 1965. STUDENT, HISTORY, U. OF CALIF., SANTA BARBARA. National Defense Education Act fellow, 1963-66. Membership: Phi Alpha Theta. Research: Latin American history; inter-American relations with major emphasis on Mexico. Language: Spanish 4,2,2,3. Home: 11121 See Dr., Whittier, Calif.

MORTON, LUIS M., JR., b. Laredo, Tex., Nov. 29, 1925. HISTORY AND EDUCATION. B.S., U. of Houston, 1948; LL.B., St. Mary's U., 1951; M.L., U. of Houston, 1953; Ph.D., U. of Tex., 1956. Instr., Odessa Coll., 1956-60; dean of admissions, 1960-61; DEAN OF DAY COLL., ODESSA COLL., 1961- . Membership: Phi Alpha Theta; Phi Delta Kappa; Pi Sigma Alpha. Research: the Mexican Revolution; junior college education. Author: The Profs Go Back to School (Texas Outlook, Nov.

1960); The Faculty Incentive Plan at Odessa College (Junior College Journal, Dec. 1960); The Faculty Incentive Plan at Odessa College (The Bulletin, National Association of Secondary School Principals, Oct. 1961). Language: Spanish 5,5,5,5; Portuguese 3,3,3,3; French 2,2,2,2. Home: 1440 Englewood Lane, Odessa, Tex. Office: P.O. Box 3752, Odessa Coll., Odessa.

MOSELEY, EDWARD HOLT, b. Selma, Ala., July 13, 1931. HISTORY. B.S., U. of Ala., 1953; M.A., 1957; U. of Nuevo León (Mexico), 1959-60; Ph.D., U. of Ala., 1963. ASST. PROF., HISTORY, LA. POLYTECHNIC INSTITUTE, 1960- . U.S. Dept. of State grant (Mexico), 1959-60. Membership: Louisiana Historical Association; Southern Historical Association; Southwestern Social Sciences Association. Research: 19th century Mexico; the Mexican Revolution; Mexican novel of the Revolution. Language: Spanish 4,3,3,3; German 2,2,2,2. Home: Glenwood Dr., Ruston, La. Office: Dept. of History, La. Polytechnic Institute, Ruston.

MOTTEN, CLEMENT GILE, b. Colorado Springs, Colo., Feb. 16, 1917. HISTORY. B.S., Trinity Coll. (Conn.), 1938; Universidad Nacional de México, 1941; Ph.D., U. of Pa., 1947. PROF., HISTORY, DIR. OF INTERNATIONAL CULTURAL ACTIVITIES, TEMPLE U., 1946- ; vis. prof., U. of Pa., 1962-63. Social Science research fellow (Mexico), 1945-46; Beveridge Award, American Historical Association, 1948; Doherty fellow (Chile), 1950; Smith-Mundt lectr., U. of Havana (Cuba), 1959-60; Organization of American States research fellow (South America), 1960; Latin American Adviser, American Friends Service Committee; Board of Directors, International Institute of Philadelphia. Membership: American Historical Association; Conference on Latin American History. Research: university education and political organization in Latin America. Author: Mexican Silver and the Enlightenment (1950). Editor: Latin American Development Programming and United States Investments (1956). Language: Spanish 4,4,4,4; Portuguese 3,2,1,1; French 4,3,3,2; German 2,3,2,1; Italian 2,2,1,1. Home: 22 Pennock Ter., Lansdowne, Pa. Office: Dept. of History, Temple U., Philadelphia 22, Pa.

MULLER, HERMAN JOSEPH, S.J., b. Cleveland, Ohio, Apr. 9, 1909. HISTORY. M.A., Loyola U. (Ill.), 1936; S.T.L., St. Louis U., 1943; Ph.D., Loyola U. (Ill.), 1950. Instr., Xavier U., 1943-47; instr., Loyola U. (Ill.), 1950-52; asst. prof., John Carroll U., 1952-56; assoc. prof., U. of Detroit, 1956-64; CHMN., 1959- ; PROF., HISTORY, U. OF DETROIT, 1964- . Membership: American Catholic Association; American Historical Association; Michigan Academy of Arts and Sciences; Phi Alpha Theta. Research: Anglo-Hispanic American trade relations in the 17th and 18th centuries; the Renaissance and the Reformation; Europe, 1914-1939. Author: Trade Interests of XVIII Century British Travel (Mid-America, July

(Mid-America, Jan. 1953); British Business and 1951); British Travel Writers and the Jesuits Spanish America, 1700-1800 (Mid-America, Jan. 1957). Language: Spanish 2,1,1,1; Portuguese 1,1,1,1; French 3,2,2,1; German 2,3,3,1; Latin 3,3,3,3. Office: Dept. of History, U. of Detroit, 4001 West McNichols, Detroit 21, Mich.

MUNRO, DANA G., b. Providence, R.I., July 18, 1892. HISTORY. A.B., Brown U., 1912; A.B., U. of Wis., 1912; U. of Munich, 1912-13; Ph.D., U. of Pa., 1917; LL.D., Brown U., 1940. Economist, U.S. Dept. of State, 1919-20; economist, Consulate (Valparaiso, Chile), Foreign Service, 1920-21; staff, Div. of Latin American Affairs, 1921-25; first secretary, Legation (Panama), 1925-27, (Nicaragua), 1927-29; chief, Div. of Latin American Affairs, 1929-30; minister to Haiti, 1930-32; prof., Princeton U., 1932-61; dir., Woodrow Wilson School of Public and International Affairs, 1939-58; RETIRED, 1958- . Carnegie Peace Endowment grant (Central America), 1914-16; Carnegie vis. prof. (South America), 1935; president, Foreign Bondholders Protective Council, 1938- ; National Advisory Committee on Inter-American Affairs, 1959-61. Membership: American Historical Association; Council for Latin American Affairs; Inter-American Academy. Research: United States diplomatic history; history of intervention policy in the Caribbean. Author: The Five Republics of Central America (1918); The Latin American Republics, a History (1942); Intervention and Dollar Diplomacy in the Caribbean (1964). Language: Spanish 4,3,3,3; Portuguese 3,2,1,1; French 4,3,2,1; German 2,2,2,1. Home: 345 Harrison St., Princeton, N.J.

MURDOCH, RICHARD KENNETH, b. Ancón, C.Z., May 8, 1913. HISTORY. A.B., Harvard Coll., 1936; M.A., U. of Calif., Los Angeles, 1940; Ph.D., 1947. Asst. prof., Carnegie Institute of Technology, 1947-56; vis. instr., U. of N.C., 1950-51, 1955-56; ASSOC. PROF., HISTORY, U. OF GA., 1956- ; DIR., UNIVERSITY CENTER, 1959- . National Defense Foreign Language post-doctoral fellow in Spanish, U. of Calif., Los Angeles, Summer 1963. Membership: American Association of University Professors; American Historical Association; Bolivarian Society; Hispanic American Historical Association; Mississippi Valley Historical Association; Southeastern Conference on Latin American Studies. Research: Argentina; Brazil; Chile; borderlands. Author: The Georgia-Florida Frontier, 1793-1796 (1951); Citizen Mangourit and the Projected Attack on East Florida in 1794 (Journal of Southern History, Nov. 1948); The Battle of Orleans, Mass., 1814, and Associated Events (American Neptune, Winter 1963-64). Language: Spanish 4,3,3,3; Portuguese 2,—,—,—; French 4,3,3,3; German 3,3,3,3; Russian 1,—,—,—. Home: Box 1292, Athens, Ga. Office: Dept. of History, U. of Ga., Athens.

MURPHY, PETER FRANCIS, JR., b. Milwaukee, Wis., Apr. 13, 1905. HISTORY. B.A., Marquette U., 1927; M.A., 1941. Teacher,

Marquette U. High School, 1927-31; vice president, Murphy Warehouse Company, 1931-34; EXECUTIVE SECRETARY, CATHOLIC YOUTH ORGANIZATION, ARCHDIOCESE OF MILWAUKEE, 1934- . Secretary-treasurer, Wisconsin Association, Amateur Athletic Union of the United States, 1934- ; member, United States Olympic Committee, 1938- . Membership: American Historical Association; Conference on Latin American History; Governor's Conference on Children and Youth; National Recreation Association. Research: athletic programming; colonial Latin American history. Language: Spanish 3,3,3,2. Home: 2268 North 59th St., Milwaukee, Wis. 53208. Office: Catholic Youth Organization, 207 East Michigan St., Milwaukee, Wis. 53202.

MURRAY, PAUL VINCENT, b. Chicago, Ill., July 15, 1908. HISTORY. B.A., St. Ambrose Coll., 1933; M.A., Catholic U. of America, 1934. Instr., Universidad Nacional de México, Summers 1935, 1943, 1944; teacher, American High School (México, D.F.), 1936-39; principal, 1939-46; co-founder, dean, vice-president, president, Mexico City Coll., 1940-61; ADMINISTRATOR GENERAL, MEXICO CITY CENTER OF BILINGUAL STUDIES, 1961- . Knights of Columbus fellow, Catholic U. of America, 1933-36; founding member: Mexican American Institute of Cultural Relations, 1942; Colegio Tepeyac, 1944; Colegio Junípero Serra, 1956; Lomas High School, 1961; Mexico City Center, 1951. Membership: American Catholic Historical Association; Sociedad Mexicana de Geografía y Estadística. Research: church-state relations in Mexico. Author: The Church and the First Mexican Republic, 1820-1830 (American Catholic Historical Society, Mar. 1937); Tres norteamericanos y su participación en el desarrollo del Tratado McLane-Ocampo, 1856-1860 (Revista Estudios Históricos, Cuaderno No. 3, 1946). Co-author: Inglés Elemental (1937-). Language: Spanish 5,5,5,3; Portuguese 3,2,—,—; French 3,—,—,—; Italian 5,—, —,—. Home: Corregidores 1516, México 10, D.F. Office: San Luis Potosí 154, México 7.

NASATIR, ABRAHAM P., b. Santa Ana, Calif., Nov. 24, 1904. HISTORY. A.B., U. of Calif., 1921; M.A., 1922; Ph.D., 1926. Instr., U. of Iowa, 1926-27; asst. prof.-PROF., HISTORY, SAN DIEGO STATE COLL., 1928- . Native Sons of the Golden West traveling fellow (Spain), 1923-24; Social Science Research Council fellow (Spain and France), 1930-31; Fulbright fellow (France), 1950-51; fellow, Huntington Library, Summer 1952; Fulbright lecturer, U. of Chile, 1959-60; vice consul (Paraguay). Membership: American Historical Association; Mississippi Valley Historical Association; Pacific Coast Council on Latin American Studies. Research: Spain in the Mississippi Valley in the 18th century; the French in California. Author: French Activities in California: An Archival Calendar Guide (1945); Before Lewis and Clark (1952); Latin America: Development of its Civilization (1960). Language: Spanish 4,3,4,3; French 4,3,3,2; German 2,—,—. Home: 3340 North Mountain View Dr., San Diego 16, Calif. Office: Dept. of History, San Diego State Coll., San Diego 15.

NAVA, JULIAN, b. Los Angeles, Calif., June 19, 1927. HISTORY. A.B., Pomona Coll., 1951; A.M., Harvard U., 1952; Ph.D., 1955. Teacher, Centro Venezolano-Americano (Caracas), U.S. Information Agency, 1953-54; lectr., U. of P.R., 1955-57; ASSOC. PROF., HISTORY, SAN FERNANDO VALLEY STATE COLL., 1957- . John Hay Whitney Foundation fellow, 1951 (Venezuela), 1953; Bravo Fund fellow, 1952, 1954; Fulbright exchange prof. (Spain), 1962-63; chmn., Committee to Preserve the History of Los Angeles, Mayor's Office, 1961- . Membership: American Historical Association; Conference on Latin American History; Pacific Coast Council on Latin American Studies. Research: social and cultural history of Latin America. Author: Antonio Guzmán Blanco y el progreso de Venezuela (Umbral, Mar. 1954); Orígenes del teatro criollo en Venezuela (Umbral, June 1954); La imigración a Venezuela desde el fin de la Guerra Federal al Siglo XX (Revista Shell, 1957). Language: Spanish 5,5,5,4; Portuguese 4,3,2,1; French 3,3,3,1. Home: 18240 Rayen St., Northridge, Calif. Office: Dept. of History, San Fernando Valley State Coll., Northridge.

NAYLOR, ROBERT ARTHUR, b. Wellwyn Garden City, England, Dec. 19, 1925. HISTORY. B.A., U. of Western Ontario, 1951; M.A., 1952; Ph.D., Tulane U., 1958. Instr., Tulane U., 1955-56; assoc. prof., Auburn U., 1956-66; ASSOC. PROF., HISTORY, FAIRLEIGH DICKINSON U., 1966- ; vis. prof., U. of Pittsburgh, 1963-64; vis. assoc. prof., George Washington U., 1964-65; vis. prof., U. of Va., 1965-66. International exchange student, Oberlin Coll., 1949-50; Governor General's Gold Medal, U. of Western Ontario, 1951; graduate fellow, Tulane U., 1953; research grant and Latin American Studies scholarship, 1954; fellow, Institute of Historical Research, U. of London, 1954-55; Latin American Studies grant, Tulane U., 1955-56. Membership: Southeastern Conference on Latin American Studies; Southern Historical Association. Research: 19th century British economic penetration of Latin America. Author: British Role in Central America Prior to the Clayton-Bulwer Treaty of 1850 (Hispanic American Historical Review, Aug. 1960); A Mexican Monarchist Views the American Civil War in November, 1861 (Iowa Civil War Journal, Mar. 1962); Research Opportunities in Modern Latin America: Central America and Mexico (The Americas, Apr. 1962). Language: Spanish 4,3,3,3. Office: Social Science Dept., Fairleigh Dickinson U., Teaneck, N.J. 07666.

NEAL, JAMES H. Home: Box 2472, Station B, Vanderbilt U., Nashville, Tenn. 37203.

NEUKAMM, DAVID JOSEPH, b. Detroit, Mich., Feb. 4, 1933. HISTORY. B.A., Wayne State U., 1957; U. of Calif., Los Angeles. Membership: American Historical Association. Research: Latin American history; Caribbean region, especially Cuba. Language: Spanish 3,2,3,2; Portuguese 3,2,1,1; French 3,1,1,1; German 3,2,1,2; Italian 3,2,1,1. Home: 2652 Gray, Detroit, Mich. 48215.

NEWTON, RONALD CHARLES, b. Newark, N.J., Feb. 8, 1933. HISTORY. B.A., Rutgers U., 1955; M.A., U. of Fla., 1960; Ph.D., 1963. Admin. asst., Summer School, Universidad de San Carlos (Guatemala), 1960; teacher, Bi-National Center (Buenos Aires), Summer 1961; ASST. PROF., HISTORY, PURDUE U., 1963- . Henry Rutgers fellow, 1955; Graduate School fellow, U. of Fla., 1959-61; National Defense Foreign Language fellow, 1962-63. Membership: American Historical Association; Conference on Latin American History; Congreso Internacional de Americanistas; Southern Historical Association. Research: modern Spanish American corporate interest groups and the political process; colonial guilds and corporations; Argentine frontier in the 18th and 19th centuries. Language: Spanish 5,4,4,4; Portuguese 4,3,3,2; French 4,3,3,3; German 5,5,5,4; Italian 4,3,3,3. Home: 1034 Happy Hollow Rd., West Lafayette, Ind. Office: Dept. of History, Purdue U., West Lafayette.

NEWTON, WESLEY PHILLIPS, JR., b. Montgomery, Ala., Apr. 2, 1925. HISTORY. A.B., U. of Mo., 1949; M.A., U. of Ala., 1953; Ph.D., 1964. Expert consultant, Historical Div., Maxwell Air Force Base, U.S. Air Force, 1957-61; ASST. PROF., HISTORY, AUBURN U., 1964- . Graduate fellow, U. of Ala., 1954-57. Membership: Phi Alpha Theta. Research: aviation in Latin American-United States relations; development of aviation in Latin America. Author: What is the Alliance for Progress? (Comment, University of Alabama Quarterly, 1963). Collaborator: Air Force Combat Units of World War II (1961). Language: Spanish 3,2,2,2; Portuguese 3,1,1,1. Home: Rt. 1, Box 2-F, Montevallo, Ala. Office: Dept. of History, Auburn U., Auburn, Ala.

NICHOLS, LAWRENCE RICHARD, b. Winston-Salem, N.C., Jan. 7, 1924. HISTORY. B.A., Wake Forest Coll., 1948; Ph.D., Duke U., 1954. Asst. prof., Queens Coll. (N.C.), 1953-56; assoc. prof., Coll. of Charleston, 1956-62; ASST. PROF., HISTORY, EASTERN ILL. U., 1962- . Padre Varela fellow (Cuba), 1951-52; Hispanic fellow, Duke U. (Spain), 1963. Membership: American Association of University Professors; American Historical Association; Southern Historical Association. Research: Antonio Maceo, hero of Cuban independence movement. Language: Spanish 4,4,4,4; Portuguese 2,2,2,2; German 2,2,2,—. Home: R.F.D. 4, Ashby Dr., Charleston, Ill. Office: Dept. of History, Eastern Ill. U., Charleston.

NICHOLS, MADALINE WALLIS, b. Ipswich, Mass., Jan. 21, 1898. HISTORY AND SPANISH AMERICAN LITERATURE. B.A., Mt. Holyoke Coll., 1918; M.A., Cornell U., 1922; Ph.D., U. of Calif., Berkeley, 1937. Reference asst., Hispanic Foundation, Library of Congress and research asst., Committee on Latin American Studies, American Council of Learned Societies, 1939-42; editor, Agriculture in the Americas, U.S. Dept. of Agriculture, 1942-43; assoc. prof., Goucher Coll., 1943-45; asst. prof., Duke U., 1945-46; lectr. in Latin American History, U. of Calif., Los Angeles, 1946-47; assoc. prof., Fla. State U., 1948-50; RETIRED, 1950- ; vis. prof., U. of N. Mex., 1950-51; honors prof. in Latin American Studies, State U. of N.Y., Coll. at Geneseo, 1963-64. Carnegie travel grant (Chile), 1937; National Committee on International Relations, American Association of University Women, 1945-46; chmn., Conference on Latin American History, 1949-50; chmn. Robertson Prize Committee, 1960. Membership: Hispanic Society of America; Sociedad de Geografía e Historia de Guatemala; Unión Cultural Argentina. Research: inter-American relations. Author: Bibliographic Guide to Materials on American Spanish (1941); The Gaucho (1942; Portuguese edition, 1946; Spanish edition, 1953); A Colombian Pattern for Peace, 1819-1830 (in The Caribbean: Contemporary Colombia, 1962). Language: Spanish 5,3,3,3; Portuguese 2,2,1,1; French 3,3,2,2; German 2,1,1,—; Italian 2,1,1,—. Home: 1107½ Gold Ave., SW., Albuquerque, N. Mex. 87102.

NICHOLS, THEODORE EDWARD, b. Oakland, Calif., July 24, 1921. HISTORY. A.B., U. of Calif., Berkeley, 1944; M.A., 1946; Ph.D., 1951. Instr., U. of Ariz., fall 1949; instr., San Francisco State Coll., spring 1950; asst. prof., U. of Ga., 1951-56; vis. asst. prof., Yale U., 1953-54; 1956-64; PROF., HISTORY, LONG BEACH STATE COLL., 1964- . Mills traveling fellow (Colombia), 1948-49; Carnegie Intern in General Education, Yale U., 1953-54; Del Amo Foundation fellow (Sevilla, Spain), Spring 1963. Research: Colombian and Chilean history. Author: The Establishment of Political Relations between Chile and Great Britain (Hispanic American Historical Review, Feb. 1948); The Rise of Barranquilla (Hispanic American Historical Review, May 1954); Colombia: the History of the Colonial Period (in The Caribbean: Contemporary Colombia, 1962). Language: Spanish 3,3,3,3; Portuguese 2,—,—,—; French 3,2,2,1. Home: 3261 Oak Knoll Dr., Los Alamitos, Calif. Office: Dept. of History, Long Beach State Coll., Long Beach 4, Calif.

NIEMEYER, EBERHARDT VICTOR, JR., b. Houston, Tex., Sept. 28, 1919. HISTORY. Ph.D., U. of Tex., 1958. Dir., Instituto Hondureño de Cultura Interamericana (Tegucigalpa), U.S. Information Agency, 1953-55; dir., Instituto de Cultura Peruano Americano (Lima), 1955-56; asst. editor, Hispanic American Historical Review, U. of Tex., 1956-57; asst. prof., Tex. Coll. of Arts & Industries, 1957-58; vis. prof., U. of P.R., Summer 1958; dir., Instituto Guatemalteco Americano, U.S. Information Agency, 1958-60; dir., Philippine American Cultural Center (Manila), 1961-63; ASST. CULTURAL AFFAIRS OFFICER (MEXICO), U.S. INFORMATION AGENCY, 1963- . Carnegie Foundation grant, U. of

N.C., Summer 1950. Membership: Sociedad de Georgrafía e Historia de Guatemala; Sociedad Nuevoleonesa de Geografía, Historia, y Estadística; Texas State Historical Association. Research: Mexican Constitutional Convention of 1916-17. Author: Anticlericalism in the Mexican Constitutional Convention of 1916-17 (The Americas, July 1954); Bernardo Reyes, fundador del moderno Nuevo León (Anales de la Sociedad de Geografía e Historia de Guatemala, 1959). Co-editor: Guide to the Hispanic American Historical Review, 1946-55 (1958). Language: Spanish 4,4,4,4. Home: 2508 Indian Trail, Austin, Tex. 78703. Office: U.S. Information Agency, Washington, D.C. 20521.

NORRIS, ROBERT EUGENE, b. Kilgore, Tex., Aug. 6, 1939. HISTORY AND SPANISH AMERICAN LITERATURE. B.A., Tex. Christian U., 1961; U. of N. Mex. Teacher, English, Centro Ecuatoriano-Norteamericano (Quito), 1961-62; teacher, English, Universidad Central, Instituto de Idiomas (Quito), Spring 1962; teacher, Spanish, Peace Corps Training Center for Latin America, U. of N. Mex., Summer 1963; STUDENT, IBERO-AMERICAN STUDIES, U. OF N. MEX. Fulbright scholar (Ecuador), 1961-62; National Defense Education Act fellow in Ibero-American Studies, 1962-65. Membership: Phi Alpha Theta; Phi Sigma Iota. Research: Latin American history and government. Language: Spanish 4,4,4,4; Portuguese 4,4,3,3; French 3,3,2,3; German 2,2,2,2. Home: 3011 Brandon, Dallas 11, Tex.

NOWELL, CHARLES E. Office: Dept. of History, U. of Ill., Champaign, Ill. 61822.

NUNN, FREDERICK McKINLEY, b. Portland, Oreg., Oct. 29, 1937. HISTORY. B.A., U. of Oreg., 1959; U. of Calif., Berkeley, 1960; M.A., U. of N. Mex., 1963; Ph.D., 1963. Co-ordinator, El Salvador-Costa Rica, U.S. Peace Corps Projects, U. of Okla., Summer 1963; ASST. PROF., HISTORY, ELBERT COVELL COLL., U. OF THE PACIFIC, 1963- . National Defense Education Act graduate fellow in Ibero-American Studies, U. of N. Mex., 1959-63; Doherty fellow (Chile and Peru), 1962. Membership: American Association of University Professors; American Historical Association. Research: Brazilian history and literature; the armed forces and political change in Latin America; Chilean history and politics. Language: Spanish 5,5,5,5; Portuguese 5,5,5,4; French 4,3,3,2; German 2,2,1,1; Italian 4,3,1,1. Home: 814 North Tuxedo, Stockton, Calif. 95204. Office: Dept. of History, Elbert Covell Coll., U. of the Pacific, Stockton.

NUTTALL, DONALD ANDREW, b. San Diego, Calif., Mar. 14, 1926. HISTORY. A.B., San Diego State Coll., 1951; M.A., 1959; Ph.D., U. of Southern Calif., 1964. Instr.-ASST. PROF., HISTORY, WHITTIER COLL., 1961- . Membership: American Historical Association; California Historical Society. Research: Pedro Fages and the Advance of the northern frontier of New Spain, 1767-1782. Language: Spanish 3,2,2,2. Home: 11045

Trudie St., Whittier, Calif. Office: Dept. of History, Whittier Coll., Whittier.

OGELSBY, JOHN C.M., b. Philadelphia, Pa., Sept. 22, 1931. HISTORY. A.B., Stanford U., 1953; U. of London, 1955-56; M.A., U. of Wash., 1960; Ph.D., 1963. Asst. prof., U. of Victoria (Canada), 1961-66; ASST. PROF., HISTORY, UNIVERSITY COLL., U. OF WESTERN ONTARIO, 1966- . Teaching fellow, U. of Wash., 1958-60; University grant, 1964. Membership: Canadian Historical Association; Conference on Latin American History; Hispanic American Society; Navy Records Society. Research: 18th century Caribbean history; colonial preiod in history of New World; logwood trade in the Caribbean. Author: Graduate Research in Europe (The Historian, May 1963); British and Panama, 1742 (Caribbean Studies, July 1963); Argentina: No Habrá Progreso (Canadian Forum, Nov. 1963). Language: Spanish 3,3,3,2; French 3,3,3,1. Office: Dept. of History, University Coll., U. of Western Ontario, London, Ontario.

OPPMANN, T. RODNEY, b. Cleveland, Ohio, Dec. 3, 1943. HISTORY. A.B., Princeton U., 1965. STUDENT, CATHOLIC U. (RIO DE JANEIRO), 1965-66. Princeton U. regional studies grant (Brazil), Summer 1964; Fulbright fellow (Brazil), 1965-66. Research: Latin American history and politics; the novels and short stories of Machado de Assis. Language: Spanish 5,5,4,4; Portuguese 5,5,5,4; German 3,3,3,3. Home: 2834 Courtland Blvd., Cleveland 22, Ohio 44122.

OSWALD, J. GREGORY, b. Chicago, Ill., Mar. 18, 1922. HISTORY. B.A., U. of Calif., Berkeley, 1948; M.A., Loyola U. (Ill.), 1950; Ph.D., Stanford U., 1958. Instr., Stanford U., 1955-58; ASSOC. PROF., HISTORY, U. OF ARIZ., 1958- . Mershon post-doctoral fellow, Ohio State U., 1962-63; consultant and project director, Hispanic Foundation, Library of Congress, 1963- . Contributing editor, Handbook of Latin American Studies. Membership: American Association for the Advancement of Slavic Studies; Far West Slavic Conference. Research: Soviet history; Soviet historical writing on Latin America; an analysis of Soviet interpretations of Latin American history, particularly their emphasis on problems of Mexican history. Author: A Soviet Criticism of the Hispanic American Historical Review (Hispanic American Historical Review, Aug. 1960); Soviet News and Notes (Hispanic American Historical Review, Feb. 1961); La Revolución Mexicana en la historiografía soviética (Historia Mexicana, Jan. 1963). Language: Spanish 3,3,3,3; French 3,2,3,2; Czech 5,5,5,5; German 4,4,4,4; Russian 5,5,5,5; Slovak 5,5,5,5. Home: 2708 East Glenn St., Tucson, Ariz. Office: Dept. of History, U. of Ariz., Tucson.

PACKARD, GORDON OTTO, JR., b. San Francisco, Calif. HISTORY. B.A., Stanford U., 1959; U. of Calif., Berkeley; U. of Ariz.

STUDENT, HISTORY, U. OF ARIZ. Fulbright fellow (Argentina), 1962-63; U. of Ariz. scholar. Research: Latin American history; Argentine social developments. Language: Spanish 4,3,3,3; Portuguese 3,2,1,1; French 2,1,1,1. Home: 1322 East Lee St., Tucson, Ariz. 85719.

PADDEN, ROBERT CHARLES, b. St. Paul, Minn., Sept. 14, 1922. HISTORY. B.A., U. of Calif., Santa Barbara, 1952; M.A., U. of Calif., Berkeley, 1954; Ph.D., 1959. Lectr., U. of Calif., Berkeley, 1957-58; asst. prof., 1958-64; ASSOC. PROF., HISTORY, ST. NORBERT COLL., 1964- . Membership: American Historical Association; Conference on Latin American History. Research: ethnohistory; the ethnohistory of nationalism; cultural history of mestizaje in Mexico; colonial Church in New Spain; Araucanian Chile. Language: Spanish 4,4,4,4; Portuguese 4,4,3,3; French 3,3,2,3; German 3,3,2,3; Italian 3,3,2,3. Home: R.F.D. 2, West De Pere, Wis. Office: Dept. of History, St. Norbert Coll., West De Pere.

PAGE, A. NAYLAND, b. Luling, Tex., July 30, 1931. HISTORY. B.A., Tex. Coll. of Arts & Industries, 1952; M.A., 1953; Ph.D., U. of Okla., 1958. ASSOC. PROF., HISTORY, TEX. COLL. OF ARTS & INDUSTRIES, 1959- . Fulbright fellow (Chile), 1958-59. Membership: American Association of University Professors; Hispanic American Historical Association; Southwestern Social Science Association. Research: current political parties and attitude in South America; Chile. Language: Spanish 4,4,4,3. Office: Dept. of History, Tex. Coll. of Arts & Industries, Kingsville, Tex.

PAREJA DIEZCANSECO, ALFREDO, b. Guayaquil, Ecuador, Oct. 12, 1908. POLITICAL SCIENCE, HISTORY, AND SPANISH AMERICAN LITERATURE. Licenciado, Universidad de Guayaquil, 1931; special doctorate, Universidad Central (Ecuador), 1960. Prof., Colegio Nacional Vicente Rocafuerte (Guayaquil, Ecuador), 1931-33; inspector general, secondary education, Ministry of Education, Government of Ecuador, 1934-36; prof., Universidad Central (Ecuador), 1950-61; prof., deputy dir., Inter-American Institute of Political Education (Costa Rica), 1961-62; assoc. prof., U. of Fla., 1962; PROF., POLITICAL SCIENCE, U. OF FLA., 1964- . Guggenheim fellow, 1963-64. Research: Ecuador; political thought in Gran Colombia. Author: Vida y leyenda de Miguel de Santiago (1952); Historia del Ecuador (1955); La lucha por democracia en el Ecuador (1956). Language: Spanish 5,5,5,5; Portuguese 3,3,3,2; French 4,4,3,2. Home: 508 Northwest 34th Ter., Gainesville, Fla. Office: Dept. of Political Science, U. of Fla., Gainesville.

PARISEAU, EARL JOSEPH, b. Methuen, Mass., Aug. 14, 1928. BIBLIOGRAPHY. B.A., U. of Fla., 1957; M.A., American U., 1959. Asst. to editor, Handbook of Latin American Studies, Hispanic Foundation, Library of Congress, 1961; EDITOR, HANDBOOK OF LATIN AMERICAN STUDIES, ASST. DIR., HISPANIC FOUNDATION, LIBRARY OF CON-

GRESS, 1964- . Committee on Bibliography, Seminars on the Acquisition of Latin American Library Materials. Membership: American Historical Association; Conference on Latin American History; Delta Sigma Pi; Inter-American Council; Phi Alpha Theta. Research: development of national acquisition plan for Latin America; Latin American history and economics. Editor: Handbook of Latin American Studies, Nos. 23-27 (1961-65). Language: Spanish 3,3,3,3; Portuguese 3,3,2,2. Home: 5515 Margate St., Springfield, Va. Office: Hispanic Foundation, Library of Congress, Washington, D.C. 20540.

PARKER, FRANKLIN DALLAS, b. Baltimore, Md., Jan. 7, 1898. HISTORY. B.A., Greenville Coll., 1939; M.A., U. of Ill., 1949; Ph.D., 1951. Asst. prof., Woman's Coll., U. of N.C., 1951-60; assoc. prof., 1960-63; ASSOC. PROF., HISTORY, U. OF N.C., GREENSBORO, 1963- . Southern Fellowships Fund grant, Summer 1955; Doherty fellow (Central America), 1955-56; Southern Fellowships Fund and Woman's College Research Council grants (Central America), 1960. Membership: Conference on Latin American History; Sociedad de Geografía e Historia de Guatemala; Southeastern Conference of Latin American Studies. Research: archival research in Central America. Author: José Cecilio del Valle and the Establishment of the Central American Confederation (1954); The Central American Republics (1964). Language: Spanish 4,4,4,4; French 4,2,2,1; German 2,1,1,1. Home: 2009 Wright Ave., Greensboro, N.C. 27403. Office: Dept. of History, U. of N.C., Greensboro, 27412.

PARKES, HENRY B., b. Sheffield, United Kingdom, Nov. 13, 1904. HISTORY. B.A., Oxford U., 1927; Ph.D., U. of Mich., 1929. Instr.-PROF., HISTORY, N.Y.U., 1930- . Research: American history; Western culture. Author: A History of Mexico (1938, 1949, 1960). Language: Spanish 3,1,1,1; French 3,1,1,1. Home: 210 East 15th St., New York 3, N.Y. Office: Dept. of History, N.Y.U., Washington Square East, New York 3.

PARKS, E. TAYLOR, b. Mulberry, Tenn., Aug., 14, 1898. HISTORY AND INTERNATIONAL RELATIONS. B.A., Carson-Newman Coll., 1927; M.A., U. of Tenn., 1928; Ph.D., Duke U., 1931. Instr., Duke U., 1930-32; chmn., Berea Coll., 1932-45; CHIEF, RESEARCH GUIDANCE AND REVIEW DIV., HISTORICAL OFFICE, U.S. DEPT. OF STATE, 1945- . Staff member, Joint United States-Brazil Technical Commission, 1948-49; delegate, Pan American Institute of Geography and History, 1961. Membership: American Historical Association; Conference on Latin American History; Mississippi Valley Historical Association; Southern Historical Association. Research: diplomatic history of United States and Latin America. Author: Colombia and the United States, 1765-1934 (1935). Editor: American Foreign Policy: Basic Documents (1950-63); The Diary and Journal of Richard Clough Anderson, Jr., 1814-1826 (1964). Language:

Spanish 3,—,—,—. Home: 407 Independence Ave., SE., Washington, D.C. 20003. Office: Historical Office, U.S. Dept. of State, Washington, D.C. 20520.

PARR, CHARLES McKEW, b. Baltimore, Md., Nov. 23, 1884. HISTORY. U.S. Military Academy; Columbia U.; LL.D., U. of Bridgeport, 1962. Export manager, Hart & Hegeman Manufacturing Company (Hartford, Conn.), 1909-19; president, Parr Electric Export Corporation (New York, N.Y.), 1925-39; president, Parr Marine & Export (Brooklyn), 1939-53; RETIRED, 1953- . Knight commander, Order of Knights of Christ (Lisbon, Portugal). Membership: Biblioteca Capitular Colombina (Spain); Conference on Latin American History; Linschoten Society (Netherlands); Sociedade de Geografia de Lisboa (Portugal). Research: the age of discovery. Author: Over and Above Our Pacific (1941); So Noble a Captain: The Life and Times of Ferdinand Magellan (1953); Linschoten (1964). Language: Spanish 4,4,4,4; Portuguese 3,3,3,3; French 2,2,2,2; Dutch 3,3,3,3. Home: Straits Rd., Chester, Conn. 06412. Office: McKew Parr Library, Chester.

PARRISH, MARY ALICE, b. Trenton, Mo., July 13, 1886. HISTORY. B.A., U. of Mo., 1909; M.A., Bryn Mawr Coll.; Ph.D., 1917. Teacher, history and Latin, Vandalia High School (Mo.), 1909-11; head, History Dept., Shipley School (Bryn Mawr, Pa.), 1915-19; assoc. prof., Extension Div., U. of Mo., 1931-36; SELF-EMPLOYED. Bryn Mawr Coll. resident fellow, 1912-13, 1914-15; Bryn Mawr Coll. foreign fellow, 1913-14. Membership: American Geographical Society; American Historical Association; Conference on Latin American History; National Geographic Society; Hispanic American Historical Association. Research: American history; trade of the Delaware District, 1763-1775. Language: Spanish 2,—,—,—; French 2,—,—,—; German 3,—,—,—. Home: 206 West State St., Vandalia, Mo. 63382.

PATCH, RICHARD W., b. Lansing, Mich., Apr. 12, 1929. ANTHROPOLOGY. B.A., Cornell U., 1951; Ph.D., 1956. Vis. asst. prof., Tulane U., 1956-57; STAFF MEMBER, AMERICAN UNIVERSITIES FIELD STAFF, INC., 1957- ; VIS. PROF., ANTHROPOLOGY, U. OF WIS., 1962- ; staff member, Land Tenure Center, 1962. Doherty fellow; Institute of Current World Affairs fellow, 1954-57; Inter-American Development Bank Mission for Rural Development of Bolivia, 1962; dir., Colonization Study for Bolivian Government and U.S. Agency for International Development, 1962. Membership: American Anthropological Association; American Ethnological Society; Midwest Council of the Association for Latin American Studies; Society for Applied Anthropology. Research: cultural anthropology; social and economic development in the Andes; land tenure and social change in Peru and Bolivia. Author: Social Change in Latin America Today (1960); Emergent Peoples (in Expectant Peoples, 1963). Language: Spanish 5,5,5,4; Portuguese 3,3,2,1; French 4,3,3,2. Office: American Universities Field Staff, Inc., 366 Madison Ave., New York 17, N.Y.; or Dept. of Anthropology, U. of Wis., Madison 6, Wis.

PATTERSON, JERRY EUGENE, b. Fort Worth, Tex., May 2, 1931. BIBLIOGRAPHY AND HISTORY. B.A., U. of Tex., 1952; M.A., 1955; Yale U., 1955-57; Columbia U., 1958-60. ASST. EDITOR, LATIN AMERICA: A GUIDE TO THE HISTORICAL LITERATURE, LIBRARY OF CONGRESS, 1964- . Asst., Hispanic American Historical Review, 1954; asst., Historical Manuscripts Div., Yale U. Library, Membership: Conference on Latin American History. Research: rare books; the literary criticism of Pedro Henríquez Ureña; history of mining in Latin America. Author: Prescott Manuscripts (Hispanic American Historical Review, Feb. 1959); Manuscritos Mexicanos (Historia Mexicana, Jan. 1960); The Mexican War, 1846-1848 (Yale U. Library Gazette, Jan. 1960). Language: Spanish 3,3,3,1. Home: 176 E. 77th St., New York, N.Y.

PAYNE, WALTER ARVILLE, b. Lodi, Calif., Jan. 30, 1924. HISTORY. B.A., U. of Calif., Berkeley, 1945; M.A., Universidad de San Carlos de Guatemala, 1951; Ph.D., U. of Fla., 1955. Instr., Grant Union High School (Calif.), 1946-47; registrar, catedrático, Escuela de Verano, Universidad de San Carlos de Guatemala, 1948-51; instr., American School of Guatemala, 1950, 1958; asst. prof., asst. dir., School of Inter-American Studies, U. of Fla., 1952-58; lectr., U. of Glasgow (Scotland), 1956-57; asst. prof., U. of Fla., 1958-61; catedrático, Escuela de Verano, Universidad de San Carlos de Guatemala, 1958, 1959, 1960; ASSOC. PROF., HISTORY, U. OF THE PACIFIC, 1961- . Latin American Studies fellow, Tulane U., 1951; Homenaje de Mérito, Facultad de Humanidades, Universidad de San Carlos, 1951; asst. managing editor, Hispanic American Historical Review, 1960- . Membership: American Historical Association; Conference on Latin American History; Pacific Coast Council on Latin American Studies. Research: republican period in Central America. Author: A Central American Historian—José Milla y Vidaurre, 1822-1882 (1957); Aportes principales de la historia norteamericana (in Notes and Lectures for the Second Bolivian Economic Seminar Project, 1960); Recent Central American Relations with Non-Hemisphere States (in The Caribbean: The Central American Area, 1961). Language: Spanish 4,4,4,4; Portuguese 3,3,3,3; French 2,2,2,2. Home: 1514 Calhoun Way, Stockton 7, Calif. Office: Dept. of History, U. of the Pacific, Stockton 4.

PECKHAM, EDMUND T., b. Worcester, Mass., Feb. 30, 1924. HISTORY AND POLITICAL SCIENCE. A.B., Brown U., 1948; M.A., Harvard U., 1949; Ph.D., 1954. Asst. prof., Rice U., 1952-58; assoc. prof., U. of the Pacific, 1958-62; PROF., SOCIAL SCIENCE, DEAN OF STUDENT LIFE, RAYMOND COLL., U. OF THE PACIFIC, 1962- . Business research fellow, Lever Brothers. Membership: Conference on Latin American History; Hispanic

American Historical Association; Phi Beta Kappa; Phi Eta Sigma; Phi Kappa Phi. Research: United States foreign relations; inter-American diplomacy. Language: Spanish 3,3, 3,3; Portuguese 2,1,1,1; French 3,2,2,3. Home: 1924 Meadow, Stockton, Calif. Office: Dept. of Social Science, Raymond Coll., U. of the Pacific, Stockton.

PEFFER, E. LOUISE, b. Natrona, Pa., Nov. 15, 1898. HISTORY. B.S., Purdue U., 1937; M.A., U. of Calif., 1939; Ph.D., 1942. Research assoc., assoc. prof.-PROF., FOOD RESEARCH INSTITUTE, STANFORD U., 1946- . Fulbright fellow (Argentina), 1958. Membership: Agricultural History Society; American Historical Association; Conference on Latin American History; Mississippi Valley Historical Association; Pacific Coast Conference on Latin American Studies. Research: agricultural history; history of Argentine cattle and beef industry. Author: The Argentine Cattle Industry under Perón (Food Research Institute Studies, May 1960); State Intervention in the Argentine Meat Packing Industry, 1946-58 (Food Research Institute Studies, Feb. 1961); Foot-and-Mouth Disease in United States Policy (Food Research Institute Studies, May 1962). Language: Spanish 3,2,2,1; French 3,2,2,1. Home: 1314 College Ave., Palo Alto, Calif. 94306. Office: Food Research Institute, Stanford U., Stanford, Calif. 94305.

PERKINS, DEXTER, b. Boston, Mass., June 20, 1889. HISTORY. A.B., Harvard U., 1909; Ph.D., 1914; LL.D. (honorary), U. of Rochester, 1955. Prof., U. of Rochester, 1915-1953; PROF. EMERITUS, ROCHESTER U., 1954- ; John L. Senior prof., Cornell U., 1953-59; PROF. EMERITUS, CORNELL U., 1959- ; Robert Campbell prof., Wells Coll., 1963-64. Commonwealth lectr., U. Coll. (London), 1937; Pitt prof., Cambridge U., 1945-46; president, Salzburg Seminar on American Studies, 1950-62. Membership: American Association of University Professors; American Historical Association; Phi Beta Kappa. Research: American foreign policy. Author: Hands Off: A History of the Monroe Doctrine (1941; revised edition, 1963); The United States and Latin America (1961); American Quest for Peace (1962). Language: Spanish 1,—,—,—; Portuguese 1,—,—,—; French 1,—,—,—. Home: 316 Oxford St., Rochester 7, N.Y.

PERRIGO, LYNN IRWIN, b. Delphi, Ind., Feb. 21, 1904. HISTORY. B.A., Ball State Teachers Coll., 1933; M.A., U. of Colo., 1934; Ph.D., 1936. Social Studies teacher, Muncie City Schools, 1922-27; Scout executive, Muncie Council, Boy Scouts of America, 1927-33; instr.-assoc. prof., U. of Kansas City, 1936-45; dir., Midwest Inter-American Center, 1943-44; asst. dir., extension div., U. of Colo., 1946-47; PROF., CHMN., HISTORY AND SOCIAL SCIENCE, N. MEX. HIGHLANDS U., 1947- ; dir., Inter-American Workshops, U. of Kansas City, Summers 1942, 1943; Latin American specialist, Teachers' Workshop, Graduate School of Education, Harvard U., Summer

1944. Membership: American Historical Association; Mississippi Valley Historical Association; New Mexico Historical Society; Rocky Mountain Conference on Latin American Studies; Rocky Mountain Social Science Association. Research: inter-American programs. Author: Latin America, Its History and Culture (1944); Our Spanish Southwest (1960); The Rio Grande Adventure: A History of New Mexico (1964). Language: Spanish 3,2,2,3; French 2,1,1,2. Home: 1038 Fifth, Las Vegas, N. Mex. Office: Dept. of History, N. Mex. Highlands U., Las Vegas.

PETERS, THELMA PETERSON, b. Independence, Mo., Apr. 22, 1905. HISTORY. A.B., Brenau Coll., 1926; M.A., Duke U., 1938; Ph.D., U. of Fla., 1960. Teacher, Miami Edison Senior High School, 1930-57; instr., U. of Miami, 1960-61; DIR., DIV. OF SOCIAL SCIENCE, MIAMI-DADE JUNIOR COLL., 1961- . Membership: Florida Historical Association; Historical Association of Southern Florida; Southern Historical Association. Research: Bahama Islands; American history. Author: Blockade-Running during the American Civil War (Tequesta, 1945); The American Loyalists in the Bahama Islands (Florida Historical Quarterly, Jan. 1962). Language: Spanish 3,2,2,2. Home: 11377 NE. West Biscayne Canal Rd., Miami, Fla. Office: Div. of Social Science, Miami-Dade Junior Coll., 11380 NW. 27th Ave., Miami.

PETERSON, HAROLD F(ERDINAND), b. Galesburg, Ill., Oct. 1, 1900. HISTORY. A.B., Knox Coll., 1922; M.A., U. of Minn., 1925; Ph.D., Duke U., 1933. Asst. prof., State U. of N.Y., Coll. at Buffalo, 1933-42; lectr., Committee on Cultural Relations with Latin America, 1940; captain, Joint Intelligence Committee, U.S. Joint Chiefs of Staff, 1942-43; captain-lieutenant colonel, Military Intelligence Div., War Dept., 1943-46; PROF. OF LATIN AMERICAN HISTORY, STATE U. OF N.Y., COLL. AT BUFFALO, 1945- . Two research fellowships, Research Foundation, State U. of N.Y., 1960. Membership: American Historical Association; Conference on Latin American History; National Council for Social Studies. Research: United States-Argentine diplomatic relations; inter-American relations. Author: Argentina and the United States, 1810-1960 (1964). Co-author: Builders of Latin America (1942). Language: Spanish 3,3,3,2. Home: 230 Knowlton Ave., Kenmore, N.Y. 14217. Office: Dept. of History, State U. of N.Y., Coll. at Buffalo, 1300 Elmwood Ave., Buffalo, 14222.

PETERSON, JOHN DeLON, b. Mt. Pleasant, Utah, Nov. 25, 1933. HISTORY. B.A., Brigham Young U., 1959; M.A., U. of Utah, 1962; U. of Calif., Los Angeles. Missionary (Brazil), Church of the Latter Day Saints, 1954-56; representative, college dept., McGraw-Hill Book Company, 1960-62; STUDENT, HISTORY, U. OF CALIF., LOS ANGELES. National Defense Education Act fellow, U. of Calif., Los Angeles; National Defense Foreign Area fellow (Brazil), 1965-66. Research: Latin American history;

national period in Brazil; Mormon missionary movement in South America. Language: Spanish 3,2,2,2; Portuguese 4,4,4,3; German 2,1,1,1. Home: 10560 Wyton Dr., Los Angeles 24, Calif.

PFLAUM, IRVING PETER, b. Chicago, Ill., Apr. 9, 1906. HISTORY AND JOURNALISM. Ph.B., U. of Chicago, 1928; J.D., 1930; J.D., De Paul U., 1931. Reporter, Chicago Evening Post, 1930-33; staff correspondent and bureau chief, United Press Associations of America (Spain), 1933-39; foreign news editor, The Chicago Sun-Times, 1939-61; prof., professional lectr., Law, Journalism, Northwestern U., 1940-59; assoc., Cuba and the Caribbean, American Universities Field Staff, 1959-61; PROF., SOCIAL STUDIES, DIR., LATIN AMERICAN CENTER, INTER AMERICAN U. (P.R.), 1961- . Marshall Field Fellowship Award, 1958; consultant, seminars, Foreign Relations Club of U.S.A.; consultant, U. of Fla. and Inter American U., summer seminars; Ford Foundation fellow (Cuba), 1960-61. Membership: American Association of University Professors; Political Science Association; Sigma Delta Chi. Research: Cuban revolution; the Carribean. Author: American Universities Field Staff Reports on Cuba, 1960-1961 (1960-61); Tragic Island: How Communism Came to Cuba (1961); Arena of Decision: Latin America in Crisis (1964). Language: Spanish 4,4,4,4; Portuguese 1,1,1,1; French 2,2,1,2. Home: Box 152, Inter American U., San German, P.R. Office: Latin American Center, Inter American U., San German, P. R.

PHELAN, JOHN LEDDY, b. Fall River, Mass., July 19, 1924. HISTORY. A.B., Harvard U., 1946; M.A., U. of Calif., Berkeley, 1947; Ph.D., 1951. Asst. prof., U. of Wis., Milwaukee, 1956-58; assoc. prof., 1958-60; ASSOC. PROF., HISTORY, U. OF WIS., MADISON, 1960- . Fulbright fellow (France), 1951-52; fellow in Philippine Studies, Newberry Library, 1953-55; Guggenheim award (Archivo General de Indias, Spain), 1960-61. Membership: American Academy of Franciscan History; American Historical Association; Conference on Latin American History. Research: colonial period in Latin America with emphasis on institutional, cultural, and intellectual history. Author: The Millennial Kingdom of the Franciscans in the New World: A Study of the Writings of Gerónimo de Mendieta, 1524-1604 (1956); The Hispanization of the Philippines: Spanish Aims and Filipino Responses, 1525-1700 (1959). Language: Spanish 4,4,4,3; Portuguese 3,3,2,1; French 4,3,3,1. Home: 346 East Lakeside, Madison, Wis. Office: Dept. of History, U. of Wis., Madison.

PIETRASZEK, BERNADINE. Home: 3254 N. Normandy, Chicago, Ill. 60634. Office: Dept. of History, De Paul U., Chicago.

PIKAZA, OTTO, b. Sestao, Vizcaya, Spain, Sept. 1, 1928. HISTORY. Ph.D., Universidad de Sevilla (Spain), 1961. Instr., Ind. U., 1961-64; ASST. PROF., HISTORY, IND. U.,

1964- . Latin American Studies Committee, Ind. U. Research: beginnings of diplomatic relations between the United States and Spain, 1776-1785; research in Archivo General de Indias; 17th century Bolivia. Author: Don Gabriel José de Zuloaga, Gobernador de Venezuela, 1737-1747 (Escuela de Estudios Hispanoamericanos, 1963). Language: Spanish 5,5,5,5; Portuguese 4,4,1,1; French 4,4,2,4; Italian 4,4,2,1. Home: 13 West University Apts., Bloomington, Ind. Office: Dept. of History, Ind. U., Bloomington.

PIKE, FREDERICK BRAUN, b. Los Angeles, Calif., Dec. 23, 1926. HISTORY. B.A., Loyola U. (Calif.), 1949; M.A., U. of Tex., 1950; Ph.D., 1956. Assoc. prof., U. of Notre Dame, 1952-66; PROF., HISTORY, U. OF PA., 1966- ; vis. asst. prof., Rutgers U., Summer 1961; vis. prof., U. of Pa., 1964-65. Doherty Foundation grant (Chile), 1959-60; Social Science Research Council grant (Peru), 1963-64. Membership: American Historical Association; Conference on Latin American History. Research: republican history of Chile and Peru. Author: Chile and the United States, 1880-1962 (1963). Editor: Freedom and Reform in Latin America (1959); Conflict Between Church and State in Latin America (1963). Language: Spanish 4,4,3,2. Home: 635 Sussex Rd., Wynnewood, Pa. Office: Dept. of History, U. of Pa., Philadelphia, Pa.

PINE, JOHN CRANE, b. East Aurora, N.Y., Oct. 25, 1921. HISTORY. B.A., Dartmouth Coll., 1945; M.A., U. of Chicago, 1948; Ph.D., U. of Colo., 1955. Instr., Hastings Coll., 1947-50; Joplin Junior Coll., 1955-56; ASSOC. PROF., HISTORY, U. OF ARK., 1956- . Membership: American Historical Association; Mississippi Valley Historical Association. Research: Latin American-United States relations. Language: Spanish 2,3,2,2; French 1,1,1,1. Home: 1228 West Cleveland, Fayetteville, Ark. Office: Dept. of History, U. of Ark., Fayetteville, 72701.

PITCHFORD, LOUIS CLEVELAND, JR., b. Weatherford, Tex., Dec. 14, 1916. HISTORY. B.A., Tex. Christian U., 1938; M.A., U. of Colo., 1962; Ph.D., 1965. Research: Latin American history; United States ministers to Mexico, 1836-1848. Language: Spanish 3,3,3,3; French 2,2,2,2. Home: 2275 Bluebell Ave., Boulder, Colo. 80302.

PLETCHER, DAVID MITCHELL, b. Faribault, Minn., June 14, 1920. HISTORY. B.A., U. of Chicago, 1941; M.A., 1941; Ph.D., 1946. Instr., U. of Iowa, 1944-46; assoc. prof., Knox Coll., 1946-56; assoc. prof.-prof., Hamline U., 1956-65; PROF., HISTORY, IND. U., 1965- ; assoc. prof., U. of Mo., Summers 1955-59. Fulbright grant, U. of London, 1953-54; Beveridge Memorial Award, 1957; McKnight Foundation Award, 1961; Social Science Research Council grant (Mexico), 1962-63. Membership: American Historical Association; Upper Midwest Historical Association. Research: history of United States foreign relations; United States-Mexican

relations. Author: Rails, Mines, and Progress: Seven American Promoters in Mexico, 1867-1911 (1958); The Awkward Years: American Foreign Relations under Garfield and Arthur (1962). Language: Spanish 4,3,3,4; French 4,3,3,4. Office: Dept. of History, Ind. U., Bloomington, Ind.

POOLE, RICHARD STAFFORD, C. M., b. Oxnard, Calif., Mar. 6, 1930. HISTORY. A.B., St. Mary's Seminary, 1952; M.A., St. Louis U., 1958; Ph.D., 1961. Instr., Cardinal Glennon Coll., 1958-59; dean of men, 1959-63; vice president, 1963-64; PROF., HISTORY, ST. MARY'S SEMINARY, 1964- . Cardinal Glennon Coll. summer research grants (Mexico), 1960, 1962. Membership: American Catholic Historical Association; American Historical Association; Hispanic American Historical Association; Judeo-Christian Studies Institute; Mississippi Valley Historical Association. Research: church history in colonial Mexico. Author: Research Possibilities of the Third Council (Manuscripta, 1961); The Church and the Repartimientos in the Light of the Third Mexican Council, 1585 (The Americas, July 1963). Language: Spanish 4,3,3,3; Portuguese 2,1,1,1; French 2,1,1,1; Italian 2,2,1,1. Home and office: St. Mary's Seminary, Perryville, Mo.

POPHAM, LEWIS C., III. Office: Orange Coll., State U. of N.Y., Middletown, N.Y. 10940.

POPPINO, ROLLIE EDWARD, b. Milwaukie, Oreg., Oct. 4, 1922. HISTORY. B.A., Stanford U., 1948; M.A., 1949; Ph.D., 1953. Instr., Stanford U., 1953-54; intelligence research specialist, U.S. Dept. of State, 1954-61; lectr., American U., 1959-61; asst. prof., U. of Calif., Davis, 1961-64; ASSOC. PROF., HISTORY, U. OF CALIF., DAVIS, 1964- . Doherty fellow (Brazil), 1950-51; consultant, U.S. Dept. of State, 1962- ; Social Science Research Council fellow (Brazil), 1963. Membership: American Historical Association; Conference on Latin American History; Pacific Coast Council on Latin American Studies. Research: history of Brazil; communism in Latin America; Latin American international relations; socio-political change since 1900 in Latin America. Author: Cattle Industry in Colonial Brazil (Mid-America, Oct. 1949); A Century of the Revista do Instituto Histórico e Geografico Brasileiro (Hispanic American Historical Review, May 1953); Imbalance in Brazil (Current History, Feb. 1963). Language: Spanish 4,4,3,3; Portuguese 4,5,4,3; French 3,2,1,1. Home: 1221 Eureka Ave., Davis, Calif. Office: Dept. of History, U. of Calif., Davis, 95616.

PORTELL-VILÁ, HERMINO, b. Cárdenas, Cuba, June 18, 1901. HISTORY. LL.D., Universidad de la Habana, 1927; Ph.D., 1934. Instr., Black Mountain Coll., 1935-39; prof., U. of Havana, 1939-60; vis. prof., U. of Calif., Los Angeles, 1940, U. of Fla., 1960-61; commentator, Latin American Div., Voice of America, U.S. Information Agency, 1961-63. Guggenheim fellow, 1931-33, 1935; Chubb fellow, Yale U., 1957; Rockefeller grant, 1960. Research: Cuban-

POTASH

United States relations. Author: Narciso López y su época (1930-58); Céspedes, el Padre de la Patria Cubana (1931); Historia de Cuba en sus relaciones con los Estados Unidos y España (1938-1941). Language: Spanish 5,5, 5,5; Portuguese 4,4,4,3; French 3,3,3,3. Home: 4740 Connecticut Ave., NW., Washington, D.C.

POTASH, ROBERT A., b. Boston, Mass., Jan. 2, 1921. HISTORY. A.B., Harvard U., 1942; A.M., 1947; Ph.D., 1953. Instr., U. of Mass., 1950-55; political analyst, U.S. Dept. of State, 1955-57; PROF., HISTORY, U. OF MASS., 1957- . Organization of American States fellow (Argentina), 1961-62; consultant, U.S. Dept. of State; Board of Editors, Hispanic American Historical Review. Membership: American Historical Association; Conference on Latin American History. Research: contemporary Argentina; 19th century Mexico. Author: El Banco de Avío de México (1959); The Historiography of Mexico since 1821 (Hispanic American Historical Review, Aug. 1960); The Changing Role of the Military in Argentina (Journal of Inter-American Studies, Oct. 1961). Language: Spanish 4,4,4,4; Portuguese 3,3,3,2; French 3,2,2,2; German 2,2,2,2. Home: 130 Red Gate Lane, Amherst, Mass. Office: Dept. of History, U. of Mass., Amherst.

POWELL, PHILIP WAYNE, b. Chino, Calif., Oct. 30, 1913. HISTORY. B.A., U. of Calif., Berkeley, 1936; Ph.D., 1941. Divisional asst., U.S. Dept. of State, 1941-43; vis. prof., U. of Pa., 1943-44; asst. prof., Northwestern U., 1944-48; vis. prof. in Ecuador, U.S. Dept. of State, 1947; special adviser to secretariat, 9th International Conference of American States (Bogotá, Colombia), 1948; PROF., HISTORY, U. OF CALIF., SANTA BARBARA, 1948- . Rockefeller Foundation fellow (Latin America), 1938-39; American Philosophical Society grant-in-aid (Mexico), 1945; chmn., Latin American Conference of the American Historical Association, 1948; Del Amo Foundation traveling fellow, 1950, 1954-55. Membership: American Historical Association. Research: inter-American relations; Spanish-United States relations; Spanish history; Mexican colonial history. Author: Soldiers, Indians and Silver: The Northward Advance of New Spain, 1550-1600 (1952). Language: Spanish 5,5,5,4; Portuguese 4,3,3,3; French 3,3,2,1; Dutch 2,2,1,1; German 2,2,1,1. Home: 1216 Shoreline Dr., Santa Barbara, Calif. Office: Dept. of History, U. of Calif., Santa Barbara.

PRATT, LUCILE, b. Chihuahua, Mexico, Nov. 1, 1926. HISTORY. B.A., Brigham Young U., 1957; M.A., Columbia U., 1959. INSTR., HISTORY, UTAH STATE U., 1964- . Membership: Phi Alpha Theta; Phi Kappa Phi. Research: Latin American and United States history; immigration to Mexico; agrarian policy of Mexico as shown by Mormon immigrant agrarian rights. Language: Spanish 5,5,4,4; Portuguese 4,3,3,1; French 4,4,2,2; Italian 2,2,1,1. Home: 349 South First West, Providence, Utah. Office: Dept. of History, Utah State U., Logan.

PREECE, MARGOT. Office: Box 765, Hato Rey, P.R.

PRUITT, AMY M. Home: 2456 20th St., NW., Apt. 109, Washington, D.C. 20009.

QUIGLEY, ROBERT EDWARD, b. Philadelphia, Pa., Oct. 10, 1927. HISTORY. A.B., Catholic U., 1954; A.M., U. of Pa., 1955; Ph.D., 1965. Instr., La Salle Coll., 1957-59; asst. prof., chmn., History, Holy Family Coll., 1959-64; ASSOC. PROF., CHMN., HISTORY, CABRINI COLL., 1964- . Herman V. Ames fellow in American history, U. of Pa., 1955-56; editor, Records of the American Catholic Historical Society of Philadelphia, 1960- . Membership: American Association of University Professors; American Catholic Historical Association; American Historical Association; Conference on Latin American History; Hispanic American Society; Historical Society of Philadelphia; Mississippi Valley Historical Association. Research: United States-Mexican relations; American Catholicism. Language: Spanish 2,2,2,1; French 2,2,2,1. Home: 4010 Wells St., Philadelphia, Pa. Office: Dept. of History, Cabrini Coll., Radnor, Pa.

QUIRK, ROBERT E., b. Akron, Ohio, Sept. 22, 1918. HISTORY. A.B., Wayne State U., 1946; M.A., Harvard U., 1948; Ph.D., 1951. Instr., Wayne State U., 1946-47; instr., Mexico City Coll., 1950; instr.-PROF., HISTORY, INDIANA U., 1950- ; vis. assoc. prof., U. of Tex., 1960. Woodbury Lowery traveling fellow (Mexico), 1949-50; Social Science Research Council fellow, 1961-62. Membership: American Historical Association; Association of Latin American Studies; Conference on Latin American History. Research: United States-Latin American relations; Mexican Revolution of 1910; church and state in Mexico. Author: The Mexican Revolution, 1914-1915 (1960); An Affair of Honor: Woodrow Wilson and the Occupation of Veracruz (1962); The Mexican Revolution and the Catholic Church (1964). Language: Spanish 4,4,4,4; Portuguese 2,2,2,2; French 2,2,2,2; German 4,4,4,4. Office: Dept. of History, Ind. U., Bloomington.

RAAT, WILLIAM DIRK, b. Ogden, Utah, July 1, 1939. HISTORY. B.S., U. of Utah, 1961. STUDENT, HISTORY, U. OF UTAH. U. of Utah research fellow, 1961-64. Membership: American Historical Association; Mississippi Valley Historical Association; Phi Alpha Theta; Phi Beta Kappa; Utah Historical Society. Research: history of Mexico; positivism and the role of the Cientificos during the Díaz era; Latin American philosophy. Language: Spanish 4,3,3,3. Home: Apt. 3, 1212 East 5th South, Salt Lake City, Utah.

RADY, DONALD EDMUND, b. Cleveland, Ohio, Dec. 1, 1930. HISTORY. B.A., U. of N. Mex., 1953; M.A., 1957; U. of Calif., Berkeley. ASST. PROF., HISTORY, WASHINGTON U., 1963- . William Harrison Mills fellow (Brazil), 1961-63. Membership: American Association of University Professors; American Historical Association; Phi Alpha Theta; Phi Kappa Phi; Phi Sigma Iota. Research: Latin American history; Volta Redonda, a Brazilian steel community; Latin American industrial development. Language: Spanish 4,4,4,4; Portuguese 5,4,4,4; French 3,3,3,3. Home: 4011 Ave. La Resolana, NE., Albuquerque, N. Mex. Office: Box 62, Dept. of History, Washington U., St. Louis, Mo. 63130.

RAFFELD, HERBERT, b. Chicago, Ill., June 9, 1920. HISTORY. B.A., Northwestern U., 1942; M.A., U. of Calif., Berkeley, 1947; Ph.D., 1951. Intelligence research analyst, U.S. Dept. of State, 1951-53; SECRETARY-TREASURER, MAXIS STORE FOR MEN, INC. (CHICAGO), 1954- . Membership: Conference on Latin American History. Research: Latin American history; viceroyalty of Peru, 1808-1824. Language: Spanish 3,2,2,1; Portuguese 1,1,—,—; French 1,—,—,—. Home: 9015 South Merrill Ave., Chicago 17, Ill.

RANDALL, ROBERT WILLIAM, b. Twin Falls, Idaho, Sept. 28, 1925. HISTORY. B.A., Brown U., 1951; Ph.D., Harvard U., 1965. Trainee and program specialist, Pan American Union, 1958-59; acting chief, Social Science Section, 1959-61; coordinator of training programs in Social Affairs, 1961; lectr., U. of the Americas, 1962; asst. prof., 1963-64; ASST. PROF., HISTORY, WESTERN RESERVE U., 1964- . Membership: American Association of University Professors; American Historical Association; Delta Sigma Rho; Phi Beta Kappa. Research: economic history of Mexico; the British Real del Monte Mining Company in Mexico. Language: Spanish 3,3,3,2; Portuguese 2,1,1,1; French 2,1,1,1. Home: 2523 North Moreland Blvd., Cleveland, Ohio. 44120. Office: Dept. of History, Western Reserve U., Cleveland, 44106.

RAUSCH, GEORGE JAY, JR., b. Aurora, Ill., Apr. 9, 1930. LIBRARY SCIENCE AND HISTORY. B.A., North Central Coll. (Ill.), 1955; M.A., U. of Ill., 1958; Ph.D., 1960; M.S., 1961. Research asst., U. of Ill., 1959-60; acquisitions asst., U. of Ill. Library, 1962-63; CHIEF, SOCIAL SCIENCE LIBRARY, WASH. STATE U., 1963- . Membership: American Historical Association; Conference on Latin American History. Research: Canadian history; Mexican history; British Commonwealth. Author: The Exile and Death of Victoriano Huerta (Hispanic American Historical Review, May 1962). Language: Spanish 3,2,2,1; Portuguese 2,1,1,1; French 2,2,1,1; German 2,2,2,1; Italian 2,1,1,1. Home: 700 Polaris, Pullman, Wash. 99163. Office: Washington State U. Library, Pullman.

RAYBURN, JOHN C., b. Bellbuckle, Tenn., Oct. 6, 1912. HISTORY. M.A., U. of Chicago, 1949; Ph.D., 1952. DIR., GRADUATE DIV., TEX. COLL. OF ARTS & INDUSTRIES, 1952- . Membership: Southwestern Social Science Association; Texas State Historical Asso-

ciation. Research: Venezuela and Mexico; Mexican history along the Rio Grande. Author: U.S. Investments in Venezuelan Asphalt (Inter-American Economic Affairs, Summer 1953); Investments in Venezuelan Telephones (Inter-American Economics Affairs, Autumn 1955); Rail Transportation in Venezuela (Inter-American Economic Affairs, Spring 1957). Language: Spanish 2,2,2,1. Home: 1222 West Lee, Kingsville, Tex. Office: Graduate Div., Tex. Coll. of Arts & Industries, Kingsville.

RAYFIELD, JO A. Home: 150 N. Bishop Lane, Mobile, Ala. 36608.

REINHART, HELEN KATHERINE, b. Quincy, Ill., Feb. 28, 1929. HISTORY. B.A., Quincy Coll., 1950; M.A., U. of Ill., 1956; Ph.D., 1960. Instr., Superior State Coll., 1959; INSTR., SOCIAL SCIENCE, ODESSA COLL., 1960- . Fellowship, U. of Ill. Membership: American Academy of Political and Social Sciences; American Association of University Professors; American Historical Association; Conference on Latin American History; Permian Basin Historical Society. Research: political history of the Brazilian regency, 1831-1840. Language: Spanish 4,2,2,3; Portuguese 4,1,1,2; French 4,1,1,2; German 3,1,1,1. Home: 1007 West 19th St., Odessa, Tex. Office: Dept. of Social Science, Odessa Coll., Odessa.

REISNER, SHERWOOD H., b. Nanking, China, Mar. 12, 1920. HISTORY. B.D., Yale Divinity School, 1945; Th.M., Princeton Theological Seminary, 1946; U. of Tex. Missionary, Presbyterian Church in the United States (Mexico), 1946-50; pastor, Primera Iglesia Presbiteriana Mexicana (Brownsville, Tex.), 1950-51; pastor, First Presbyterian Church (Falfurrias, Tex.), 1952-57; PRESIDENT, PRESBYTERIAN PAN AMERICAN SCHOOL, 1957- . Research: Latin American history and literature; the Dialogo de Doctrina Christiana of Juan de Valdés. Language: Spanish 2,2,2,2; Portuguese 3,3,5,5; French 4,5,5,5. Home: Presbyterian Pan American School, R.F.D. 1, Box 531, Kingsville, Tex. 78363.

RESNICK, ENOCH. Home: 8001 Eastern Dr., Silver Spring, Md.

RILES, BOBBY RAY, b. Laurel, Miss., Feb. 1, 1941. HISTORY. B.A., Miss. State U., 1962; M.A., 1963; Ball State Teachers Coll. STUDENT, HISTORY, BALL STATE TEACHERS COLL. Membership: American Historical Association; Mississippi Valley Historical Association. Research: United States and European history; United States, Mexico and the A.B.C. mediation of 1914. Language: Spanish 2,1,1,1; German 3,3,3,3. Home: Anthony Apts. 56, Bethel Ave., Muncie, Ind. 47304.

RILEY, G. MICHAEL, b. Silver City, N. Mex., Apr. 22, 1934. HISTORY. B.S., Ariz. State U., 1956; M.A., U. of N. Mex., 1961; Ph.D., 1964. Vis. asst. prof., U. of N. Mex., 1963-64; asst. prof., Colo. State U., 1964-66; ASST. PROF., HISTORY, MARQUETTE U.,

1966- . Social Science Research Council fellow (Spain), 1962-63. Membership: American Historical Association; Conference on Latin American History; Phi Alpha Theta; Phi Kappa Phi. Research: colonial Latin American history; the estate of Fernando Cortés in the Cuernavaca Valley (Mexico) to 1547; archival research in Spain and Mexico. Language: Spanish 4,3,3,3; Portuguese 2,1,1,1; French 3,1,1,1. Office: Dept. of History, Marquette U., Milwaukee, Wis.

RIPPY, JAMES FRED, b. Sumner County, Tenn., Oct. 27, 1892. HISTORY. B.A., Southwestern U. of Tex., 1913; A.M., Vanderbilt U., 1915; Ph.D., U. of Calif., 1920; D. Litt. (honorary), Southwestern U. of Tex., 1961. Instr., U. of Chicago, 1920-23; asst. prof., 1923-24; assoc. prof., 1924-26; prof., Duke U., 1926-36; prof., U. of Chicago, 1936-58; PROF. EMERITUS, HISTORY, U. OF CHICAGO, 1958- . Native Sons fellow, U. of Calif., 1917-18; editorial staff, Hispanic American Historical Review, 1926- ; Guggenheim fellow (Central America), 1927; Carnegie fellow (Colombia), 1928; Albert Shaw lectr., Johns Hopkins U., 1928; lectr., Instituto Interamericano of the National U. of Mexico, 1929; American Historical Review, 1933-38; delegate, Pan American Conference on History and Geography, 1935; Walter Fleming lectr., U. of La., 1941; Walker Ames lectr., U. of Wash., 1945; recipient, William Volker award, 1960. Membership: American Academy of Political and Social Science; American Association of University Professors; American Historical Association; Mississippi Valley Historical Association; North Carolina Historical and Literary Society; Phi Alpha Theta; Phi Beta Kappa. Research: the national period in Latin America; the industrial age in Latin America. Author: Modern Latin America (1958); Globe and Hemisphere (1958); British Investments in Latin America (1959). Language: Spanish 5,4,4,—; French 4,3,—,—; German 3,2,—,—; Italian 2,2,—,—. Home: 814 East Forest Hills Blvd., Durham, N.C.

RIPPY, NOBLE MERRILL, b. Fort Worth, Tex., Aug. 8, 1917. HISTORY. A.A., Decatur Baptist Coll., 1936; B.A., Tex. Christian U., 1938; M.A., 1939; Ph.D., U. of Tex., 1950. Teacher-counselor, Fort Worth Public Schools, 1938-45; part-time instr., U. of Tex., 1945-46; asst. prof.-assoc. prof., Tex. Christian U., 1947-53; asst. prof.-assoc. prof., Lamar State Coll., 1954-58; asst. prof.-ASSOC. PROF., HISTORY, BALL STATE TEACHERS COLL., 1959- ; vis. lectr. and researcher, U. of P.R., Summers 1959, 1960, 1961. E.D. Farmer international fellow, Universidad Nacional Autónoma de México, 1947; Ford Foundation post-doctoral fellow, U. of Chicago-U. of Tex., 1952-53; Smith-Mundt exchange prof., U. of Panama, 1956-57; National Defense Foreign Language post-doctoral fellow in Spanish, U. of Calif., Los Angeles, Summer 1963. Membership: American Historical Association; Bolivarian Society of the United States; Conference on Latin American History; Indiana Academy of the Social Sciences; Midwest Council, Association

for Latin American Studies; Texas State Historical Association. Research: intellectual history of Mexico and the Caribbean; Spanish origins of Latin American intellectuality. Author: El Petróleo y la Revolución Mexicana (1954); The Mexican Oil Industry (in Essays in Mexican History, 1958); Theory of History: Twelve Mexicans (The Americas, Jan. 1961). Language: Spanish 4,4,4,3; Portuguese 2,2,2,2; French 2,2,2,2. Home: 2613 North Janney Ave., Muncie, Ind. 47304. Office: Dept. of Social Sciences, Ball State Teachers Coll., Muncie.

RITTENHOUSE, FLOYD OLIVER, b. Bozeman, Mont., Mar. 10, 1906. HISTORY. B.A., Andrews U., 1928; M.A., Ohio State U., 1932; Ph.D., 1947. Assoc. prof., Wash. Missionary Coll., 1939-48; prof., Southern Missionary Coll., 1948-52; prof., Andrews U., 1952-63; PROF., HISTORY, PACIFIC UNION COLL., 1963- . Membership: American Historical Association; Phi Alpha Theta. Research: Mexico; the Mexican Revolution, 1910-1920. Language: Spanish 4,3,3,3; French 3,2,2,2. Home: 495 South White Cottage Rd., Angwin, Calif. Office: Dept. of History, Pacific Union Coll., Angwin.

ROBERTSON, DONALD, b. Elizabeth, N.J., May 12, 1919. ART. B.A., U. of N. Mex., 1942; M.A., Yale U., 1944; Ph.D., 1956. Instr., Queens Coll., 1946-47; asst. prof., U. of Tex., 1947-50; instr., Pomona Coll., 1954-56; vis. asst. prof., U. of Kans., 1956-57; ASSOC. PROF., ART, NEWCOMB COLL., TULANE U., 1957- . Pomona Coll. faculty research grant (Mexico), Summers 1958, 1962, Winter 1963; American Council of Learned Societies fellow, Summers 1960, 1961; Guggenheim fellow, 1964-65; Social Science Research Council grant, 1965; contributing editor, Handbook of Latin American Studies. Membership: College Art Association; Conference on Latin American History; Renaissance Society; Society for American Archaeology; Society of Architectural Historians; Southeastern Conference on Latin American Studies. Research: pre-Columbian, colonial and modern art, especially of Mexico; Mexican manuscript painting. Author: Mexican Manuscript Painting of the Early Colonial Period: The Metropolitan Schools (1959); Pre-Columbian Architecture (1963); The Relaciones Geográficas of Mexico (Actas, 33 Congreso Internacional de Americanistas, July 1958). Language: Spanish 4,4,4,1; Portuguese 3,2,2,1; French 4,4,4,1; German 3,2,2,1; Italian 4,3,3,1; Latin 2,1,1,1. Home: 7707 Plum St., New Orleans, La. 70118. Office: Dept. of Art, Newcomb Coll., Tulane U., New Orleans, 70118.

ROBBINS, DAVID. Home: 54 Springbrook Dr., N. Chili, N.Y. 14514.

RODRÍGUEZ, MARIO, b. Colusa, Calif., Oct. 1, 1922. HISTORY. A.B., U. of Calif., Berkeley, 1946; M.A., 1948; Ph.D., 1952. Instr., Tulane U., 1952-54; faculty research adviser, Graduate Seminar in Central America, Tulane U. and U. of San Carlos (Guatemala), Summer 1953; instr.-asst. prof., Yale U., 1954-60; assoc. prof.-

prof., U. of Ariz., 1960-66; PROF., HISTORY, GEORGE WASHINGTON U., 1966- . Robertson Prize, Conference on Latin American History, 1955; Morse Fellowship in History, Yale U., 1958-59; contributing editor, Handbook of Latin American Studies, 1959- . Membership: American Historical Association; Conference on Latin American History; Pacific Coast Council of Latin American Studies. Research: 19th and 20th century Central American history; Río de la Plata area. Author: The Livingston Codes in the Guatemalan Crisis of 1837-1838 (1955); The Genesis of Economic Attitudes in the Río de la Plata (Hispanic American Historical Review, May 1956); Dom Pedro of Braganza and Colônia do Sacramento, 1680-1705 (Hispanic American Historical Review, May 1958). Language: Spanish 5,5,5,5; Portuguese 5,3,3,2; French 5,3,3,2; German 2,2,1,1; Italian 3,3,2,1. Office: Dept. of History, George Washington U., Washington, D.C.

ROGERS, ROLLAND C., b. Kent, Wash., Mar. 20, 1910. HISTORY. A.B., U. of Wash., 1933; M.A., 1937; Ph.D., Stanford U., 1953. Research asst., Div. of Press Intelligence, Executive Office of the White House, 1935-37; instr., Wash. Public Schools, 1937-46; instr., San Francisco State Coll., Spring 1951; asst. prof., Stanford U., 1951-57; instr., Foothill Coll., 1958-59; asst. prof., San Jose State Coll., 1959-64; ASSOC. PROF., HISTORY, SAN JOSE STATE COLL., 1964- . Membership: American Historical Association; Pacific Coast Council of Latin American Studies. Research: Brazil. Author: Latin American Transportation (in Encyclopedia Americana, 1955). Language: Spanish 2,2,2,1; Portuguese 3,3,3,1; French 2,2,2,1. Home: P.O. Box 3581, Stanford, Calif. Office: Dept. of History, San Jose State Coll., San Jose 14, Calif.

ROMEO, ROBERT J., b. Alexandria, Egypt, May 24, 1922. SCIENTOLOGY AND HISTORY. B.A., Stanford U., 1957; M.A., 1960. SCIENTOLOGIST, SELF-EMPLOYED, 1960- . Membership: Conference on Latin American History; Hubbard Association; Scientologists International; Phi Alpha Theta. Research: human communication and relations; roots of Argentine nationalism, 1810-1910. Language: Spanish 5,5,5,5; Portuguese 5,5,4,4; French 5,5,5,5; Arabic 3,3,3,3; Italian 5,5,5,5. Home: Box 273, Cupertino, Calif. 95014.

RONAN, CHARLES EDWARD, S.J., b. Chicago, Ill., June 1, 1914. HISTORY. A.B., Loyola U. (Ill.), 1940; M.A., 1954; Ph.D., U. of Tex., 1958. Instr., U. of Detroit, 1956-57; asst. prof., Loyola U. (Ill.), 1957-60; asst. prof., Xavier U. (Ohio), 1960-63; ASST. PROF., HISTORY, LOYOLA U. (ILL.), 1963- . Membership: American Division of the Jesuit Institute of History; American Historical Association; Catholic Historical Association. Research: biography of Francisco Javier Clavigero, Mexican Jesuit, 1731-1787; 18th century Latin America. Author: On the Word Gringo (Historia Mexicana, Apr. 1959). Language: Spanish 4,4,4,4; Portuguese 2,2,2,1; French 3,—,—,—;

Latin 2,2,3,3. Office: Dept. of History, Loyola U., 6525 Sheridan Rd., Chicago, 60626.

ROSS, CARL A., b. Spring Place, Ga., Nov. 5, 1931. HISTORY. A.B., Berry Coll., 1953; M.A., U. of Ga., 1957. ASST. PROF., HISTORY, U. OF DUBUQUE, 1962- . Research: Latin American history; Chile. Language: Spanish 3,2,1,2; Portuguese 3,1,1,1; Japanese —,2,—,—. Home: 1957 University Ave., Dubuque, Iowa 52002. Office: Dept. of History, U. of Dubuque, Dubuque.

ROSS, OLIVER DELL, b. Lorain, Ohio, Oct. 12, 1925. HISTORY. B.A., U. of Wis., 1948; M.A. 1950; Ph.D., Ohio State U., 1953. Manager-PRESIDENT, SAM ROSS AND SONS, 1953- . Membership: American Historical Association; Phi Alpha Theta. Research: studies of selected Mexican communal institutions in the colonial period. Language: Spanish 4,3,2,3; French 2,—,—,—; German 2,—,—,—. Home: 317 Euclid Ave., Lorain, Ohio. Office: 1351 Broadway, Lorain.

ROSS, STANLEY ROBERT, b. New York, N.Y., Aug. 8, 1921. HISTORY. A.B., Queens Coll., 1942; M.A., Columbia U., 1943; Ph.D., 1951. Asst. prof., U. of Nebr., 1951-57; assoc. prof., 1957-60; vis. assoc. prof., Columbia U., Summer 1960; prof., dir., Latin American Program, U. of Nebr., 1960-62; vis. prof., U. of Colo., Summer 1962; PROF., CHMN., HISTORY, STATE U. OF N.Y., COLL. AT STONY BROOK, 1962- ; ACTING DEAN, COLL. OF ARTS AND SCIENCES, 1963- . U.S. Dept. of State travel grant (Mexico), Summers 1947, 1948; Doherty fellow (Mexico), 1952-53; U. of Nebr. grant (Mexico), Summer 1955; Rockefeller Foundation grants (Mexico), 1958-59, 1961-62. Membership: American Association of University Professors; American Historical Association; Conference on Latin American History; Mississippi Valley Historical Association. Research: 20th century Mexico; effects of revolutionary movement; diplomatic history. Author: Francisco I. Madero, Apostle of Mexican Democracy (1955). Language: Spanish 4,4,4,3; Portuguese 2,3,1,1. Home: Mud Rd., Setauket, N.Y. Office: Dept. of History, State U. of N.Y., Coll. at Stony Brook, Stony Brook.

ROTHSTEIN, MIGNON. Home: 6074 Pickford St., Los Angeles, Calif. 90035.

ROUT, LESLIE BRENNAN, JR., b. Chicago, Ill., Feb. 26, 1936. HISTORY. B.S., Loyola U. (Chicago), 1957; M.A., 1961; U. of Minn. Teacher, Wendell Phillips Public High School (Chicago), 1959-62; INSTR., HISTORY, U. OF MINN., 1964- . Commonwealth Edison scholar, 1956-57; John Hay Whitney fellow, U. of Minn., 1964. Research: Latin American history; colonial Argentina; Chaco War. Language: Spanish 3,2,3,3; Portuguese 1,2,1,1; French 3,1,2,3. Home: 727 East 83rd St., Chicago 19, Ill. Office: Dept. of History, Social Science Bldg., U. of Minn., Minneapolis, 55455.

ROWE, JOHN HOWLAND, b. Sorrento, Maine, June 10, 1918. ANTHROPOLOGY AND HISTORY. A.B., Brown U., 1939; M.A., Harvard U., 1941; Ph.D., 1947; Litt. D. (honorary), Universidad Nacional de Cuzco, 1954. Supervisor, Southern Peruvian Project, Institute of Andean Research, 1941-42; prof., dir., Instituto de Arqueología, U. Nacional de Cuzco, 1942-43; representative in Colombia, Institute of Social Anthropology, Smithsonian Institution, 1946-48; asst. prof., U. of Calif., Berkeley, 1948-51; assoc. prof., 1951-56; PROF., ANTHROPOLOGY, U. OF CALIF., BERKELEY, 1956- ; CHMN., 1963- ; CURATOR OF SOUTH AMERICAN ARCHAEOLOGY, LOWIE MUSEUM OF ANTHROPOLOGY. Peabody Museum fellow (Peru), 1946; Guggenheim fellow (Peru), 1958; research prof., Miller Institute for Basic Research in Science, 1964-65. Membership: American Anthropological Association; Institute of Andean Studies; Sociedad Científica del Cuzco; Sociedad Peruana de Historia; Société des Américanistes; Society for American Archaeology. Research archaeology; ethnology; Peru; Colombia. Author: An Introduction to the Archaeology of Cuzco (1944); Inca Culture at the Time of the Spanish Conquest (in Handbook of South American Indians, 1946); The Incas Under Spanish Colonial Institutions (Hispanic American Historical Review, May 1957). Language: Spanish 5,4,4,4; Portuguese 3,2,1,1; French 4,4,3,2; German 3,1,1,1; Italian 3,1,1,1; Quechua 3,1,1,1. Linguistic studies: Guambian; Quechua. Home: 2137 Rose St., Berkeley, Calif. 94709. Office: Dept. of Anthropology, U. of Calif., Berkeley, 14720.

ROWLAND, DONALD WINSLOW, b. Mariposa, Calif., Jan., 12, 1898. HISTORY. A.B., U. of Calif., Berkeley, 1925; A.M., 1926; Ph.D., 1931. Asst. prof., U. of Hawaii, 1930-35; vis. prof., U. of Oreg., Summer 1933; PROF., HISTORY, U. OF SOUTHERN CALIF., 1935- ; summer vis. prof., U. of Calif., Berkeley, 1935, 1941, 1955, U. of Mich., 1957; political analyst, Office of Coordinator of Inter-American Affairs, 1943-47. Native Sons of the Golden West traveling fellow (Spain), 1927-28. Membership: American Historical Association; Conference on Latin American History; Pacific Coast Council on Latin American Affairs. Research: colonial Latin America. Author: History of the Office of the Coordinator of Inter-American Affairs (1947). Contributor: Greater America (1933). Language: Spanish 3,—,2,2. Home: 1205 Chavez St., Burbank, Calif. Office: Dept. of History, U. of Southern Calif., University Park, Los Angeles 7, Calif.

ROYAL, LESLIE JOHN, b. Frederick, S. Dak., Oct. 11, 1930. HISTORY. B.A., U. of Calif., Riverside, 1958; M.A., U. of Calif., Berkeley, 1960. ASST. PROF., HISTORY, SACRAMENTO STATE COLL., 1964- . Woodrow Wilson fellow, 1960-61; Woodrow Wilson traveling fellow (Spain), 1961-62. Research: Latin American history, especially colonial period; popular diversions in 16th century Mexico. Language: Spanish 4,4,4,3; Portuguese

4,2,2,2; French 3,2,1,2; German 3,3,2,1. Home: 500 38th St., Sacramento, Calif. 95820. Office: Dept. of History, Sacramento State Coll., 6000 J St., Sacramento, 95819.

RUIZ, RAMÓN EDUARDO, b. Pacific Beach, Calif., Oct. 9, 1921. HISTORY. B.A., San Diego State Coll., 1947; M.A., Claremont Coll., 1948; Ph.D., U. of Calif., Berkeley, 1954. Lectr., U. of Calif., San Francisco, 1953-54; vis. lectr., Claremont Coll., Summers 1954-57; asst. prof., U. of Oreg., 1955-57; asst. prof., Southern Methodist U., 1957-58; assoc. prof., Smith Coll., 1958-64; vis. prof., U. of Tex., Summer 1964; PROF., HISTORY, SMITH COLL., 1964- . John Hay Whitney fellow, 1950-51; Huntington Library grant, 1958; American Philosophical Society grant, 1959. Membership: Conference on Latin American History. Research: political and cultural history of Mexico; rural education in Latin America; the Caribbean, particularly Cuba. Author: An American in Maximilian's Mexico (1959); Mexico: The Challenge of Poverty and Illiteracy (1963); The Mexican War—Was It Manifest Destiny? (1963). Language: Spanish 5,5,5,4. Home: 66 Paradise Rd., Northampton, Mass. Office: Dept. of History, Smith Coll., Northampton.

RYDJORD, JOHN, b. Webster, S. Dak., Sept. 5, 1893. HISTORY. B.A., U. of Wis., 1922; M.A., Northwestern U., 1923; Ph.D., U. of Calif., Berkeley, 1925. Head, History, U. of Wichita, 1926-51; vis. prof., George Washington U., Summer 1929, U. of Calif., Berkeley, 1943-44, Northwestern U., Summer 1945, U. of Calif., Los Angeles, 1945-46; dean, Graduate School, U. of Wichita, 1949-58; PROF. EMERITUS, U. OF WICHITA, 1958- ; vis. prof., U. of Nebr., 1961-62. Bolton Prize Committee; Native Sons of the Golden West traveling fellow; William Smith Mason fellow, Northwestern U. Membership: American Historical Association; Hispanic American Historical Association; Kansas State Historical Association; Phi Alpha Theta; Pi Sigma Alpha. Research: Mexico. Author: Foreign Interest in the Independence of New Spain (1935); French Revolution and Mexico (Hispanic American Historical Review, Feb. 1929); Spanish Defeat of the Napoleonic Confederation (U. of Wichita Studies, Dec. 1944). Language: Spanish 3,3,3,3; French 3,2,2,1; German 3,2,2,1. Home: 1730 North Lorraine, Wichita, Kans. 67214. Office: Dept. of History, Wichita State U., Wichita.

Sable, MARTIN H. Home: 416½ N. Maple Dr., Beverly Hills, Calif.

SAFFORD, FRANK ROBINSON, b. El Paso, Tex., June 4, 1935. HISTORY. A.B., Harvard U., 1957; M.A., Columbia U., 1959; Ph.D., 1965. Instr., Dartmouth Coll., 1962-66; ASST. PROF., HISTORY, NORTHWESTERN U., 1966- . Harvard College scholar, 1953-57; Woodrow Wilson fellow, 1957-58; Columbia U. faculty scholar, 1959-60; Doherty fellow (Colombia), 1961. Membership: American Historical Association; Conference on Latin

American History; Instituto Paraguayo de Investigaciones Históricas. Research: Latin American history; 19th century Colombia; Latin American economic history. Language: Spanish 5,4,4,4; Portuguese 3,3,1,3; French 3,2,1,2. Office: Dept. of History, Northwestern U., Evanston, Ill.

SANDELS, ROBERT LYNN, b. Akron, Ohio, Mar. 23, 1933. HISTORY. B.A., Mexico City Coll., 1958; M.A., U. of Oreg., 1962. ASST. PROF., HISTORY, CHICO STATE COLL., 1964- . Carnegie summer research fellow (Costa Rica), 1963. Membership: American Historical Association. Research: Latin American history; modern Mexico; the Mexican Revolution; the soldier's life in the Spanish American War. Language: Spanish 4,4,4,3; Portuguese 3,1,1,1; French 3,1,1,1. Home: 1734 Villard St., Eugene, Oreg.

SANTANA, ARTURO F., b. Santurce, P.R., June 9, 1921. HISTORY. B.A., U. of P.R., 1941; M.A., U. of Chicago, 1942; Ph.D., 1952. Instr., U. of P.R., 1944-49; asst. prof., 1949-54; assoc. prof., 1954-63; PROF., HISTORY, U. OF P.R., 1963- . Board of Directors, Institute of Puerto Rican Culture; consultant in history, Dept. of Education, Commonwealth of Puerto Rico; contributing editor, Handbook of Latin American Studies. Research: early relations between the United States and Puerto Rico, 1790-1830. Language: Spanish 5,5,5,5; French 2,2,2,2. Home: Box 21822, U. of P.R. Station, Rio Piedras, P.R. Office: Dept. of History, U. of P.R., Rio Piedras, P.R.

SATZ, ARTHUR R. Home: 671 W. 162nd St., New York, N.Y. 10032.

SAVELLE, MAX, b. Mobile, Ala., Jan. 8, 1896. HISTORY. A.B., Columbia U., 1925; M.A., 1926; Ph.D., 1932. Instr., Columbia U., 1926-32; prof. Stanford U., 1932-47; PROF., HISTORY, U. OF WASH., 1947- . Fulbright scholar (France), 1950; Fulbright teacher (Spain), 1960-61; Rockefeller Foundation grant (Chile), 1963; editorial board, American Historical Review and Western Humanities Review. Membership: American Historical Association; Mississippi Valley Historical Association; Phi Alpha Theta. Research: United States colonial history; American Revolution. Author: Seeds of Liberty (1948); Short History of American Civilization (1957); Diplomatic History of the Canadian Boundary, 1748-1763 (1960). Language: Spanish 4,3,4,4; Portuguese 2,—,—,—; French 4,3,4,4. Home: 4545 55th Ave., NE., Seattle, Wash. Office: Dept. of History, U. of Wash., Seattle 5.

SCHEIPS, PAUL JOSEPH, b. Peru, Ind., Oct. 24, 1914. HISTORY. A.B., Evansville Coll., 1935; M. of Mich., 1947; M.A., U. of Chicago, 1949; Ph.D., American U., 1965. Teacher, English, Narciso Rebell Cabrero School (San Sebastian, P.R.), 1935-36; teacher, English and Social Studies, Bosse and Central High Schools (Evansville, Ind.), 1936-40; instr., Denison U., 1943-45; technical adviser and chief clerk, U.S.

Census Bureau (South Bend, Ind.), 1950; historian, Historical Div., Air Proving Ground Command, Dept. of the Air Force (Elgin Air Force Base, Fla.), 1951-52; historian, Signal Corps, Historical Div., Dept. of the Army (Washington, D.C.), 1952-62; HISTORIAN, OFFICE OF THE CHIEF OF MILITARY HISTORY, DEPT. OF THE ARMY, 1962- . Membership: American Association of University Professors; American Historical Association; Conference on Latin American History; Phi Alpha Theta. Research: American and Latin American history; the Caribbean and Isthmian area; inter-American relations; archives history and administration. Author: Buchanan and the Chiriqui Naval Station Sites (Military Affairs, Summer 1954); Gabriel LaFond and Ambrose W. Thompson: Neglected Isthmian Promoters (Hispanic American Historical Review, May 1956); United States Commercial Pressures for a Nicaragua Canal in the 1890's (The Americas, Apr. 1964). Language: Spanish 2,—,—,—; French 2,—,—,—; German 2,—,—,—. Home: 3483 South Wakefield St., Arlington, Va. 22206. Office: Office of the Chief of Military History, Dept. of the Army, Tempo C, 2nd and R Sts., SW., Washington, D.C. 20315.

SCHELLENBERG, THEODORE R., b. Harvey County, Kans., Feb. 24, 1903. HISTORY AND ARCHIVAL MANAGEMENT. A.B., U. of Kans., 1928; A.M., 1930; Ph.D., U. of Pa., 1934. Executive secretary, Joint Committee on Materials for Research, American Council of Learned Societies and Social Science Research Council, 1934-35; history asst., Works Progress Administration, National Park Service, U.S. Dept. of the Interior, 1935; deputy examiner-asst. archivist of the United States, U.S. National Archives, 1935-63; assoc. national dir., Survey of Federal Archives, U.S. Government, 1936; records officer, U.S. Office of Price Administration, 1945-48; RETIRED, 1963- . Fulbright lectr. (Australia, New Zealand), 1954; Rockefeller Foundation consultant in Trinidad and Tobago, 1958; American specialist, International Education Exchange Program (South American countries), 1960; dir., Inter-American Archival Seminar, National Archives, 1961; chmn., Inter-American Archives Council, 1961. Membership: Pan American Institute of Geography and History. Research: preservation and administration of archives; archival situations in South American countries. Author: Archivos modernos: principios y técnicas (1958); Archivos privados e públicos: arranjo e descrição (1963); Manual de archivos (1959; 1961). Language: Spanish 3,2,2,1; Portuguese 3,1,1,1; French 3,2,2,1; Dutch 3,3,2,1; German 5,5,4,4. Home: 2637 Military Rd., Arlington 7, Va.

SCHIFF, WARREN, b. Pforzheim, Baden, Germany, June 22, 1924. HISTORY. B.S., Georgetown U., 1948; M.A., U. of Calif., Berkeley, 1949; Universidad de la República (Uruguay), 1950-51; Ph.D., U. of Calif., Berkeley, 1957. Assoc. prof., chmn., Div. of Social Sciences, Little Rock U., 1957-61; ASSOC. PROF., HISTORY, COLL. OF THE HOLY CROSS,

1961- . Membership: American Historical Association; Worcester Academy of Historians and Political Scientists. Research: study of German influence in Mexico; Uruguay. Author: German Military Penetration into Mexico during the Late Díaz Period (Hispanic American Historical Review, Nov. 1959); An East German Survey Concerning Recent Soviet Historical Writings on Latin America (Hispanic American Historical Review, Feb. 1960). Language: Spanish 4,4,4,4; Portuguese 2,1,1,1; French 2,1,1,1; German 5,5,5,4. Home: 8 Lenox St., Worcester, 2, Mass. Office: Dept. of History and Political Science, Coll. of the Holy Cross, Worcester.

SCHMITT, KARL MICHAEL, b. Louisville, Ky., July 22, 1922. HISTORY AND POLITICAL SCIENCE. B.A., Catholic U., 1947; M.A., 1949; Ph.D., U. of Pa., 1954. Asst. prof., Niagara U., 1950-55; analyst for Latin America, Intelligence Research, U.S. Dept. of State, 1955-58; ASSOC. PROF., GOVERNMENT, U. OF TEX., 1958- ; asst. prof., U. of Calif., Los Angeles, Summer 1959. Consultant, U.S. Dept. of State, 1962- ; consultant on education in Central America, U.S. Government, 1963. Membership: Catholic Historical Association; Conference on Latin American History. Research: government and politics of Latin America; Mexico. Author: Evolution or Chaos: Dynamics of Latin American Government and Politics (1963); Communism in Mexico Today (Western Political Quarterly, Mar. 1962); The Catholic Response to the Secular State: The Case of Mexico, 1867-1911 (Catholic Historical Review, July 1962). Language: Spanish 4,3,3,—; Portuguese 2,2,2,—; French 2,2,2,—. Home: 2603 Pinewood Ter., Austin, Tex. Office: Dept. of Government, U. of Tex., Austin.

SCHNEIDER, RONALD MILTON, b. Minneapolis, Minn., Sept. 29, 1932. POLITICAL SCIENCE. B.S., Northwestern U., 1954; M.A., Princeton U., 1956; Ph.D., 1958. Research asst., Foreign Policy Research Institute (Washington, D.C. and Guatemala), 1956-57; intelligence research specialist, U.S. Dept. of State, 1957-63, Embassy (Brazil), 1962; lectr., Catholic U., 1960-61; vis. assoc. prof., Catholic U., Summer 1963; VIS. ASSOC. PROF., GOVERNMENT, COLUMBIA U., 1963- ; acting asst. dir., Institute of Latin American Studies, Columbia U.; dir., Metropolitan Summer Graduate Field Training Program in Latin America. Research: Latin American comparative politics and government; communism in Latin America; Brazilian politics; Guatemala; Colombia; Panama. Author: Communism in Guatemala, 1944-1954 (1959); Introduction (in Evolution or Chaos: The Dynamics of Latin American Government and Politics, 1963); Five Years of the Cuban Revolution (Current History, Jan. 1964). Language: Spanish 4,4,3,3; Portuguese 4,4,4,4. Home: 36 E. Glen Ave., Ridgewood, N.J. Office: Dept. of Government, Columbia U., 417 W. 117th St., New York, N.Y. 10027.

SCHOLES, FRANCE VINTON, b. Bradford, Ill., Jan. 26, 1897. HISTORY. A.B., Harvard U., 1919; A.M., 1922; Ph.D., 1943. Instr., Mass. Institute of Technology, 1919-20; instr., U. of N. Mex., 1925-26; asst. prof., Colo. Coll., 1926-27; assoc. prof., U. of N. Mex., 1928-30; prof., 1930-31; investigator, Div. of Historical Research, Carnegie Institution of Washington, 1931-36; prof., History, U. of N. Mex., 1946-63; RETIRED, 1963- . Serra Award Academy of American Franciscan History, 1956. Membership: Academy of American Franciscan History; American Academy of Arts and Sciences; American Anthropological Association; American Historical Association; Phi Beta Kappa; Phi Kappa Phi. Research: colonial history of Latin America. Author: Church and State in New Mexico, 1610-1650 (1937); Troublous Times in New Mexico, 1659-1670 (1942). Coauthor: The Maya Chontal Indians of Acalan-Tixchel (1948). Language: Spanish 5,4,4,4; Portuguese 3,2,1,1; French 4,2,2,1; German 4,1,1,1. Home: 115 Harvard Dr., SE., Albuquerque, N. Mex.

SCHOLES, WALTER V., b. Bradford, Ill., July 26, 1916. HISTORY. B.A., U. of Mich., 1938; M.A., 1940; Ph.D., 1943. Prof., Stephens Coll., 1943-45; PROF., HISTORY, U. OF MO., 1945- . Membership: American Historical Association; Conference on Latin American History. Research: 19th century Mexico; early 20th century United States diplomacy. Author: Diego Ramírez Visita (1946); Mexican Politics during the Juárez Regime (1957). Editor: Mexico during the War with the United States (1950). Language: Spanish 3,—,—,—; Portuguese 1,—,—,—; French 3,—,—,—. Home: 1515 Ross. Columbia, Mo. Office: Dept. of History, U. of Mo., Columbia.

SCHUSTER, ALICE K., b. Pittsburgh, Pa., Apr. 13, 1903. HISTORY. A.B., U. of Pittsburgh, 1936; M.A., 1938; Ph.D., 1946. Asst. prof., Westminster Coll. (Pa.), 1945-51; instr., Frostburg State Teachers Coll., 1951-57; ASSOC. PROF., SOCIAL STUDIES, EDINBORO STATE COLL., 1957- . Membership: American Historical Association; Conference on Latin American History; Pennsylvania Historical Association. Research: Nicholas P. Trist and peace mission to Mexico. Language: Spanish 2,—,—,—. Home: 340 South Highland Ave., Pittsburgh, Pa. 15206. Office: Dept. of Social Studies, Edinboro State Coll., Edinboro, Pa.

SCHWEMMER, ORA-WESTLEY, b. Mohrsville, Pa., Dec. 12, 1935. HISTORY. B.A., Ursinus Coll., 1957; M.A., Tulane U., 1960. ASST. PROF., U. OF SOUTHWESTERN LA., 1963- . American Association of University Women research fellow, 1961-62. Membership: American Association of University Professors; American Association of University Women; American Historical Association. Research: Latin American history; Belgian commercial and territorial expansion in Central America, 1840-1856. Language: Spanish 3,2,2,—; French 5,4,4,4. Home: Apt. 6, 610 Wilson St., Lafayette, La. Office: Box 1143, U. of Southwestern La., Lafayette.

SCOBIE, JAMES ROBERT, b. Valparaiso, Chile, June 16, 1929. HISTORY. A.B., Princeton U., 1950; M.A., Harvard U., 1951; Ph.D., 1954. Part-time instr., U. of Md. Overseas Program, 1956-57; instr.-asst. prof., U. of Calif., Berkeley, 1963-64; vis. prof., U. of Tex., Summer 1961; ASSOC. PROF., HISTORY, IND. U., 1964- . Doherty fellow (Argentina), 1952-53; Social Science Research Council and Organization of American States Faculty research fellow (Argentina), 1959-60; vis. scholar, Institute of Latin American Studies, Columbia U., 1962-63. Membership: American Historical Association; Conference on Latin American History; Pacific Coast Council on Latin American Studies. Research: Rio de la Plata area, 1840-1900; 19th and 20th century Argentine development. Author: Argentina: A City and a Nation (1964); Consolidación de la nación argentina, 1852-1862 (1964). Co-author: Correspondencia Mitre-Elizalde (1956). Language: Spanish 5,5,5,4; Portuguese 4,4,3,3; French 5,5,4,3; German 3,3,3,1; Italian 2,2,2,1. Office: Dept. of History, Ind. U., Bloomington.

SCRUGGS, OTEY MATTHEW, b. Vallejo, Calif., June 29, 1929. HISTORY. B.A., U. of Calif., Santa Barbara, 1951; M.A., Harvard U., 1952; Ph.D., 1958. Instr., U. of Calif., Santa Barbara, 1957-59; ASST. PROF., HISTORY, U. OF CALIF., SANTA BARBARA, 1959- . Membership: Agricultural History Society; American Historical Association; Mississippi Valley Historical Association. Research: United States history; Mexican agricultural labor in the United States; recent Mexican history and culture. Author: Mexican Farm Labor Agreement of 1942 (Agricultural History, July 1960); The United States, Mexico, and the Wetbacks (Pacific Historical Review, May 1961); Mexican Farm Labor Program under the Farm Security Administration (Labor History, Spring 1962). Language: Spanish 3,2,2,2; Portuguese 1,1,1,1; French 2,1,1,1. Home: 6784 Sueno Rd., Goleta, Calif. 93018. Office: Dept. of History, U. of Calif., Santa Barbara.

SEHLINGER, PETER JOSEPH, JR., b. Louisville, Ky., Aug. 18, 1940. HISTORY. B.A., U. of the South, 1962; M.A., Tulane U., 1964; U. of Ky. Instr., Catherine Spalding Coll., 1964-65; STUDENT, HISTORY, U. OF KY., 1965- . National Defense Foreign Language fellow in Spanish, Tulane U., 1962-64, U. of Ariz. Summer School (Guadalajara, Mexico), Summer 1963; U. of Ky. fellow, 1965-66. Research: Latin American history; Hispanidad in Mexico, 1936-1945 Language: Spanish 4,4,4,4; Portuguese 3,3,3,2; French 3,3,3,2; German 3,2,2,2. Home: 2307 Wetstein Ave., Louisville, Ky. 40205.

SENSABAUGH, LEON F., b. Dublin, Tex., Oct. 9, 1903. HISTORY. A.B., Vanderbilt U., 1925; Ph.D., Johns Hopkins U., 1928. Asst. prof., Birmingham-Southern Coll., 1928-29; prof., Okla. City U., 1929-36; assoc. prof.-prof., Birmingham-Southern Coll., 1936-56; dean, Washington & Lee U., 1956-60; PROF., HISTORY, WASHINGTON & LEE U., 1960- .

Rosenwald fellow (Brazil), 1941-42. Membership: Conference on Latin American History; Southern Historical Association. Research: Brazilian diplomatic history; United States-Brazilian relations; Latin American boundary disputes. Author: American Interest in the Mexican-Guatemalan Boundary Dispute (Birmingham-Southern College Bulletin, Dec. 1940); The Attitude of the United States toward Colombia-Costa Rica Arbitral Proceedings (Hispanic American Historical Review, Feb. 1939); The Coffee-Trust Question in United States-Brazilian Relations (Hispanic American Historical Review, Nov. 1946). Language: Spanish 2,1,1,1; Portuguese 3,2,2,1; French 2,1,1,1. Home: 6 University Pl., Lexington, Va. Office: Dept. of History, Washington & Lee U., Lexington.

SERVIN, MANUEL PATRICIO, b. El Paso, Tex., Aug. 8, 1920. HISTORY. M.S.W., Boston Coll., 1951; A.M., U. of Southern Calif., 1954; Ph.D., 1959. Instr., El Camino Coll., 1958-60; lectr., Summer School (Mexico), U. of Southern Calif., 1960; ASST. PROF., HISTORY, U. OF SOUTHERN CALIF., 1961- . Del Amo Foundation fellow (Spain), 1957-58; editor, California Historical Society Quarterly, 1961- ; advisory editor, Southern California Quarterly, 1962. Research: colonial church; colonial social history. Author: Religious Aspects of Symbolic Acts of Sovereignty (The Americas, Jan. 1957); La toma de posesión inglesa (Revista de Indias, Apr. 1958); The Instructions of Viceroy Bucareli to Ensign Juan Pérez (California Historical Society Quarterly, Sept. 1961). Language: Spanish 5,5,5,5; Latin 1,—,—,—. Home: 1625 Bushnell Ave., South Pasadena, Calif. Office: Dept. of History, U. of Southern Calif., Los Angeles 7.

SHAFER, ROBERT JONES, b. South Salem, Ohio, Jan. 29, 1915. HISTORY. B.A., Ohio State U., 1938; M.A., U. of Calif., Los Angeles, 1943; Ph.D., 1947. PROF., HISTORY, SYRACUSE U., 1945- ; vis. prof., U. of Calif., Los Angeles, Summer 1953. U. S. Office of Education research fellow, 1946; Ford Foundation grant (Mexico), 1961-63; consultant on Latin American marketing and data handling problems, Itek Corporation. Membership: American Historical Association; Association for Latin American Studies; Conference on Latin American History. Research: recent economic development; Mexican economic development planning; military institutions in Latin America. Author: The Economic Societies in the Spanish World (1958). Language: Spanish 4,3,3,3; Portuguese 3,—,—,—; French 4,2,2,2. Home: 311 Houston Ave., Syracuse 10, N.Y. Office: Dept. of History, Syracuse U., Syracuse 10.

SHANNON, EDITH REED, b. Paterson, N.J. EDUCATION. Columbia U.; Ph.D., N.Y.U., 1932. Teacher, elementary school (Paterson, N.J.), 1907-17; prof., supervisor for practice teaching, State Teachers Coll. (Paterson), 1917-54; prof., Fairleigh Dickinson U., 1954-63; RETIRED, 1963- . Membership: Conference on

Latin American History; Kappa Delta Pi; National Education Association; Pi Gamma Mu. Research: teacher placement; teacher education; visual education. Language: German 3,—,—,—. Home: 65 Glen Ave., Glen Rock, N.J. 07452.

SHAPIRO, SAMUEL, b. Ellenville, N.Y., Aug. 23, 1927. HISTORY. Ph.D., Columbia U., 1958. Asst. prof., Oakland U., 1960-63; ASST. PROF., LATIN AMERICAN HISTORY, U. OF NOTRE DAME, 1963- . Fulbright prof., Tucumán U. (Argentina), 1959. Membership: American Historical Association; Hispanic American Historical Association; Midwest Council of the Association of Latin American Studies; Mississippi Valley Historical Association; Southern History Association. Research: contemporary Latin America; the Cuban revolution; current economic and political affairs in Argentina. Author: Richard Henry Dana, Jr. (1961); Invisible Latin America (1963); Fidel Castro and John Brown (Columbia University Forum, Winter, 1963). Language: Spanish 5,4,4,4; Portuguese 3,2,3,1; French 5,4,4,4. Home: 1828 Crestwood, South Bend, Ind. Office: Dept. of History, U. of Notre Dame, Notre Dame, Ind.

SHEARER, ERNEST CHARLES, b. Denton, Tex., July 6, 1903. HISTORY. B.A., West Tex. U., 1930; M.A., U. of Colo., 1933; Ph.D., U. of Tex., 1940. Teacher, acting president, Amarillo Coll., 1935-46; chmn., U. of Houston, 1946-56; PROF., HISTORY, SUL ROSS STATE COLL., 1956- ; summer lectr., U. of Tex., 1931, 1932, West Tex. State Coll., 1952, Mexico City Coll., 1954, U. of Tenn., 1956. Research: Mexico. Author: Robert Potter, Remarkable North Carolinian and Texan (1954). Home: Alpine, Tex. Office: Dept. of History, Sul Ross State Coll., Alpine.

SHERIDAN, GERARD, REV. Office: Church of the Assumption, Chestnut St., Centereach, Long Island, N.Y. 11720.

SHERMAN, WILLIAM LEWIS, b. Pasadena, Calif., Apr. 9, 1927. HISTORY. B.B.A., Woodbury Coll., 1949; B.F.T., American Institute for Foreign Trade, 1950; M.A., Mexico City Coll., 1958; U. of N. Mex. Cryptographer and courier (Frankfurt and Munich, Germany), U.S. Dept. of State, 1951-53; instr., asst. to the President, Mexico City Coll., 1959-60; Peace Corps coordinator, Area Studies Program, U. of N. Mex., 1962-65; ASST. PROF., HISTORY, CALIF. WESTERN U., 1965- . Baird fellow, 1962. Membership: Hispanic American Historical Association; Hispanic American Society; Phi Alpha Theta. Research: Latin American history, especially colonial period; paleography; Spanish-Indian relations in Guatemala, 1524-1562. Author: Victoriano Huerta: A Reappraisal (1960). Language: Spanish 4,4,4,4; Portuguese 2,2,1,1; French 2,2,1,1; German 2,2,2,1. Office: Dept. of History, Calif. Western U., San Diego, Calif.

SHIELS, W(ILLIAM) EUGENE, S.J., b. Cincinnati, Ohio, Feb. 2, 1897. HISTORY. A.B., Gonzaga U. (Wash.), 1922; M.A., St. Louis U.,

1928; Ph.D., U. of Calif., Berkeley, 1933. Instr., Campion Coll., 1923-25; instr., Loyola U. (Ill.), 1930-31; asst. prof., St. John's Coll. (Ohio), 1934-35; assoc. prof., Loyola U. (Ill.), 1935-42; assoc. prof., U. of Detroit, 1944-46; PROF., CHMN., HISTORY, XAVIER U., 1946- . Canisius fellow, 1958-59. Membership: American Catholic Historical Association; American Historical Association; Conference on Latin American History; Mississippi Valley Historical Association. Research: colonial church history in Mexico and Paraguay. Author: Gonzalo de Tapia: Founder of Jesuit Missions of North America (1934; Spanish edition, 1958); King and Church (1961). Language: Spanish 5,3,2,3; French 4,2,2,1; German 3,3,2,1; Latin 5,5,5,5. Office: Dept. of History, Xavier U., Cincinnati 7, Ohio.

SHINE, KATHRYN. Home: 8502 16th St., Apt. 417, Silver Spring, Md.

SIMMONS, CHARLES E.P., b. Boston, Mass., Mar. 11, 1931. HISTORY. B.A., Seattle U., 1959; M.A., Drake U., 1960; Washington State U. Instr., Notre Dame U., 1960-61; instr.-ASST. PROF., HISTORY, U. OF IDAHO, 1963- . Fellow, Dalhousie U., 1965-66. Membership: Conference on Latin American History; Pacific Coast Historical Association; Phi Alpha Theta. Research: Latin American history; colonial Mexico church history. Language: Spanish 3,3,3,1; Latin 3,—,—,—. Office: Dept. of History, U. of Idaho, Boise, Idaho.

SIMMONS, MERLE EDWIN, b. Kansas City, Kans., Sept. 27, 1918. SPANISH AMERICAN LITERATURE. A.B., U. of Kans., 1939; M.A., 1941; Ph.D., U. of Mich., 1952. Instr.-PROF., SPANISH, IND. U., 1942- . American Philosophical Society grant, 1955; American Council of Learned Societies grant (Peru), 1962. Membership: American Association of Teachers of Spanish and Portuguese; American Association of University Professors; American Folklore Society; Conference on Latin American History; Instituto Internacional de Literatura Iberoamericana; Modern Language Association of America; Phi Beta Kappa; Phi Sigma Iota. Research: the romance, folklore, and history of ideas in Spanish America; U.S. influence and intellectual currents at the time of Peruvian independence. Author: The Mexican Corrido as a Source for Interpretive Study of Modern Mexico, 1870-1950 (1957); A Bibliography of the Romance and Related Forms in Spanish America (1963). Language: Spanish 5,5,5,5; Portuguese 4,2,2,2; French 4,2,2,2; German 2,—,—,—. Home: 4233 Saratoga Dr., Bloomington, Ind. Office: Dept. of Spanish and Portuguese, Ind. U., Bloomington.

SIMS, HAROLD DANA, b. Oct. 19, 1935. HISTORY. B.A., Stetson U., 1962; M.A., U. of Fla., 1963. INSTR., HISTORY, U. OF PITTSBURGH, 1966- . Graduate Council fellow, U. of Fla. Membership: American Historical Association; Conference on Latin American History; Phi Alpha Theta. Research: Latin American history; Napoleon's emissaries to Spanish America, 1808-1812. Language: Spanish 3,3,3,3; Portuguese 2,2,2,2. Office: Dept. of History, U. of Pittsburgh, Pittsburgh, Pa.

SKIDMORE, THOMAS ELLIOTT, b. Troy, Ohio, July 22, 1932. HISTORY. B.A., Denison U., 1954; B.A., M.A., Oxford U., 1956; Ph.D., Harvard U., 1961. Instr., Harvard U., 1960-61; research fellow in Latin American studies, 1961-64; asst. prof., Harvard U., 1964-66; ASST. PROF., HISTORY., U. OF WIS., 1966- . Social Science Research Council fellow, 1958-59, 1959-60; Harvard U. research fellow (Brazil), 1963-64. Membership: American Historical Association. Research: modern Brazilian history; Brazilian politics, 1889-1918. Author: Survey of Unpublished Sources on the Government and Politics of the Second Empire: 1871-1918 (American Historical Review, July, 1960). Language: Spanish 4,3,2,—; Portuguese 4,4,3,—; French 3,2,2,—; German 4,3,3,—. Office: Dept. of History, U. of Wis., Madison, Wis.

SKLAR, BARRY A. Home: 1715 Preston Rd., Alexandria, Va. 22302.

SLAUGHTER, JOHN EIDELL, b. Ft. Missoula, Mont., Dec. 16, 1912. HISTORY. B.S., U.S. Military Academy, 1935; M.A., U. of Fla., 1963. Officer, U.S. Army, 1935-59; INSTR., SOCIAL SCIENCE, U. OF FLA., 1959- . Membership: American Historical Association; Hispanic American Historical Association; Medieval Academy of America; Phi Alpha Theta. Research: Portuguese and Spanish medieval history; Alfonso Henriques and Portuguese nationality. Language: Spanish 3,2,2,2,; Portuguese 4,3,3,3; French 3,3,2,3; Italian 1,—,—,—; Catalan 1,—,—,—. Home: 224 NE. 10th Ave., Gainesville, Fla. Office: Dept. of Social Science, U. of Fla., Gainesville.

SLUITER, ENGEL, b. New Holland, S. Dak., June 30, 1906. HISTORY. B.A., Stanford U., 1929; M.A., U. of Calif., Berkeley, 1933; Ph.D., 1937. Instr., San Francisco State Coll., 1937-38; project dir., U.S. Works Progress Administration and Bancroft Libraran, U. of Calif., Berkeley, 1938-39; PROF., HISTORY, U. OF CALIF., BERKELEY, 1940- . Social Science Research Council grant (Europe), 1935-36; Rockefeller Foundation fellow (Latin America), 1942-43; Guggenheim fellow (Spain, Portugal), 1948-49; Fulbright fellow (Belgium), 1954-55. Membership: American Historical Association; Conference on Latin American History. Research: Dutch-Iberian rivalry in the colonial world; Brazil, decline of the Spanish and Portuguese empires. Author: The Dutch Archives and American Historical Research (Pacific Historical Review, Mar. 1937); Dutch Maritime Rivalry and the Colonial Status Quo, 1585-1641 (Pacific Historical Review, Mar. 1942); Dutch-Spanish Rivalry in the Caribbean Area (Hispanic American Historical Review, May 1948). Language: Spanish 5,5,4,3; Portuguese 5,5,4,3; French 4,3,1,1; Dutch 5,5,5,5; German 5,5,4,3. Home: 214 Yale Ave., Kensington 8,

Calif. Office: Dept. of History, U. of Calif., Berkeley, 94720.

SMITH, CARLETON SPRAGUE. Office: Luso-Brazilian Institute, N.Y. U., Washington Sq., New York, N.Y. 10003.

SMITH, PETER HOPKINSON, Brooklyn, N.Y., Jan. 17, 1940. HISTORY. B.A., Harvard Coll., 1961; M.A., Columbia U., 1963. STUDENT, HISTORY, COLUMBIA U. Harvard Coll. scholar, 1960-61; New England Society scholar, 1960-61; Woodrow Wilson fellow, 1961-62; International Fellows scholar, 1962-63; National Defense Education Act fellow, 1963-64; Foreign Area fellow (Argentina), 1964-65. Membership: American Association of University Professors; Society for International Development. Research: Latin American history; Argentine economic nationalism; Gabriel García Moreno; Mexican response to the space race. Author: Development and Dictatorship in Nicaragua (American Economist, June 1963). Language: Spanish 4,4,3,3; Portuguese 3,3,3,3; French 2,2,1,1. Home: 789 West End Ave., New York, N.Y. 10025.

SMITH, RALPH ADAM, b. San Augustine, Tex., Apr. 1, 1912. HISTORY. B.A., Stephen F. Austin State Coll., 1934; M.A., U. of Tex., 1936; Ph.D., 1938. Prof., Okla. Coll. for Women, 1939-42; prof., Hardin-Simmons U., 1945-50; PROF., HISTORY, ABILENE CHRISTIAN COLL., 1950- . Membership: Southwestern Historical Association; West Texas Historical Association. Research: Mexico and the American Southwest. Author: Indians in American-Mexican Relations before the War of 1846 (Hispanic American Historical Review, Feb. 1963). Language: Spanish 2,2,2,—; French 2,—,—,—. Home: 665 NE. 15th St., Abilene, Tex. Office: Dept. of History, Abilene Christian Coll., Abilene.

SMITH, ROBERT FREEMAN, b. Little Rock, Ark., May 13, 1930. HISTORY. B.A., U. of Ark., 1952; M.A., 1953; Ph.D., U. of Wis., 1958. Instr., U. of Ark., 1953; asst. prof., Lutheran Coll., 1958-62; asst. prof., U. of R.I., 1962-64; ASSOC. PROF., HISTORY, U. OF R.I., 1964- . Advanced Knapp fellow, U. of Wis., 1957-58. Membership: American Historical Association; Economic History Society; Hispanic American Society; Mississippi Valley Historical Association; Southern Historical Association. Research: Cuban history; United States foreign policy. Author: The United States and Cuba: Business and Diplomacy, 1917-1960 (1960); What Happened in Cuba: A Documentary History (1963); The U.S. and Latin American Revolutions (Journal of Inter American Studies, Jan. 1962). Language: Spanish 3,2,1,1; Portuguese 1,1,1,1; French 2,1,1,1. Home: Greenwood Dr., Peace Dale, R.I. Office: Dept. of History, U. of R.I., Kingston.

SMITH, ROBERT SIDNEY, b. Waterbury, Conn., June 13, 1904. ECONOMICS AND HISTORY. A.B., Amherst Coll., 1927; A.M., 1928; Ph.D., Duke U., 1932. PROF., ECONOMICS, DUKE

U., 1932- ; vis. prof., Universidad de San Carlos (Guatemala), Summer 1949, Universidad del Valle (Colombia), 1963. Amherst Memorial fellow, 1930-32; Guggenheim fellow (Mexico), 1942; U.S. Dept. of State grants (Costa Rica), 1945, (Guatemala), 1949, (Latin America), 1955, 1956, 1957; research grant (Peru, Chile), 1946; Ford Foundation fellow (Central America), 1959-60; Rockefeller grant (Colombia), 1963; Board of Editors, Hispanic American Historical Review, 1947-53; Southern Economic Journal, 1959-62. Membership: Academia de Historia del Valle del Cauca; American Economic Association; Economic History Association; Inter-American Statistical Institute; Southern Economic Association. Research: the Consulados in Spain and America; Spanish and Hispanic economic thought, 1500-1850. Author: The Spanish Guild Merchant: A History of the Consulado, 1250-1700 (1940); Population and Economic Development in Latin America (Southern Economic Journal, July 1957); Population and Economic Growth in Central America (Economic Development and Cultural Change, Jan. 1962). Language: Spanish 4,4,4,4; Portuguese 3,1,1,1; French 4,2,2,1. Home: 2236 Cranford Rd., Durham, N.C. Office: Dept. of Economics, Duke U., Durham.

SMITH, ROBERT WAYNE, b. Kansas City, Mo., June 6, 1903. HISTORY. B.A., U. of Kans., 1924; M.A., U. of Idaho, 1932; Ph.D., U. of Calif., Berkeley, 1937. Instr., Yuba Junior Coll., 1937-41; PROF., HISTORY, OREG. STATE U., 1943- ; part-time vis. prof., U. of Oreg., 1963-64. Membership: American Association of University Professors; American Historical Association. Research: Mexico; South America. Author: Coeur D'Alene Mining War of 1892 (1961). Language: Spanish 4,4,4,4; Portuguese 3,3,3,3; French 4,3,3,3; German 2,2,2,2; Italian 2,2,1,1; Russian 1,1,1,1. Home: 105 North 32nd St. Corvallis, Oreg. Office: Dept. of History, Oregon State U., Corvallis.

SMITH, WILLARD HARVEY, b. Eureka, Ill., Oct. 15, 1900. HISTORY. B.A., Goshen Coll., 1928; M.A., U. of Mich., 1929; Ph.D., Ind. U., 1939. PROF., HISTORY, GOSHEN COLL., 1929- . Dir. of relief work, Mennonite Central Committee (Paraguay), 1944-45; (Mexico), 1954-55. Membership: American Historical Association; American Political Science Association; Hispanic American Society; Mississippi Valley Historical Association. Research: United States-Latin American relations. Author: Paraguayan Interlude-Observations and Impressions (1950); Schulyer Colfax, the Changing Fortunes of a Political Idol (1952); Mennonites in Latin America (Mennonite Quarterly Review, Oct. 1952). Language: Spanish 3,3,3,3; German 3,3,3,3. Home: 1619 South Eighth St., Goshen, Ind. Office: Dept. of History, Goshen Coll., Goshen.

SOLBERG, CARL EDWARD, b. St. Paul, Minn., Apr. 4, 1940. HISTORY. B.A., U. of Minn., 1962; M.A., Stanford U., 1963. STUDENT, HISTORY, STANFORD U. Woodrow Wilson fellow, 1962-63; National Defense Foreign Language fellow in Spanish, 1963-64. Membership: Phi Beta Kappa. Research: Latin American history, especially social and economic history of the 20th century; Argentine reactions to immigration, 1880-1940. Language: Spanish 4,4,4,4; Portuguese 4,2,2,2; French 3,1,1,1. Home: 3721 Lowry Ave. North, Robbinsdale 22, Minn.

SOLNICK, BRUCE B., b. New York, N.Y., Sept. 7, 1933. HISTORY. A.B., N.Y.U., 1954; M.A., 1955; Ph.D., 1960. Instr., N.Y.U., Summers 1957, 1958, 1959; instr., Hunter Coll., 1959-61; ASST. PROF., HISTORY, STATE U. OF N.Y., COLL. AT ALBANY, 1961- . Penfield fellow, 1956-57, 1957-58; Samuel S. Fels Fund grant, 1958-59; Research Foundation of the State U. of N.Y., Inc. grant-in-aid (Jamaica), 1962. Membership: American Historical Association; Conference on Latin American History; Society for the History of Discoveries. Research: history of inter-American relations; period of Latin American Independence; American opinion concerning the Spanish American Wars of Independence, 1808-1824. Language: Spanish 4,3,3,3; Portuguese 3,3,2,1; French 2,1,1,1; German 3,2,2,2; Italian 2,2,1,1. Home: 499 Livingston Ave., Albany, N.Y. 12203. Office: Dept. of History, State U. of N.Y., Coll. at Albany, 135 Western Ave., Albany, 12203.

SPECTOR, ROBERT MELVYN, b. Boston, Mass., Mar. 5, 1926. HISTORY AND POLITICAL SCIENCE. A.B., Boston U., 1948; M.A., 1949; LL.B., Boston Coll., 1959; Ph.D., Boston U., 1961. Teacher, William Howard Taft Junior High School (Boston), 1954-56; master, Boston Latin School, 1956-63; lectr., University Coll., Northeastern U., 1960; ASST. PROF., HISTORY, WORCHESTER STATE COLL., 1963- . Membership: American Historical Association; Mississippi Valley Historical Association; Worcester Association of Historians and Political Scientists. Research: constitutional history; United States-Latin American relations; judicial structure of Caribbean countries; American investment and expropriation problems in the Caribbean. Language: Spanish 2,1,1,2; French 2,1,1,2. Home: 7 Old Wood Rd., Framingham, Mass. 01704. Office: Dept. of History, Worcester State Coll., 486 Chandler St., Worcester, Mass.

SPINDLER, FRANK MacDONALD, b. Columbus, Ohio, Dec. 17, 1917. HISTORY. B.A., U. of Tex., 1939; S.T.B., General Theology Seminary, 1948; M.A., U. of Houston, 1955; American U. Rector, St. Bartholomew's Church (Hempstead, Tex.), 1950-56; curate, Grace and St. Peter's Church (Baltimore), 1956-57; assoc. rector, Church of St. Michael and All Angels (Baltimore), 1957-62; asst. minister, St. Paul's Church (Washington, D.C.), 1962; St. John's Church (Washington, D.C.), 1962-63; ASST. MINISTER, CHURCH OF ASCENSION AND ST. AGNES, 1963- ; STUDENT, HISTORY, AMERICAN U. Membership: American Historical Association; American Institute of Archaeology; Historical Society of the Protestant Episcopal Church; Phi Alpha Theta;

Texas State Historical Association. Research: Latin American and United States history; intellectual history; the political thought of Juan Montalvo. Author: Concerning Hempstead and Waller County (Southwestern Historical Quarterly, Apr. 1956); The History of Hempstead and the Formation of Waller County, Texas (Southwestern Historical Quarterly, Jan. 1960); St. Bartholomew's Church, Hempstead, Texas (Historical Magazine of the Protestant Episcopal Church, Mar. 1960). Language: Spanish 4,3,3,3; French 4,2,2,2. Home: 1233 4th St., SW., Washington, D.C. Office: The Church of the Ascension and St. Agnes, 1217 Massachusetts Ave., NW., Washington, D.C. 20005.

SPINDLER, RUSSELL STEPHEN, b. Duluth, Minn., Nov. 16, 1914. HISTORY AND EDUCATION. B.S., U. of Minn., 1943; M.A., 1950. Education specialist, Eastern Air Defense Force, Stewart Air Force Base (Newburgh, N.Y.), 1950-54; EDUCATION SPECIALIST, SOCIAL SCIENCE, U.S. ARMED FORCES INSTITUTE, 1954- . Membership: American Historical Association; American Sociological Association; Midwest Council of the Association for Latin American Studies; Phi Beta Kappa; Phi Delta Kappa. Research: Latin American history; military history; correspondence education; development of Spanish military institutions, 800-1643. Language: Spanish 3,3,3,3; Portuguese 2,1,1,1; Italian 2,2,1,2. Home: 615 West Dean Ave., Madison 16, Wis. Office: U.S. Armed Forces Institute, 102 North Hamilton, Madison 3.

STAFFORD, JOSEPH EDWARD, O.S.F.S., b. Philadelphia, Pa., June 11, 1926. HISTORY. A.B., Catholic U., 1949; M.A., 1963. Teacher, Northeast Catholic High School (Philadelphia), 1945-47, 1953-54; teacher, DeSales Catholic High School (Lockport, N.Y.), 1954-58; TEACHER, HEAD, SOCIAL STUDIES, FATHER JUDGE HIGH SCHOOL, 1958- . Membership: American Catholic Historical Association; American Catholic Historical Society of Philadelphia; American Historical Association; Conference on Latin American History. Research: United States and Latin American history. Language: Spanish 3,2,2,2; French 3,1,1,1. Home and office: Father Judge High School, 3301 Solly Ave., Philadelphia, Pa. 19136.

STANSIFER, CHARLES LEE, b. Garden City, Kans., Dec. 13, 1930. HISTORY. B.A., Wichita U., 1953; M.A., 1954; Ph.D., Tulane U., 1959. Asst. prof., U. of Southwestern La., 1958-63; ASST. PROF., HISTORY, U. OF KANS., 1963- . Doherty fellow (Chile), 1962-63. Membership: American Association of University Professors; Conference on Latin American History; Mississippi Valley Historical Association. Research: United States relations with Central America; Latin American politics, 1920-40. Author: Cumulative Index to Volumes XXXVI-XLV (1949-1959) of the Mississippi Valley Historical Review (1961); Mexican Foreign Policy in the United Nations: The Advocacy of Moderation in an Era of Revolution (South-

western Social Science Quarterly, Sept. 1963). Language: Spanish 5,4,4,4; Portuguese 4,3,1,1; French 3,2,2,2; Italian 3,2,2,1. Home: 1023 Highland Dr., Lawrence, Kans. Office: Dept. of History, U. of Kans., Lawrence.

STAUFFER, DAVID HALL, b. Shanghai, China, Nov. 3, 1921. HISTORY. B.A., Amherst Coll., 1946; M.A., Columbia U., 1952; Ph.D., U. of Tex., 1955. Teacher, Kiskiminitas Springs School (Pa.), 1949-51; asst. prof., Union Coll., 1955-56; diplomatic historian, U.S. Dept. of State, 1956-62; REPRESENTATIVE, U.S. PEACE CORPS, 1962- ; dir., U.S. Peace Corps Education Project (British Honduras), 1962-64. Membership: Phi Alpha Theta; Phi Delta Kappa. Research: Brazil; British Honduras. Author: Central American Sections (in Foreign Relations of the United States, Diplomatic Papers, 1943-44); Origin and Establishment of Brazil's Indian Service (Revista de História, São Paulo, 1957). Language: Spanish 3,2,1,1; Portuguese 2,1,1,1; French 2,1,1,1; Chinese —,1,1,—. Office: U.S. Peace Corps, Washington 25, D.C.

STEELE, ARTHUR ROBERT, b. Oakland, Calif., Oct. 28, 1916. HISTORY. A.B., U. of Calif., Berkeley, 1937; M.A., U. of N. Mex., 1950; Ph.D., Duke U., 1957. Asst. prof., State U. of N.Y., Coll. at Buffalo, 1957; instr.-ASSOC. PROF., HISTORY, DIR., UNIVERSITY HONORS PROGRAM, U. OF TOLEDO, 1957- . Doherty fellow (Peru and Chile), 1951-52. Membership: American Historical Association; Conference on Latin American History; Midwest Council of the Association for Latin American Studies. Research: colonial period; intellectual history. Author: Flowers for the King: The Expedition of Ruiz and Pavón and the Flora of Peru (1964). Language: Spanish 4,3,3,3; Portuguese 2,1,1,1; French 3,1,1,1. Office: Dept. of History, U. of Toledo, Toledo, Ohio 43606.

STEIGERWALT, ALBERT K., b. New York, N.Y., Dec. 20, 1919. ECONOMICS. A.B., Wayne State U., 1946; A.M., U. of Mich., 1951; Ph.D., 1952. Research assoc., U. of Mich., 1953-57; prof., U. of Mich., 1953-66; DEAN, COLL. OF BUSINESS ADMINISTRATION, DETROIT INSTITUTE OF TECHNOLOGY, 1966- . U. of Mich. fellow, 1950-51; chmn., Conference on Business History, 1954- ; executive committee, Program in International Business; dir., Venezuelan Student Leader Seminar, 1960-63. Membership: American Historical Association; Conference on Business History; Mississippi Valley Historical Association. Research: business and economic development; higher education in Venezuela. Author: Locational Factors in Iron and Steel Industry (1954); The National Association of Manufacturing (1963); Student Tyranny in Latin America (Michigan Quarterly, Autumn 1963). Language: Spanish 3,2,2,2; French 3,2,2,2; German 4,2,2,2. Office: Coll. of Business Administration, Detroit Institute of Technology, Detroit, Mich.

STEIN, STANLEY J., b. New York, N.Y., June 8, 1920. HISTORY, B.A., City Coll. (N.Y.), 1941; M.A., Harvard U., 1948; Ph.D., 1951. PROF., HISTORY, PRINCETON U., 1953- . Social Science Research Council fellow (Brazil), 1948-49; Woodbury Lowery fellow, 1948-49; research fellow, Research Center in Entrepreneurial History, Harvard U., 1950-53; Guggenheim fellow (Mexico), 1958-59; Joint Committee on Latin American Studies, Social Science Research Council-American Council of Learned Societies; Translation Committee, Association of American University Presses. Membership: American Historical Association; Conference on Latin American History. Research: history of Brazil and Mexico, 1750-1900. Author: Vassouras, a Brazilian Coffee County, 1850-1900 (1957); The Brazilian Cotton Manufacture: Textile Enterprise in an Underdeveloped Area, 1850-1950 (1957); Brazilian Historiography (Hispanic American Historical Review, May 1960). Language: Spanish 4,4,4,4; Portuguese 4,4,4,4; French 4,4,3,3. Home: 12 Edgehill St., Princeton, N.J. Office: Dept. of History, Princeton U., Princeton.

STEVENS, ROBERT CONWAY, b. Elgin, Ill., Mar. 2, 1924. HISTORY. B.A., U. of Ariz., 1953; M.A., 1954; Ph.D., U. of Calif., Berkeley, 1963. RESEARCH ASSOC., HISTORY, U. OF ARIZ., 1962- . Arizona Historical Convention Committee, 1963-64. Membership: American Historical Association; Pacific Coast Council on Latin American Studies. Research: archival research on northern Mexico; history of Sonora, 1821-1846. Author: A History of Chandler, Arizona (1955). Language: Spanish 4,2,3,1; Portuguese 2,1,1,1; French 2,1,1,1. Home: 7005 East Kingston Dr., Tucson, Ariz. Office: Dept. of History, U. of Ariz., Tucson.

STEWART, DONALD EDWARD JAMES, b. La Ceiba, Honduras, Feb. 24, 1932. HISTORY AND BIBLIOGRAPHY. B.A., Washington & Lee U., 1955; M.A., George Washington U., 1960. Asst. to the editor, Handbook of Latin American Studies, 1962-64; Foreign Service officer, U.S. Dept. of State, 1964-65; VICE-CONSUL (YOKOHAMA, JAPAN), U.S. DEPT. OF STATE, 1965- . U.S. Dept. of State Foreign Service Institute guest lectr.; George Washington U. guest lectr. on international politics of the Western Hemisphere; administrative asst. and dir. of evening programs for participants in the Andean Seminar, International Study Center. Membership: American Historical Association; Association of Latin American Studies; Inter-American Council. Research: Latin American history, especially that of Central America; Latin American bibliography. Language: Spanish 5,5,5,5; Portuguese 4,3,3,1; French 4,4,4,2. Home and office: American Consulate General, FPO, San Francisco, Calif. 96660.

STEWART, WATT, b. Flatwoods, W. Va., Mar. 21, 1892. HISTORY. B.A., West Va. Wesleyan, 1920; M.A., U. of Chicago, 1925; Ph.D., 1928. Prof., Okla. State U., 1928-40; prof., chmn., History, State U. of N.Y., Coll. at Albany,

1940-57; PROF. EMERITUS, 1957- . Smith-Mundt lectr., U. of Guayaquil, U. of Cuenca, and Central U. (Ecuador), 1957-58; Guggenheim fellow (Costa Rica), 1958-59. Membership: American Historical Association; Conference on Latin American History; Sociedad Chilena de Historia y Geografía; Sociedad Costarricense de Geografía e Historia. Research: Latin American diplomatic relations. Author: Henry Meiggs: Yankee Pizarro (1946); Chinese Bondage in Peru (1951); Keith and Costa Rica (1964). Language: Spanish 4,4,4,3; French 4,3,2,1. Home: 204 Charleston, NE., Albuquerque, N. Mex.

STOKES, WILLIAM SYLVANE, b. Willcox, Ariz., Feb. 21, 1916. POLITICAL SCIENCE. B.A., U. of Calif., Los Angeles, 1938; Ph.D., 1943. Instr.-asst. prof., Northwestern U., 1943-46; assoc. prof.-prof., U. of Wis., 1946-58; vis. prof., U. of Calif., Berkeley, 1951-52; prof.-senior prof., Claremont Men's Coll., 1958-62; prof., National War Coll., 1962-63; SENIOR PROF., POLITICAL SCIENCE, CLAREMONT MEN'S COLL., 1963- . Volker Fund fellow; Reim Foundation fellow; Del Amo Foundation fellow; Social Science Research Council fellow; executive council, Inter-American Defense Coll., 1962-63. Membership: American Political Science Association; Western Political Science Association. Research: comparative government; international relations; political institutions and governmental development in Honduras; Cuba; Mexico; Central America. Author: Honduras, an Area Study in Government (1950); Latin American Politics (1959); U.S. Policy and Inter-American Misunderstandings (1964). Language: Spanish 5,5,5,5; Portuguese 4,2,1,1; French 3,1,1,1; German 3,1,1,1. Home: 1401 North Mountain Ave., Claremont, Calif. Office: Dept. of Political Science, Claremont Men's Coll., Claremont.

STREET, JAMES H. Office: Dept. of Economics, Rutgers U., New Brunswick, N.J. 08903.

SUGHRUE, JUDITH ANN, b. Worcester, Mass., Aug. 2, 1935. HISTORY. A.B., Regis Coll., 1957; M.A., Catholic U., 1965. Data systems analyst, National Security Agency, 1957-61; computer programmer, Goddard Space Flight Center, Summers 1963, 1964; INSTR., HISTORY, STONEHILL COLL., 1964- . Regis Coll. scholar. Membership: American Association for the Advancement of Science; American Historical Association; Massachusetts Archaeological Society; Pi Gamma Mu. Research: Latin American history; Western civilization; history of computers. Language: Spanish 2,1,-1,2; French 2,1,1,2; German 2,—,—,—. Home: 74 Church St., Whitinsville, Mass. Office: Social Science Office, Stonehill Coll., North Easton, Mass.

SULLIVAN, RALPH E., b. Gary, Ind., Dec. 7, 1927. HISTORY. A.B., George Washington U., 1961; M.A., 1963. LIEUTENANT COLONEL, U.S. MARINE CORPS, 1944- . Adviser to the naval delegation, Joint Brazilian-U.S. Defense Commission and Joint Mexican-

U.S. Defense Commission, 1962- . Membership: American Historical Association; Conference on Latin American History. Research: Latin American history, especially the 19th and 20th centuries; diplomatic recognition of the government of Porfirio Díaz by the United States; amphibious warfare. Language: Spanish 4,3,3,3; Portuguese 3,2,1,1; French 2,1,1,1. Home: 910 Braeburn Dr., Fairfax, Va. Office: Marine Corps Command Center—Code AC, Headquarters, U.S. Marine Corps, Washington 25, D.C.

SVEC, WILLIAM RUDOLPH, b. Chicago, Ill., Nov. 27, 1933. HISTORY. B.S., Loyola U., 1956; M.A., Northwestern U., 1959; U. of Tex. ASST. PROF., HISTORY, CALIF. STATE COLL., LONG BEACH, 1964- . University fellow; Ford Foundation Foreign Area Training fellow. Membership: American Historical Association. Research: Latin American history; Argentina; development of the modern Argentine estancia, 1852-1914. Language: Spanish 4,4,4,4; Portuguese 3,2,2,2; French 2,2,2,2. Home: 910 North Kedvale Ave., Chicago 51, Ill. Office: Dept. of History, Calif. State Coll., Long Beach, Calif.

SWECKER, ZOE. Office: Winona State Coll., Winona, Minn. 55987.

SYNNESTVEDT, SIG, b. Bryn Athyn, Pa., Nov. 13, 1924. HISTORY AND INTERNATIONAL RELATIONS. B.A., Mich. State U., 1949; M.A., 1950; Ph.D., U. of Pa., 1959. PROF., HISTORY, ACADEMY OF THE NEW CHURCH, 1950- ; RESEARCH ASSOC., INTERNATIONAL RELATIONS, FOREIGN POLICY RESEARCH INSTITUTE, U. OF PA., 1960- . Asst. to dir., Latin American Project, Foreign Policy Research Institute; post-doctoral fellow, U. of Pa.; editorial staff, Orbis: A Quarterly Journal of World Affairs. Membership: American Historical Association; Conference on Latin American History; Phi Alpha Theta; Phi Kappa Phi. Research: Latin American foreign policy. Author: Public Service (New Church Life, Nov. 1956); Red Drive in Cuba (Current History, Oct. 1963). Language: Spanish 3,3,2,2; French 2,2,2,2. Home: 660 Woodward Dr., Huntington Valley, Pa. Office: Foreign Policy Research Institute, U. of Pa., 133 South 36th St., Philadelphia 4.

SZADLOWSKI, JOHN PHILLIP, b. Olean, N.Y., Dec. 20, 1932. HISTORY. B.A., St. Bonaventure U., 1956; M.A., 1961; Georgetown U. INSTR., COLL. OF STEUBENVILLE, 1963- . Membership: American Historical Association; Hispanic American Historical Association. Research: Latin American history and government; United States-Brazilian relations; United States-Chilean diplomatic relations, 1898-1942. Language: Spanish 3,3,3,3; Portuguese 2,2,2,2; French 3,3,3,3. Home: 711 North 4th St., Steubenville, Ohio. Office: Dept. of History, Coll. of Steubenville, Steubenville.

SZÁSZDI, ADAM M., b. Budapest, Hungary, Nov. 16, 1930. HISTORY. B.A., Western

Reserve U., 1952; M.A., Tulane U., 1954; Ph.D., Universidad de Madrid, 1956. Asst. prof., Inter American U. of P.R., 1956-58; ASSOC. PROF., HISTORY, HUMANIDADES, UNIVERSIDAD DE P.R., 1958- . Organization of American States grant (Ecuador), Summer 1963. Membership: American Historical Association; Conference on Latin American History; Phi Alpha Theta; Society for the History of Discoveries; Southeastern Conference of Latin American Studies. Research: colonial Latin America; archival research in Central America. Author: Nicolas Raoul y la República Federal de Centroamérica (1958); La municipalidad de San Germán en Puerto Rico, 1798-1808 (Journal of Inter-American Studies, Oct. 1959); Credit—without Banking—in Early 19th Century Puerto Rico (The Americas, 1962). Language: Spanish 5,5,5,5; Portuguese 4,3,2,1; French 5,5,4,4; German 4,4,3,3; Italian 3,2,1,1. Home: Ave. de los Flamboyanes 171 Río Piedras, P.R. Office Facultad de Estudios Generales, Universidad de P.R., Río Piedras.

SZÁSZDI, DORA LEÓN BORJA DE, b. Apr. 9, 1926. HISTORY. M.A., U. of Guayaquil (Ecuador), 1951; Ph.D., U. of Madrid, 1956. Asst. prof., Inter American U., 1957-58; asst. prof., U. of P.R., 1958-59; ASST. PROF., HISTORY, INTER AMERICAN U., 1961- . Membership: American Historical Association; Bolivarian Society of the United States; Conference on Latin American History; Phi Alpha Theta; Society for the History of Discoveries; Southeastern Conference of Latin American Studies. Research: colonial Latin American history; history of Guayaquil, Ecuador. Language: Spanish 5,5,5,5. Home: Ave. de los Flamboyanes 171, Río Piedras, P.R. Office: Dept. of History, Inter American U. of P.R., Hato Rey.

TALBOTT, ROBERT DEAN, b. Centralia, Ill., Feb. 18, 1928. HISTORY. B.A., U. of Ill., 1950; M.A., 1955; Ph.D., 1959. Instr., Emporia State Teachers Coll., 1958-59; assoc. prof., Valley City State Teachers Coll., 1959-62; ASSOC. PROF., HISTORY, KEARNEY STATE COLL., 1962- . Membership: American Historical Association. Research: the colonial period in Chile; history of Chilean boundaries, 1540-1955. Language: Spanish 2,2,1,1; Portuguese 1,1,1,1; French 2,1,1,1. Home: 903 East 30th Dr., Kearney, Nebr. Office: Div. of Social Science, Kearney State Coll., Kearney.

TAMBS, LEWIS A., b. San Diego, Calif., July 7, 1927. HISTORY. B.S., U. of Calif., Berkeley, 1953; M.A., U. of Calif., Santa Barbara, 1962. Asst. plant engineer, Standard Brands, Inc. (San Francisco), 1953-54; pipeline engineer, Creole Petroleum Corporation (Caracas), 1954-57; general manager, C.A. CACYP Instalaciones Petroleras (Maracaibo, Venezuela), 1957-59; STUDENT, HISTORY, U. OF CALIF., SANTA BARBARA. Salzburg Seminar in American Studies fellow, 1960; National Defence Education Act fellow in Western Hemisphere Studies, 1962-63. Membership: American

Historical Association; Pacific Coast Council on Latin American Studies. Research: Latin American history; geopolitical analysis of Bolivian-Brazilian relations in the 20th century. Language: Spanish 5,5,5,4; Portuguese 3,2,2,2. Home: 1919 El Camino de la Luz, Santa Barbara, Calif.

TANCK, DOROTHY ELIZABETH, b. San Francisco, Calif., Aug. 28, 1941. HISTORY. B.A., Trinity Coll. (Washington, D.C.), 1963. STUDENT, HISTORY, U. OF CALIF., BERKELEY. Fulbright scholar (Argentina), 1963-64. Research: Latin American history; archeology of Guatemala and Argentina; liberal-conservative conflicts in 19th century Argentina. Language: Spanish 5,4,5,4; Portuguese 4,3,3,3; French 3,2,2,2. Home: 197 Wicks Lane, Malvern, Long Island, N.Y. 11565.

TANNENBAUM, FRANK, b. Austria, Mar. 4, 1893. HISTORY AND ECONOMICS. B.A., Columbia Coll., 1921; Ph.D., Brookings Institution, 1927. Newspaper correspondent (Mexico), 1922-24; surveyor in Mexico, Institute of Economics (Washington, D.C.), 1925-27; staff member in P.R., 1928-30; instr., Cornell U., Summer 1932; lectr., Columbia U., 1935-37; assoc. prof., 1937-45; prof., 1945-61; vis. lectr., Universidad de San Marcos (Peru), 1947; PROF. EMERITUS, LATIN AMERICAN HISTORY, COLUMBIA U., 1961- . Guggenheim fellow, 1932-33. Membership: Academy of Political Science; American Economic Association; American Geographical Association; American Historical Association; Instituto Geográfico e Histórico de Bahía (Brazil). Research: economic and social history; Mexico. Author: Mexico, the Struggle for Peace and Bread (1950); A Philosophy of Labor (1951); Ten Keys to Latin America (1962). Language: Spanish 4,4,4,—; Portuguese 4,4,4,—. Office: Dept. of History, Columbia U., 409 West 117th St., New York 27, N.Y.

TANNER, EARL CHAPIN, b. Providence, R.I., Nov. 16, 1919. PHYSICS. A.M., Brown U., 1947; Ph.D., Harvard U., 1951; Sc. M., Brown U., 1959. ASST. TO THE DIR., PLASMA PHYSICS LABORATORY, PRINCETON U., 1959- ; assoc. dir., Summer Institute in Plasma Physics, Princeton U. Membership: American Historical Association; American Physical Society; Conference on Latin American History. Language: Spanish 4,—,—,—; Portuguese 4,—,—,—; French 4,2,2,2; German 2,2,2,2. Home: 354 Cold Soil Rd., Princeton, N.J. Office: Plasma Physics Laboratory, P.O. Box 451, Princeton U., Princeton.

TANNER, HELEN HORNBECK, b. Northfield, Minn., July 5, 1916. HISTORY. A.B., Swarthmore Coll., 1937; M.A., U. of Fla., 1949; Ph.D., U. of Mich., 1961. LECTR., EXTENSION SERVICE, U. OF MICH., 1961- . American Association of University Women fellow, 1958-59. Membership: American Historical Association; American Indian Ethnohistoric Conference; Central States Anthropological Society; Conference on Latin American History; Florida Historical Society. Research: Spanish Florida. Author: Zéspedes in East Florida (1963). Language: Spanish 3,2,2,2; French 3,2,2,3; German 3,2,2,3. Home: 1319 Brooklyn Ave., Ann Arbor, Mich. 48104. Office: Extension Service, U. of Mich., Ann Arbor.

TAPIA, FRANCISCO XAVIER, S. J., b. Zaragoza, Spain, Jan. 8, 1925. HISTORY. S.T.B., Woodstock Coll., 1958; M.A., Georgetown U., 1961; Ph.D., 1963. Assoc. prof., Sophia U. (Japan), 1960-66; ASSOC. PROF., HISTORY, U. OF P.R., 1966- . Private grant for archival research in Central and South America, 1963. Membership: American Historical Association; Hispanic American Society. Research: colonial Spanish America; Latin American economic geography. Author: El cabildo abierto colonial (1964); Democracia en el absolutismo (Estudios Americanos, 1960). Language: Spanish 5,5,5,5; Portuguese 4,3,2,1; French 3,3,1,1; Italian 4,4,4,3; Japanese 4,4,4,3. Home: 19 Media Lequerica, Madrid 4, Spain. Office: Dept. of History, U. of P.R., Mayaguez, P.R. 00709.

TAPSON, ALFRED JOSEPH, b. Feb. 21, 1909. HISTORY. A.B., U. of Calif., Berkeley, 1933; M.A., 1942; Ph.D., 1952. Teacher, San Francisco Unified School District, 1935-55; INSTR., HISTORY, CITY COLL. OF SAN FRANCISCO. Membership: California Historical Society; Conference on Latin American History; Pacific Historical Society. Research: Argentine plains frontier and other similar frontier areas; the Indian problem on the Argentine Pampa, 1735-1852. Author: The Sutler and the Soldier (Military Affairs, Winter 1957); Indian Warfare on the Pampa during the Colonial Period (Hispanic American Historical Review, Feb. 1962). Language: Spanish 4,3,3,3; Portuguese 3,2,2,1; French 4,3,2,1. Home: 110 Walnut St., San Francisco 18, Calif. Office: Dept. of History, City Coll. of San Francisco, San Francisco.

TARR, TERENCE STEPHEN, b. Everson, Wash., Nov. 17, 1935. HISTORY. B.A., State U. of Wash., 1957; M.A., U. of Fla., 1958; Ph.D., 1960. Asst. prof., U. of Miss., 1960-62; vis. asst. prof., U. of Wash., 1962-63; ASST. PROF., HISTORY, U. OF DENVER, 1963- . U. of Fla. fellow, 1957-59; Doherty fellow (Chile), 1959-60. Membership: American Association of University Professors; American Historical Association; Conference on Latin American History. Research: modern Chile; military intervention and the civilian reaction in Chile, 1924-1938. Language: Spanish 4,4,4,2; Portuguese 2,3,3,1; French 2,2,1,1. Home: 2309 South Columbine, Denver 10, Colo. Office: Dept. of History, U. of Denver, Denver 10.

TePASKE, JOHN JAY, b. Grand Rapids, Mich., Dec. 8, 1929. HISTORY. B.A., Mich. State U., 1951; M.A., Duke U., 1953; Ph.D., 1959. Asst. prof., Memphis State U., 1958-59; asst. prof., Ohio State U., 1959-64; ASSOC. PROF., HISTORY, OHIO STATE U., 1964- . Institute of International Education fellow (Spain), 1956-57; Ford Foundation Foreign Area Training fellow, U. of Calif., Berkeley, 1962-63. Membership: American Historical Association; Conference on Latin American History; Phi Beta Kappa. Research: Peru, Bolivia, and Chile in the 18th century; Spanish Florida. Author: Economic Problems of Governors of Florida, 1700-1763 (Florida Historical Quarterly, July 1958). Co-editor: The Character of Philip II: The Problem of Moral Judgments in History (1963); Explosive Forces in Latin America (1964); The Governorship of Spanish Florida, 1700-1763 (1964). Language: Spanish 4,4,3,4; Portuguese 2,—,2,1; French 2,3,2,1 Home: 351 Park Blvd., Worthington, Ohio. Office: Dept. of History, Ohio State U., Columbus 10.

THOMAS, ALFRED BARNABY, b. Belt, Mont., Apr. 14, 1896. HISTORY. A.B., U. of Calif., Berkeley, 1923; M.A., 1925; Ph.D., 1927. Asst. prof.-assoc. prof., U. of Okla., 1927-37; PROF., HISTORY, U. OF ALA., 1937- . Native Sons of the Golden West fellow (Spain), 1925-26; Social Science Research Council-Council of Learned Societies research grants (Mexico); Guggenheim fellow (Spain), 1929-30; historian for the Jicarilla, Mescalero, and Chiricahua Apache Indians, 1959-62; editorial consultant, Arizona and the West-Journal of History. Membership: American Historical Association; Hispanic American Society; Conference on Latin American History; Mississippi Valley Historical Association; New Mexico Historical Society; Southeastern Conference on Latin American Studies. Research: the Spanish Empire under Charles III. Author: After Coronado: Spanish Exploration Northeast of New Mexico, 1696-1727 (1935); Teodoro de Croix and the Northern Frontier of New Spain, 1776-1783 (1941); Latin America: A History (1956). Language: Spanish 3,3,3,3; Portuguese 3,—,—,—; French 3,3,3,3; Rumanian 3,—,—,—. Home: 96 The Highlands, Tuscaloosa, Ala. Office: Dept. of History, Box 1491, U. of Ala., University.

THOMAS, JACK RAY, b. Youngstown, Ohio, Dec. 23, 1931. HISTORY. B.A., Youngstown U., 1954; M.A., Kent State U., 1960; Ph.D., Ohio State U., 1962. Asst. prof., Wis. State Coll., 1962-65; ASST. PROF., HISTORY, BOWLING GREEN U., 1965- . Doherty fellow (Chile), 1961-62. Membership: American Historical Association; Midwest Council of the Association of Latin American Studies. Research: growth of the Socialist Party in Chile and the role of Marmaduke Grove Vallejo in its development; political economy of Chile, 1920-40. Language: Spanish 4,3,3,2; French 2,1,1,1. Office: Bowling Green State U., Bowling Green, Ohio.

THOMAS AQUINAS, SISTER. Office: St. Mary Coll., Xavier, Kan. 66098.

THORNING, JOSEPH FRANCIS, b. Milwaukee, Wis., Apr. 25, 1896. HISTORY. B.A., St. Louis U., 1921; M.A., 1929; Ph.D., Catholic U. of America, 1931. Prof., Mount St. Mary's Seminary and Coll., 1936-46; ASSOC. EDITOR, WORLD AFFAIRS, 1940- ; RECTOR, ST. JO-

SEPH'S-ON-CARROLLTON MANOR, 1946- ; DIR., INTER-AMERICAN SEMINAR, MARY-MOUNT COLL., 1958- . Dir., American Peace Society; consultant, U.S. Congress. Membership: Historical and Geographic Institute of Brazil. Research: inter-faith understanding and cooperation; political organization of Brazil. Author: Religious Liberty (1931); Builders of the Social Order (1941); Miranda: World Citizen (1952). Language: Spanish 4,4,4,4; Portuguese 3,3,3,3; French 4,4,4,4; German 3,3,3,3; Greek 5,5,5,5; Italian 3,3,3,3; Latin 5,5,5,5. Home: St. Joseph's-on-Carrollton Manor, Frederick 4, Md. Office: World Affairs, 1307 New Hampshire Ave., NW., Washington 6, D.C.

THURMAN, MICHAEL E., b. Kansas City, Mo., Oct. 7, 1933. HISTORY. A.B., U. of Southern Calif., 1955; A.M., 1960; Ph.D., 1963. Instr., Naval Reserve Officer's School, U. of Southern Calif., 1959-60; Extension Div., 1960; student professional curator, History Div., Los Angeles County Museum, 1959-60; registrar's asst., U. of Southern Calif., Summer 1961; ASST. PROF., HISTORY, EAST TEX. STATE COLL., 1962- . Del Amo fellow (Spain), 1961-62. Membership: California Historical Society; Montana Historical Society; Pacific Council on Latin American Affairs; Phi Alpha Theta; Western History Association. Research: colonial Mexico; Alta California; 19th century Central America. Author: A New Historical Depository (Los Angeles County Museum Associates Quarterly, Summer 1960); The Naval Department of San Blas and Its Initial Naval Fleet (Hispanic American Historical Review, Feb. 1963). Language: Spanish 4,4,4,4; Portuguese 2,1,1,1; French 2,1,1,1; German 2,1,1,2. Home: 643 Fourth St., Encinitas, Calif. Office: Dept. of History, East Tex. State Coll., Commerce, Tex.

TIGNER, JAMES LAWRENCE, b. Los Angeles, Calif., Apr. 18, 1918. HISTORY. A.B., U. of Redlands, 1948; A.M., Stanford U., 1949; Ph.D., 1956. Field assoc. in history, Pacific Science Board, National Academy of Sciences and Hoover Institution, Stanford U., 1951-55; instr., Hoover Institution, 1955; Stanford U., 1956-59; ASSOC. PROF., HISTORY, U. OF NEV., 1959- . Pacific Science Board, National Academy of Sciences, research grant for Ryukyuan Emigration Project in Latin America. Membership: American Historical Association; Conference on Latin American History; Pacific Coast Conference on Latin American Studies. Research: immigration and resettlement in Latin America; Japanese and Ryukyuan communities in Latin America; economic and social history. Author: The Okinawans in Latin America (1955); Shindo Remmel: Japanese Nationalism in Brazil (Hispanic American Historical Review, Nov. 1961); The Ryukyuans in Bolivia (Hispanic American Historical Review, May 1963). Language: Spanish 4,4,4,3; Portuguese 4,4,4,3; French 3,2,2,2. Home: P.O. Box 385, Virginia City, Nev. Office: Dept. of History, U. of Nev., Reno.

TILLER, ANN QUIGGINS, b. Ravenna, Ky., Aug. 2, 1921. HISTORY. B.A., U. of Houston, 1961; M.A., 1963. INSTR., HISTORY, ALVIN JUNIOR COLL., 1962- . Membership: American Association of Teachers of Spanish and Portuguese; American Historical Association; Conference on Latin American History; Mississippi Valley Historical Association; Southern Historical Association. Research: United States and Latin American history; Brazilian history; Brazilian revolution of 1930. Language: Spanish 3,3,3,3; Portuguese 3,3,3,3. Home: 7901 Montglen Dr., Houston, Tex. Office: Alvin Junior Coll., Alvin, Tex. 77511.

TIMMONS, WILBERT H., b. Springfield, Mo., June 22, 1915. HISTORY. B.A., Park Coll., 1938; M.A., U. of Chicago, 1940; Ph.D., U. of Tex., 1949. Asst. prof., Tex. Western Coll., 1949-53; assoc. prof., 1953-57; PROF., HISTORY, TEX. WESTERN COLL., 1957- ; CHMN., 1962- . Membership: American Historical Association; Southwest Social Science Association. Research: United States diplomatic history; Mexican independence period. Author: Morelos of Mexico: Priest, Soldier, Statesman (1963); Los Guadalupes (Hispanic American Historical Review, Nov. 1950). Language: Spanish 4,2,1,1. Home: 104 Crown Point Dr., El Paso, Tex. 79912. Office: Dept. of History, Tex. Western Coll., El Paso.

TINKER, EDWARD LAROCQUE, b. New York, N.Y., Sept. 12, 1881. HISTORY AND SPANISH AMERICAN LITERATURE. A.B., Columbia U., 1902; LL.B., N.Y. Law School, 1905; Ph.D., Université de Paris, 1933; LL.D. (honorary), Middlebury Coll., 1949; Ph.D., Universidad de Madrid, 1955; Litt.D. (honoris causa), Columbia U., 1962. Lectr., Carnegie Endowment for International Peace (Mexico), 1943; exchange prof., U.S. Dept. of State (Uruguay, Argentina), 1945; PRESIDENT, TINKER FOUNDATION. Palmes Academiques (France), 1933; Chevalier Legion of Honor, 1939; El Orden de Mayo al Mérito (Argentina); Award of the Americas Foundation, 1962; Comendador, Orden de Isabela Católica, 1963; vice president, Spanish Institute. Membership: American Antiquarian Society; Hispanic Society of America; Instituto González Fernández de Oviedo (Spain); Instituto Histórico y Geográfico del Uruguay. Research: gaucho literature; the Latin American cowboy and his folklore. Author: Los jinetes de las Américas y la literatura por ellos inspirada (1952; English edition, 1953); Corridos y calaveras (1961); Life and Literature of the Pampas (1961). Language: Spanish 4,4,3,2; French 5,5,4,3. Home and office: Tinker Foundation, 550 Park Ave., New York 21, N.Y.

TREE, ROBERT L. Office: Dept. of History, Parsons Coll., Fairfield, Iowa 52556.

TREMBLEY, WILLIAM ALBERT, b. Akron, Ohio, June 6, 1920. HISTORY. B.A., U. of Akron, 1942; M.A., U. of Houston, 1953. Asst. Prof., U.S. Merchant Marine Academy, 1957-59; ASST. PROF., HISTORY, RESEARCH

ASSOC., INSTITUTE OF CARIBBEAN STUDIES, U. OF P.R., 1959- ; vis. lectr., U. of the West Indies (Jamaica), 1962-63. John S. Knight scholarship, U. of Akron, 1943; Ford fellow, 1956; Fulbright fellow (Haiti), 1957. Membership: American Historical Association; Jamaica Historical Society. Research: 19th century Haiti and the French Caribbean. Author: The Status of the Church in Saint-Domingue during the Last Days of the French Monarchy, 1781-1793 (Caribbean Studies, Apr. 1960). Co-author: The Alfred Nemours Collection of Haitian History: A Catalogue (Caribbean Studies, Oct. 1962). Editor: Directory of Caribbean Studies (1962). Language: Spanish 2,3,2,1; French 3,3,3,3. Home: Calle del Sol 4 (Interior), San Juan, P.R. Office: Institute of Caribbean Studies, U. of P.R., Río Piedras.

TREUTLEIN, THEODORE EDWARD, b. San Diego, Calif., Dec. 25, 1906. HISTORY. B.A., San Diego State Coll., 1929; M.A., U. of Calif., 1930; Ph.D., 1934. PROF., HISTORY, SAN FRANCISCO STATE COLL., 1935- ; vis. assoc. prof., Stanford U., 1946. Native Sons of the Golden West traveling fellow in Pacific Coast History, 1932-33. Membership: American Association of University Professors; American Historical Association; California Historical Society; Pacific Coast Council on Latin American Studies. Research: history of Mexico. Author: The Relation of Philipp Segesser (Mid-America, July 1945). Translator and editor: Sonora: A Description of the Province, by Ignaz Pfefferkorn (1949). Language: Spanish 3,3,3,1; German 4,4,4,3. Home: 2215 Marin Ave., Berkeley 7, Calif. Office: Dept. of History, San Francisco State Coll., 1600 Holloway, San Francisco 27, Calif.

TRUE, MARSHALL M., b. Portland, Maine, June 28, 1938. HISTORY. B.A., Bates Coll., 1960; M.A., U. of Va., 1963. STUDENT, HISTORY, U. OF VA., 1960- . DuPont fellow, 1961-63. Research: Latin American history; Cuban independence period, 1890-1898. Language: Spanish 4,2,2,3; Portuguese 2,1,1,1; French 4,2,2,2. Home: 1815 Jefferson Park Ave., Charlottesville, Va. 22903.

TRUEBLOOD, FELICITY. Office: Box 13368 University Station, Gainesville, Fla.

TUDISCO, ANTHONY, b. Brooklyn, N.Y., Aug. 5, 1915. LANGUAGE. B.A., Brooklyn Coll., 1936; M.A., Columbia U., 1937; Ph.D., 1950. Instr., Long Island U., 1938-41; tutor, Queens Coll., 1943-47; ASSOC. PROF., SPANISH, COLUMBIA U., 1947- . Regional Interviewing Committee for Teacher Exchange Program, U.S. Dept. of Health, Education, and Welfare. Membership: American Association of Teachers of Spanish and Portuguese; Conference on Latin American History; Hispanic Institute; North East Conference for Latin American Studies; Sigma Delta Pi. Research: language and literature of Spanish America. Author: América en la literatura española del Siglo XVIII (Anuario de Estudios Americanos, 1954); The Land, People, and Problems of America in XVIIIth Century Spanish Literature (The

Americas, Apr. 1956); America to Some Travelers, Historians, and Political Economists of the Spanish Eighteenth Century (The Americas, July 1958). Language: Spanish 5,5,5,5; Portuguese 3,3,1,1; French 3,3,1,1; Italian 4,4,4,4. Linguistic studies: Spanish. Home: 601 West 113th St., New York, N.Y. 10025. Office: Dept. of Spanish, Columbia U., New York, 10027.

TULCHIN, JOSEPH SAMUEL, b. New York, N.Y., Jan. 13, 1939. HISTORY. B.A., Amherst Coll., 1959; Cambridge U.; Ph.D., Harvard U., 1965. Harvard U. Office of Latin American Studies traveling fellow (Argentina), 1962. Research: United States and Latin American history; inter-American relations. Language: Spanish 3,3,3,2; Portuguese 2,1,1,1; French 2,2,2,2. Home: 1218 Forest Rd., New Haven, Conn. Office: Dept. of History, Yale U., New Haven, 06520.

TURNER, ALNEA. Home: 2212 I St., NW., Washington, D.C.

TURNER, GEORGE RONALD, b. Sacramento, Calif., June 16, 1937. HISTORY. B.A., U. of the Pacific, 1963; M.A., Tex. Christian U., 1965. STUDENT, HISTORY, TEX. CHRISTIAN U. National Defense Education Act fellow, Tex. Christian U., 1964-65. Membership: Phi Alpha Theta. Research: Latin American history; world geography; Juan Alvarez of Mexico. Language: Spanish 3,2,3,3; German 3,2,3,3. Home: 1818 Fairmount Ave., Fort Worth, Tex. 76110.

ULIBARRI, GEORGE SARRACINO, b. Reserve, N. Mex., May 16, 1916. LIBRARY SCIENCE: ARCHIVAL ADMINISTRATION. B.A., U. of N. Mex., 1943; M.A., 1948; Ph.D., U. of Iowa, 1952. Instr., Spanish and Portuguese, U. of Iowa, 1948-52; prof., Spanish, U. of Wyo., 1952-53; translator and interpreter, Mayo Clinic, 1953; LATIN AMERICAN SPECIALIST, ARCHIVIST, DEPT. OF CIVIL ARCHIVES, NATIONAL ARCHIVES, 1956- . Secretary general, Consejo Interamericano Técnico para Archivos; chmn., Committee on Spanish Archival Terminology; Advisory Committee, Guide to Latin American Materials in the United States. Membership: Consejo Interamericano Técnico para Archivos; Sociedad de Archiveros Peruanos; Society of American Archivists. Research: archival management; novels of Peru, Bolivia, and Ecuador. Author: Semejanzas y diferencias entre archivos y bibliotecas (Revista Interamericana de Bibliografía, Sept. 1962); The Inter-American Technical Council on Archives (American Archivist, Jan. 1964). Translator: Técnicas descriptivas de archivos, by T. R. Schellenberg (1961). Language: Spanish 5,5,5,5; Portuguese 4,3,2,1; French 3,1,1,1. Home: 3960 Pennsylvania Ave., SE., Washington, D.C. 20020. Office: National Archives and Records Service, Washington, D.C. 20408.

UNDREINER, GEORGE JOSEPH, RT. REV. MSGR., b. Brooklyn, N.Y., Oct. 28, 1900. HISTORY. A.B., Josephinum Coll., 1920; Josephinum Seminary, 1923-27; Ph.D., U. of Fribourg (Switzerland), 1931. PROF. OF HISTORY AND CHURCH HISTORY, PONTIFICAL COLL., JOSEPHINUM, 1931- . Membership: Academy of American Franciscan History; Conference on Latin American History; New Mexico Historical Society. Research: southwest United States history; Catholic missions. Author: Monsignor Joseph Jessing, 1836-1899 (1936); Church and Culture in the Middle Ages (1956); Fray Marcos de Niza and His Journey to Cibola (The Americas, Apr. 1947). Language: Spanish 4,2,1,2; Portuguese 2,—,—,—; French 4,3,3,3; German 5,5,4,4. Home and office: Pontifical Coll. Josephinum, Worthington, Ohio.

VAN AKEN, MARK JAY, b. Elkhart, Ind., Apr. 9, 1922. HISTORY. B.A., U. of Mich., 1944; M.A., U. of Calif., Berkeley, 1952; Ph.D., 1955. Asst. prof., Memphis State Coll., 1955-56; instr., U. of Calif., Berkeley, 1952; Ph.D., asst. prof., San Diego State Coll., 1957-60; asst. prof.-assoc. prof., Alameda State Coll., 1960-63; ASSOC. PROF., HISTORY, DUKE U., 1963- . U. of Mich.-U. of Tucumán exchange fellow (Argentina), 1947-48; Institute of International Education exchange fellow (Spain), 1953-54; Fulbright fellow (Uruguay), 1963-64. Membership: American Historical Association; Conference on Latin American History; Pacific Coast Council on Latin American Studies. Research: university student movement in 20th century Latin America; Pan-Hispanism in the 19th century; diplomatic history, 19th century; the diplomatic intrigues of General Juan José Flores of Ecuador, 1840-1860. Author: Pan-Hispanism: Its Origin and Development to 1866 (1959); British Policy Considerations in Central America before 1850 (Hispanic American Historical Review, Feb. 1962). Language: Spanish 4,4,4,3; Portuguese 3,2,2,1. Home: c/o A. Gomez, 968 Alice Ave., San Leandro, Calif. Office: Dept. of History, Duke U., Durham, N.C.

VANDERBURGH, JOHN B., b. San Francisco, Calif., Oct. 12, 1917. HISTORY. A.B., Stanford U., 1938; M.A., 1939; Ph.D., 1954. Junior economic analyst, Embassy (Chile), U.S. Dept. of State, 1941-45; reference asst., Hispanic Foundation, Library of Congress, 1946; teacher, Menlo School (Calif.), 1947-48; instr., chmn. of faculty, Deep Springs Junior Coll., 1948-51; LABOR MARKET ANALYST, DEPT. OF EMPLOYMENT, STATE OF CALIF., 1951- . Inter-American exchange fellow (Chile), 1941. Membership: American Statistical Association. Research: labor market analysis. Language: Spanish 4,4,4,4; Portuguese 2,2,2,1; French 2,2,2,1. Home: 5620 State Ave., Sacramento, Calif. 95819. Office: California Dept. of Employment, 800 Capital Ave., Sacramento, 95814.

VANGER, MILTON I., b. New York, N.Y., Apr. 11, 1925. HISTORY. B.A., Princeton U., 1948; M.A., Harvard U., 1950; Ph.D., 1958. Instr., Okla. State U., 1956-58; vis. lectr., U.

of Wis., Summer 1958; asst. prof., Sacramento State Coll., 1958-62; ASSOC. PROF., HISTORY, BRANDEIS U., 1962- . Princeton U. scholarship; Princeton U., grant (Guatemala), Summer 1947; Harvard U. scholarship; Doherty fellow (Uruguay), 1950-52. Membership: American Historical Association; Conference on Latin American History; Pacific Coast Council on Latin American Studies; Phi Beta Kappa. Research: Uruguay; 20th century Latin America; Latin American historiography. Author: José Batlle y Ordoñez of Uruguay: The Creator of His Times, 1902-1907 (1963); Uruguay Introduces Government by Committee (American Political Science Review, June 1954); Latin America in Perspective (Yale Review, Winter 1959). Language: Spanish 5,5,5,4; Portuguese 4,3,2,1. Home: 32 Gray St., Cambridge, Mass. Office: Dept. of History, Brandeis U., Waltham 54, Mass.

VARGAS-BARÓN, EMILY ANN, b. Seattle, Wash., June 18, 1940. HISTORY. B.A., U. of Wash., 1962; M.A., 1964. STUDENT, HISTORY, STANFORD U., 1964- ; coordinator, Peace Corps Training Program, San Diego State Coll., Summer 1965. Fulbright scholar (Colombia), 1962-63; National Defense Education Act fellow, Stanford U., 1964-65. Membership: Phi Alpha Theta; Phi Beta Kappa. Research: Latin American history and political science; community development in Colombia; agrarian reform; urban development; the 1948 Colombian Bogotazo. Language: Spanish 5,5,4,4; Portuguese 2,2,1,1; French 2,2,2,2. Home: 7508 56th Ave., NE., Seattle, Wash.

VARNER, JOHN GRIER, b. Mt. Pleasant, Tex., Mar. 30, 1905. HISTORY AND TRANSLATION. B.A., Austin Coll., 1926; M.A., U. of Va., 1932; Ph.D., 1940. Asst. prof., Washington and Lee U., 1938-43; dir., Bi-national Institute (Venezuela), U.S. Dept. of State, 1943-47; asst. cultural attaché, Embassy (Mexico), 1947; ASSOC. PROF., ENGLISH, U. OF TEX., 1947- ; lectr. in South America, U.S. Dept. of State, 1951-52. DuPont teaching fellow, U. of Va., 1930-38; American Philosophical Society and U. of Tex. grants (Spain), 1955. Membership: Real Academia de Ciencias, Bellas Letras, y Nobles Artes de Córdoba (Spain). Research: Peruvian history; El Inca Garcilaso de la Vega. Co-author: English Grammar for Venezuelans (1946). Editor: Edgar Allan Poe and the Philadelphia Saturday Courier (1933). Co-translator: The Florida of the Inca, by El Inca Garcilaso de la Vega (1951, 1963). Language: Spanish 4,4,4,2; Portuguese 2,1,1,1; French 2,1,1,1. Home: 2510 Jarratt Ave., Austin, Tex. Office: Dept. of English, U. of Tex., Austin.

VIEIRA, DAVID GUEIROS, b. Garanhuns, Pernambuco, Brazil, Sept. 12, 1929. HISTORY. B.A., King Coll., 1952; Union Theological Seminary; M.A., U. of Richmond, 1960; American U. Sales representative, Alkor Corporation (Rio de Janeiro), 1952-53; teacher, Colegio 15 de Novembro (Garanhuns, Brazil), 1953; translator, asst. traffic manager, Dura Com-

modities Corporation (N.Y.), 1953-54; claims representative, Social Security Administration (Washington, D.C.), 1958-60; ASST. PROF., HISTORY, LONGWOOD COLL., 1961- . William fellow, U. of Richmond, 1957-58; Commonwealth of Va. research grant, 1962. Membership: American Historical Association; Phi Alpha Theta; Pi Sigma Alpha; Virginia Social Science Association. Research: Latin American history with emphasis on Brazil; the role of the Protestant element in Pernambuco, Brazil, 1872-1875. Author: A Story of Heroes (The Presbyterian Survey, Mar. 1952). Language: Spanish 4,4,4,4; Portuguese 5,5,5,5; French 3,2,2,1; Italian 3,2,2,1. Home: 708 First Ave., Farmville, Va. Office: Dept. of History, Longwood Coll., Farmville.

VIGNERAS, LOUIS ANDRÉ, b. Paris, France, May 28, 1903. HISTORY. Lic. en lettres, Bordeaux, 1920; M.A., Princeton, 1922; Ph.D., Harvard, 1934. Instr., Robert Coll. (Turkey), 1925-26, Lycée Français (Beirut, Lebanon), 1927-28, Ohio State U., 1928-30, De Pauw U., 1930-33, Duquesne U., 1934-36; instr.-prof., U. of Maine, 1936-51; PROF., ROMANCE LANGUAGES, GEORGE WASHINGTON U., 1960- . Research: history of the discovery and exploration of America, particularly of North America and the West Indies. Author: The Journal of Christopher Columbus (1960); The Voyage of Samuel Champlain to the West Indies (Anuario de Estudios Americanos, 1953); Revue d'Histoire de l'Amerique Français, Sept. 1957). Language: Spanish 5,5,4,4; Portuguese 4,3,3,2; French 5,5,5,5. Office: Dept. of Romance Languages, George Washington U., Washington, D.C. 20006.

VIGNESS, DAVID MARTELL, b. La Feria, Tex., Oct. 12, 1922. HISTORY. B.A., U. of Tex., 1943; M.A., 1948; Ph.D., 1951. Instr., U. of Tex., Summer 1951; prof., chmn., Social Sciences, Schreiner Institute, 1951-55; PROF., CHMN., HISTORY, TEX. TECHNOLOGICAL COLL., 1955- . Fulbright lectr., U. of Chile and Catholic U. of Santiago (Chile), 1957-58. Membership: American Historical Association; Conference on Latin American History; Mississippi Valley Historical Association; Rocky Mountain Council on Latin American Studies; Southwestern Social Science Association; Texas State Historical Association; Western History Conference. Research: Mexican history; Chile; Texas history. Author: The Revolutionary Decades (1964); Huatchipato: The Story of Steel in Chile (Southwestern Social Science Association Quarterly, June 1959). Co-author: Documents of Texas History (1963); Language: Spanish 5,5,5,4; Portuguese 4,3,2,2; French 3,2,1,1. Office: Dept. of History, Tex. Technological Coll., Lubbock, 79409.

WALTER, RICHARD JOHN, b. Champaign, Ill., May 3, 1939. HISTORY. B.A., Duke U., 1961; M.A., Stanford U., 1962. INSTR., HISTORY, WASHINGTON U., 1965- . Doherty fellow, 1964. Research: Latin American history; political role of university students in

Argentina. Language: Spanish 4,4,4,3; French 4,2,2,2. Home: 212 South Lee St., Falls Church, Va. Office: Dept. of History, Washington U., St. Louis, Mo.

WARREN, DAVE, b. Santa Fe, N. Mex., Apr. 12, 1932. HISTORY. B.A., U. of N. Mex., 1955; Mexico City Coll., 1960-61; M.A., U. of N. Mex., 1961; Ph.D., 1965. Teacher, Alberquerque Public Schools, 1957-58; instr. and asst. coordinator, Peace Corps Training Center, U. of N. Mex., Summer 1964; INSTR., HISTORY, OKLA. STATE U., 1964- . John Hay Whitney Opportunity fellow, 1959-61; National Defense Foreign Language fellow, U. of N. Mex, 1961-63. Research: Latin American history; colonial and pre-Conquest ethnohistory; Nahuatl native documents; post-Conquest codices materials; Olmec area at Spanish contact. Language: Spanish 3,3,2,2; Nahuatl 3,1,1,1. Home: 233½ North Duck, Stillwater, Okla. 74074. Office: Dept. of History, Okla. State U., Stillwater, 74075.

WARREN, DONALD, JR., b. Boston, Mass., Sept. 5, 1921. HISTORY. B.A., Mexico City Coll., 1947; M.A., 1948; Ph.D., Columbia U., 1959. Lectr., Columbia U., 1955-58; Instr., Long Island U., 1958-59; asst. prof., 1959-64; vis. assoc. prof., State U. of N.Y., Coll. at Buffalo, 1964-65; ASSOC. PROF., HISTORY, LONG ISLAND U., 1965- . Fulbright Summer Seminar (Brazil), 1960; National Institute of Mental Health research grant (Brazil), 1962-63; New York State grant, Columbia U., Summer 1964. Membership: American Historical Association; Association of Brazilianists; Conference on Latin American History. Research: Brazilian history, especially religion and the freeman in the 19th century. Author: The Red Kingdom of Saxony (1964); Religion, Race, and Poverty in Brazil (Helicon, 1964); The Negro and Religion in Brazil (Race, Jan. 1965). Language: Spanish 5,5,4,4; Portuguese, 5,4,3,3; French 4,3,3,3; German 4,4,4,3; Italian 3,2,1,1. Home: 12 West 83d St., New York, N.Y. 10024. Office: Dept. of History, Long Island U., Brooklyn, N.Y. 11201.

WARREN, FINTAN BENEDICT, O.F.M., b. Waterflow, N. Mex., June 30, 1930. HISTORY. B.A., Duns Scotus Coll., 1953; M.A., U. of N. Mex., 1960; Ph.D., 1963. RESIDENT MEMBER, ACADEMY OF AMERICAN FRANCISCAN HISTORY, 1958- ; EDITOR, THE AMERICAS, 1963- . Membership: Phi Alpha Theta. Research: institutional and social history of 16th century Mexico. Author: Don Vasco de Quiroga and His Pueblo-Hospitals of Santa Fe (1963); Jesuit Historians of Sinaloa-Sonora (The Americas, Apr. 1962); The Caravajal Visitation: First Spanish Survey of Michoacán (The Americas, Apr. 1963). Language: Spanish 4,4,3,3; Portuguese 3,2,1,1; French 3,2,1,1; German 3,2,1,1; Italian 3,2,1,1; Latin 4,4,4,3. Home and office: Academy of American Franciscan History, 9800 Kentsdale Dr., Box 5850, Washington, D.C. 20014.

WARREN, HARRIS GAYLORD, b. Lincoln, Nebr., Oct. 10, 1906. HISTORY. B.S., Purdue U., 1926; A.M., Stanford U., 1930; Ph.D., Northwestern U., 1937. Instr., Mountain Home High School (Idaho), 1926-28; clerk, American Legation (Asunción, Paraguay), 1928-29; instr., Joliet High School and Junior Coll. (Ill.), 1930-36; instr., Mich. State Coll., 1938-39; assoc. prof., MacMurray Coll. for Women, 1939-40; asst. prof., La. State U., 1940-46; prof., U. of Miss., 1946-57; PROF., CHMN., HISTORY, MIAMI U., 1957- . University Scholar, Stanford U., 1929-30; University Fellow, Northwestern U., 1936-37; American Philosophical Society grant, 1962; Miami U. research grant, 1962; Mississippi State Historical Commission and Ohio Civil War Centennial Commission. Membership: American Association of University Professors; American Historical Association; Association for Latin American Studies; Mississippi Historical Society; Mississippi Valley Historical Association; Ohio Academy of History; Ohio Historical Society; Southern Historical Association; Western History Association. Research: national period in Paraguay; United States-Latin American diplomacy; recent United States history. Author: The Sword Was Their Passport: A History of American Filibustering in the Mexican Revolution (1943); Paraguay: An Informal History (1949); Herbert Hoover and the Great Depression (1959). Language: Spanish 4,4,3,4; Portuguese 4,2,2,2; French 4,2,1,1; Italian 3,2,1,1. Home: 1022 South Locust St., Oxford, Ohio. Office: Dept. of History, Miami U., Oxford.

WARWICK, MAL, b. Pittsburgh, Pa., May 13, 1941. POLITICAL SCIENCE. A.B., U. of Mich., 1963; National U. of Mexico; COLUMBIA U. VOLUNTEER, U.S. PEACE CORPS (QUITO, ECUADOR), 1966-68. Membership: American Political Science Association; Conference on Latin American History; Hispanic American Historical Association; Hispanic American Society. Language: Spanish 3,2,3,2; Portuguese 2,2,1,1; German 3,2,2,1. Home: c/o U.S. Peace Corps Representative, U.S. Embassy, Quito, Ecuador.

WATERS, JOHN J. Office: Dept. of History, U. of Rochester, Rochester, N.Y. 14627.

WEBB, DORTHY ROSE, b. Los Angeles, Calif., Aug. 2, 1927. HISTORY. B.A., Stanford U., 1949; M.A., Fresno State Coll., 1963. Teacher, St. Johns School (Woodlake, Calif.), 1955-62; STUDENT, HISTORY, FRESNO STATE COLL. National Defense Foreign Language fellow in Spanish, Fresno State Coll., 1963-64. Membership: National Education Association; Phi Kappa Phi; Pi Gamma Mu; Sigma Delta Pi. Research: Latin American history; political structure of Peru, 1920-1963. Language: Spanish 4,4,3,3; Portuguese 3,1,1,1; German 2,2,2,2. Home: P.O. Box 467, Visalia, Calif. 93277.

WELCH, ROBERT J. Office: 305 Gilmore Hall, U. of Iowa, Iowa City, Iowa 52240.

WELLER, JUDITH ANN, b. Warwick, N.Y., June 9, 1935. HISTORY. B.A., Randolph-Macon Woman's Coll., 1956; M.A., McGill U., 1958; Ph.D., Columbia U., 1965. Instr., Brooklyn Coll., 1962-63. McGill U. fellow, 1956-57; Fulbright scholar (Trinidad), 1961-62. Membership: Phi Beta Kappa. Research: Latin American history and ethnography. Author: Tacitus and Tiberius' Rhodian Exile (The Phoenix, Journal of the Classical Association of Canada, Spring 1958); A Profile of a Trinidadian Steelband (Phylon, Spring 1961). Language: Spanish 4,3,3,4; Portuguese 3,1,1,2; French 4,2,2,4; German 2,1,1,2; Greek 3,—,—,2; Latin 4,—,—,4. Home: Apt. 4D, 425 Riverside Dr., New York 25, N.Y.

WELSHOFER, HARRY LEWIS, b. Detroit, Mich., Oct. 19, 1928. HISTORY. B.A., St. Bonaventure U., 1954; M.A., 1955; Ph.D., State U. of N.Y., Buffalo, 1959. Instr., St. Bonaventure U., 1955-56; teacher, Mt. Morris Central School (N.Y.), 1956-59; ASST. PROF., SOCIAL STUDIES, STATE U. OF N.Y., COLL. AT GENESEO, 1961- . Membership: American Historical Association; Conference on Latin American History. Research: Latin American history and international relations; Italian immigration to Argentina, 1852-1952. Language: Spanish 3,—,1,1; French 2,—,—,—. Home: R.F.D. 1, Reservoir Rd., Geneseo, N.Y. Office: Dept. of Social Studies, State U. of N.Y., Coll. at Geneseo.

WHITAKER, ARTHUR PRESTON, b. Tuscaloosa, Ala., June 6, 1895. HISTORY. B.A., U. of Tenn., 1915; A.M., Harvard U., 1917; Ph.D., 1924. Prof., Fla. State Coll. for Women, 1926-27; vis. prof., Vanderbilt U., 1927-28; assoc. prof., Western Reserve U., 1928-30; prof., Cornell U., 1930-36; prof., U. of Pa., 1936-65; RETIRED, 1965; vis. prof., Princeton U., 1965-66; VIS. PROF., HISTORY, U. OF TEX., 1966-67. Lectr., U. of San Marcos and Catholic U. (Peru), 1941; vis. lectr., National U. of Colombia (Bogotá), 1946; unit head, U. S. Dept. of State, 1943-45. Amherst Memorial fellow, 1924-26; Guggenheim fellow, 1929, 1950; Council on Foreign Relations fellow, 1958-59; Rockefeller Foundation grants for study of Argentine nationalism, 1959-64; Doherty Fellowship Committee; editorial boards, Hispanic American Historical Review, Hispanic American Report, and Orbis: A Quarterly Journal of World Affairs. Membership: American Academy of Political and Social Science; American Historical Association; American Philosophical Society; Council on Foreign Relations; Hispanic Society of America. Research: nationalism in Argentina; United States diplomatic history. Author: The U.S. and the Independence of Latin America, 1800-1830 (1942); The Western Hemisphere Idea: Its Rise and Decline (1954); Spain and Defense of the West: Ally and Liability (1961). Language: Spanish 4,4,4,4; Portuguese 3,2,1,1; French 4,4,3,4; German 3,2,1,1; Italian 3,1,1,1. Office: Dept. of History, U. of Tex., Austin, Tex.

WHITE, ROBERT ALLAN, b. Galveston, Tex., Oct. 10, 1941. SPANISH LITERATURE AND HISTORY. B.A., Haverford Coll., 1963; U. of Tex. STUDENT, LATIN AMERICAN STUDIES, U. OF TEX. National Defense Foreign Language fellow in Portuguese, U. of Wis. and U. of Tex. Research: Spanish literature; Latin American and Spanish history. Language: Spanish 5,5,4,4; Portuguese 3,3,2,2; French 4,4,3,3. Home: 2205 Sabine St., Austin, Tex. 78705.

WILGUS, A(LVA) CURTIS, b. Platteville, Wis., Apr. 2, 1897. HISTORY. B.A., U. of Wis., 1920; M.A., 1921; Ph.D., 1925. Assoc. prof., U. of S.C., 1924-30; assoc. prof., George Washington U., 1930-40; dir., Center of Latin American Studies, 1932-36; prof., 1940-41; PROF., HISTORY, DIR., SCHOOL OF INTER-AMERICAN STUDIES, U. OF FLA., 1951- . Latin America expert, U.S. Office of Education, 1942; dir., Education and Teacher Aids, Office Coordinator for Inter-American Affairs, 1943-44; Cervantes Medal, Hispanic Institute of Florida, 1954; Chevalier, El Compagnon Honnaire Croix de Lorraine, 1954. Membership: American Association of University Professors; American Historical Association; Association for Latin American Studies; Committee on Library Cooperation with Latin America; Hispanic Society of America; Inter-American Bibliography and Library Association. Research: the Caribbean; United States foreign relations. Author: Latin American History (1939); Development of Hispanic America (1941); Histories and Historians of Hispanic America (1942). Language: Spanish 4,4,4,1; Portuguese 3,2,1,1; French 4,4,4,1; German 2,3,2,1; Italian 2,3,2,1. Home: 32 SW. 43rd Ter., Gainesville, Fla. Office: School of Inter-American Studies, U. of Fla., Gainesville.

WILKIE, JAMES WALLACE, b. Idaho Falls, Idaho, Mar. 10, 1936. HISTORY. B.A., Mexico City Coll., 1958; M.A., U. of Calif., Berkeley, 1959. Teacher, Spanish, San Diego High School, 1959-60; STUDENT, HISTORY, U. OF CALIF., BERKELEY. Inter-American Cultural Convention fellow (Mexico), 1960-61; National Defense Foreign Language fellow, U. of Calif., Berkeley, 1962-63; William Harrison Mills traveling fellow in International Relations (Mexico), 1963-64. Research: Latin American social and political history; sociology of underdeveloped areas; Mexican social revolution and the rise of Lázaro Cárdenas, 1928-1934. Language: Spanish 4,4,4,4; Portuguese 3,2,2,2; French 3,2,2,2. Home: 1810 Ridenbaugh, Boise, Idaho.

WILKINS, CAROLINE HANKE, b. Corpus Cristi, Tex., May 12, 1937. HISTORY. B.A., U. of Tex., 1961; M.A., U. of the Americas, 1964; Oreg. State U. Research: Latin American history and international relations; 20th century history of Colombia; the two party political system in Colombia, 1949-1964. Language: Spanish 3,3,3,3. Home: 1140 Filmore St., Corvallis, Oreg.

WILLIFORD, MIRIAM, b. Rock Hill, S.C., Mar. 26, 1926. HISTORY. B.A., Winthrop Coll., 1945; M.A., U. of N.C., 1950; Ph.D., Tulane U., 1963. Teacher, Cambridge High School (Md.), 1945-47; ASSOC. PROF., HISTORY, WINTHROP COLL., 1947- ; asst. to dean of the college, 1961- ; dean, Rock Hill Community Coll., 1961- . Organization of American States research fellow (Guatemala), Summer 1962. Membership: American Association of University Professors; American Historical Association; Conference on Latin American History; Hispanic American Society; Phi Alpha Theta; Sigma Delta Pi; Southern Historical Association. Research: the reform program of Dr. Mariano Gálvez, chief of state of Guatemala, 1831-1838; adult education program. Language: Spanish 4,4,3,3; Portuguese 2,2,2,1; French 3,3,3,3; Italian 2,2,2,2. Home: Apt. 9, 517 North Wilson St., Rock Hill, S.C. Office: Box 102, Winthrop Coll. Station, Rock Hill.

WILLIMAN, JOHN B., b. Jersey City, N.J., Dec. 19, 1936. HISTORY. B.S., Coll. of Charleston, 1960; M.A., U. of Ala., 1962; W. Va. U. Instr., Fairmont State Coll., 1963-65; INSTR., HISTORICAL STUDIES, SOUTHERN ILL. U., 1965- . National Defense Education Act fellow in Latin American History, U. of Ala., 1960-62. Membership: American Association of University Professors; Conference on Latin American History; Phi Alpha Theta. Research: Latin American history; church-state relations in Mexico, 1926-1927. Language: Spanish 5,3,-4,5. Home: R.F.D. 5, Edwardsville, Ill. Office: Historical Studies Faculty, Southern Ill. U., Carbondale.

WILSON, IRIS HIGBIE, b. Los Angeles, Calif., Jan. 9, 1935. HISTORY. B.A., U. of Southern Calif., 1956; M.A., 1957; Ph.D., 1962. Teacher, Huntington Beach High School, 1957-59; translator of Spanish manuscripts, Los Angeles County Museum, 1959-60; lectr., U. of Southern Calif., 1962- ; INSTR., HISTORY, LONG BEACH CITY COLL., 1962- . University graduate fellow, U. of Southern Calif.; Del Amo fellow (Spain), 1960-62. Membership: American Historical Association. Research: history of science; Spanish scientific expeditions in South and Central America with particular emphasis on native medicinal plants and remedies. Author: Scientists in New Spain—the 18th Century (Journal of the West, July 1962); Investigación sobre la planta maguey (Revista de Indias, 1963). Editor: Pineda's Report on the Beverages of New Spain (Arizona and the West, Spring 1963). Language: Spanish 4,5,4,4; Portuguese 2,2,2,2; French 2,2,1,1; German 2,2,2,1; Italian 2,2,1,1. Home: 328 Amethyst Ave., Balboa Island, Calif. Office: Dept. of History, Long Beach City Coll., 4901 Carson St., Long Beach 8, Calif.

WILSON, JOE FOSTER, b. Huntington Beach, Calif., May 21, 1919. HISTORY. B.A., Fla. Southern Coll., 1962; M.A., U. of Ga., 1963; Ph.D., 1965. Master sergeant, U.S. Air Force, 1939-59. Research: Latin American history;

ABC powers; Tacna-Arica Plebiscitary Commission; woman's rights in Chile; Central America. Language: Spanish 3,3,3,3; Portuguese 2,2,1,1. Home: Box 4224, Campus Station, Athens, Ga.

WINN, WILKINS BOWDRE, b. Fort Worth, Tex., Jan. 19, 1928. HISTORY. A.B., Howard Coll., 1952; Th.M., Dallas Theological Seminary, 1959; M.A., U. of Ala., 1959; Ph.D., 1964. ASST. PROF., HISTORY, MOBILE COLL., 1963- . Membership: American Anthropological Association; Southern Historical Association. Research: Protestantism in Latin America; Central American missions. Language: Spanish 3,—,—,—; German 1,—,—,—; Greek 3,—,—,—; Hebrew 2,—,—,—. Home: 705 Montclaire Way, Mobile, Ala. 36609. Office: Mobile Coll., P.O. Box 13220, Mobile, 36613.

WIRTH, JOHN DAVIS, b. Dawson, N. Mex. HISTORY. B.A., Harvard Coll., 1958; Ph.D., Stanford U., 1966. ASST. PROF., HISTORY, STANFORD U., 1966- . Foreign Area fellow (Brazil), 1963-65. Membership: American Historical Association; Conference on Latin American History. Research: Latin American history; modern Brazilian social, political and intellectual history; role of the university student in Brazil since 1930. Language: Spanish 4,4,3,2; Portuguese 3,3,2,2; French 2,2,1,1. Home: 37 Park Dr., Atherton, Calif. Office: Dept. of History, Stanford U., Palo Alto, Calif.

WISAN, JOSEPH EZRA, b. New York, N.Y., Feb. 26, 1901. HISTORY. B.S.S., City Coll. (N.Y.), 1922; Ph.D., Columbia U., 1934. Instr., City Coll. (N.Y.), 1928-35; asst. prof., 1935-42; assoc. prof., 1943-49; chmn., History, City Coll. (N.Y.), 1949-66; prof., 1950-66; RETIRED, 1966- . Membership: American Academy of Political and Social Science; American Association of University Professors; Conference on Latin American History; Mississippi Valley Historical Association; Phi Alpha Theta; Phi Beta Kappa. Research: United States history; American foreign policy; diplomatic history of the United States. Author: The Cuban Crisis as Reflected in the New York Press, 1895-1898 (1934). Language: Spanish 4,3,3,—; French 4,3, 3,—. Home: 25 Monroe Pl., Brooklyn 1, N.Y. Office: Dept. of History, City Coll. of N.Y., New York 31.

WOMACK, JOHN, JR., b. Norman, Okla., Aug. 14, 1937. HISTORY. B.A., Harvard Coll., 1955; Oxford U., 1959-61; Harvard U. STUDENT, HISTORY, HARVARD U., 1961- . Bliss fellow in Latin American Studies, Harvard U., 1961-65. Research: Mexican history; the Mexican Revolution; Zapata and Zapatismo. Language: Spanish 5,5,4,4; Portuguese 4,4,3,3; French 4,4,3,3; Italian 4,3,3,3. Home: Apt. 6B, 1039 Massachussetts Ave., Cambridge, Mass. 02138.

WOOD, BRYCE, b. Everett, Wash., Mar. 13, 1909. POLITICAL SCIENCE. B.A., Reed Coll., 1931; M.A., 1933; Ph.D., Columbia U., 1940. Instr., Columbia U., 1936-42; senior administrative asst., Div. of Political Studies,

U.S. Dept. of State, 1942-43; assoc. prof., Swarthmore Coll., 1943-50; asst. dir., Div. of Social Sciences, Rockefeller Foundation, 1947-48; STAFF ASSOC., SOCIAL SCIENCE RESEARCH COUNCIL, 1950- ; vis. prof., Columbia U., 1958-60, 1965; staff, Joint Committee on Latin American Studies, American Council of Learned Societies-Social Science Research Council, 1959-63. Social Science Research Council fellow (Europe), 1935-36; William Bayard Cutting fellow, Columbia U. (Mexico, Argentina, Brazil, Chile), 1939-40; asst. secretary, International Secretariat, United Nations Conference on International Organization, 1945; Board of Editors, International Organization. Membership: American Political Science Association; Conference on Latin American History; Council on Foreign Relations. Research: United States policy in Chaco, Leticia, and Marañón disputes, 1932-1942; civil services in Latin America. Author: Peaceful Change and the Colonial Problem (1940); The Making of the Good Neighbor Policy (1961). Language: Spanish 3,3,3,2; Portuguese 3,2,1,1; French 3,3,3,2; German 2,1,1,1. Home: 4 Putnam Hill, Greenwich, Conn. 06830. Office: Social Science Research Council, 230 Park Ave., New York, N.Y. 10017.

WOOD, MARIE V., b. Altoona, Pa., Dec. 25, 1921. HISTORY. A.B., Shaw U., 1945; M.A., Howard U., 1946; Ph.D., American U., 1955. Instr., Howard U., 1946-55; research assoc., legislative aide, U.S. Congressman Adam Clayton Powell, House of Representatives, 1955-58; assoc. prof., Del. State Coll., 1958-61; dir., Virgin Islands Teacher Education Project, Hampton Institute and Dept. of Education, Government of V.I., 1961-63; ADMINISTRATIVE ASST., TO PRESIDENT, HAMPTON INSTITUTE, 1964- . John Hay Whitney fellow, Buenos Aires Convention fellow; consultant on Haiti, American Friends Service Committee. Membership: American Historical Association; American Personnel and Guidance Association; Association for Higher Education; College Personnel Association; Conference on Latin American History. Research: the Caribbean; the economic development of Haiti, 1934-53. Language: Spanish 2,3,2,2; French 5,5,4,4; Haitian Creole —,4,4,—. Home: 5206 First St., NW., Washington, D.C. Office: Hampton Institute, Hampton, Va. 23368.

WOOD, ROBERT DOUGLAS, S.M., b. St. Louis, Mo., Apr. 2, 1927. HISTORY. B.S., U. of Dayton, 1948; M.A., Catholic U., 1964. Teacher, St. Michael's High School (Chicago), 1948-49; teacher, Provencher Collegiate Institute (St. Boniface, Manitoba, Canada), 1949-52; teacher, St. Mary's High School (St. Louis), 1952-53; teacher, Villa Chaminade (Chiclayo, Peru), 1954-55; teacher, Colegio Santa María (Lima), 1955-59; teacher, St. Joseph Coll. (Yokohama, Japan), 1959-62; teacher, St. Michael's High School (Chicago), 1962-63; STUDENT, HISTORY, CATHOLIC U. Organization of American States fellow, 1964. Membership: Marianist Writers' Guild; Phi Alpha Theta. Research: Latin American and United States history and literature; education of the Andean Indian during the colonial period; Marianists in Latin America. Author: Missionary Crisis and Challenge in Latin America (1964). Language: Spanish 4,4,4,3; Portuguese 2,2,1,1; French 2,2,1,1. Home: 1311 Allison St., NE., Washington, D.C. Office: Society of Mary, Province of St. Louis, Maryhurst Preparatory, Kirkwood 22, Mo.

WOODS, KENNETH FLINT, b. Randolph, Mass., Oct. 20, 1930. HISTORY. B.S., Ball State Teachers Coll., 1954; M.A., U. of Md., 1959; Ph.D., American U., 1962. Asst. prof., Pa. State Coll., 1960-61; coordinator for Venezuelan Affairs, U.S. Peace Corps, Spring 1962; vis. lectr., Universidad Central del Ecuador, Summer 1962; asst. prof., Old Dominion Coll., 1962-63; ASST. PROF., HISTORY, SAN DIEGO STATE COLL., 1963- . Fellow, Universidad Central del Ecuador, 1962. Membership: American Historical Association; Conference on Latin American History; Pacific Coast Council on Latin American Studies. Research: problems on inter-American cooperation. Author: Intellectual and Artistic History of Panama (in Handbook of Panama, 1962). Language: Spanish 5,4,4,4; Portuguese 3,2,2,2. Home: 4628 63rd St., San Diego 15, Calif. Office: Dept. of History, San Diego State Coll., San Diego 15.

WOODWARD, RALPH LEE, JR., b. New London, Conn., Dec. 2, 1934. HISTORY. A.B., Central Coll. (Mo.), 1955; M.A., Tulane U., 1959; Ph.D., 1962. Asst. prof., U. of Southwestern La., 1962-63; ASST. PROF., HISTORY, U. OF N.C., 1963- . Doherty fellow (Guatemala), 1960-61. Membership: American Association of University Professors; American Historical Association; Conference on Latin American History; Mississippi Valley Historical Association. Research: Central America; Caribbean; southeastern South America; labor history of Cuba. Author: Octubre: Communist Appeal to the Urban Labor Force of Guatemala, 1950-53 (Journal of Inter-American Studies, July 1962); Political Economy in Guatemala (University of Wichita, Aug. 1962); Communism and Urban Labor: Cuba (Caribbean Studies, Oct. 1963). Language: Spanish 4,4,3,3; Portuguese 4,3,2,1; French 4,2,2,2; German 2,2,1,1; Italian 3,3,1,1; Russian 2,1,1,1. Home: 108 Kenan St., Chapel Hill, N.C. Office: Dept. of History, U. of N.C., Chapel Hill.

WORCESTER, DONALD EMMET, b. Tempe, Ariz., Apr. 29, 1915. HISTORY. A.B., Bard Coll., 1939; M.A., U. of Calif., Berkeley, 1940; Ph.D., 1947. Asst. prof.-prof., chmn., U. of Fla., 1947-63; PROF., CHMN., HISTORY, TEX. CHRISTIAN U., 1963- . Smith-Mundt vis. prof., U. of Madrid, 1956-57. Membership: American Historical Association; Instituto Paraguayo de Investigaciones Históricas; New Mexico Historical Society; Phi Alpha Theta. Research: independence period in Chile; Brazil. Author: Sea Power and Chilean Independence (1962); The Three Worlds of Latin America (1963). Co-author: The Growth and Culture of Latin America (1956). Language: Spanish 4,4,4,4; Portuguese 3,3,3,3; French 2,2,2,2. Home: 5800 Wedgeworth Rd., Ft. Worth, Tex. 76133. Office: Dept. of History, Tex. Christian U., Ft. Worth, 76129.

WRIGHT, ALMON ROBERT, b. Roseville, Ohio, July 23, 1903. HISTORY. Ph.B., Denison U., 1926; A.M., Harvard U., 1928; Ph.D., U. of Ill., 1935. Instr., State U. of Mont., 1928-31; asst., Div. of Classification, U.S. National Archives, 1935-41; asst. chief, 1941-47; chief, Div. of State Dept. of Archives, U.S. National Archives, 1947-49; historian, Historical Office, U.S. Dept. of State, 1949-58; SENIOR HISTORIAN, HISTORICAL OFFICE, U.S. DEPT. OF STATE, 1958- . Membership: American Historical Association; Society of American Archivist. Research: United States foreign policy; Panama-United States relations. Author: German Interests in Panama's Piñas Bay, 1910-1938 (Journal of Modern History, Mar. 1955); Defense Sites Negotiations Between the United States and Panama, 1930-48 (U.S. Dept. of State Bulletin, Aug. 1952). Compiler and editor: Foreign relations: American Republic, 1940-42 (1961-). Language: Spanish 3,—,—,—; French 3,—,—,—. Home: 3901 North Upland St., Arlington, Va. Office: Historical Office, U.S. Dept. of State, Washington, D.C.

WRIGHT, IONE STUESSY, b. La Grange, Ill., Mar. 12, 1905. HISTORY. B.A., U. of Richmond, 1926; M.A., U. of Calif., Berkeley, 1937; Ph.D., 1940. Lectr.-PROF., HISTORY, U. OF MIAMI, 1946- . Editor, Journal of Inter-American Studies, 1964- . Membership: American Association of University Professors; American Historical Association; Conference on Latin American History; Historical Association of South Florida; Southeastern Conference on Latin American Studies; Southern Historical Association. Research: 16th century Spanish American history; period of the wars of independence. Author: Voyages of Álvaro de Saavedra Cerón, 1527-1529 (1951); Early Spanish Voyages from America to the Far East, 1527-65 (in Greater America: Essays in Honor of Herbert Eugene Bolton, 1945); Factors Affecting Popular Self-government in the Caribbean (in The Caribbean: Its Political Problems, 1956). Language: Spanish 4,3,3,3; Portuguese 2,1,1,1; French 2,1,1,1. Home: 485 NE. 94th St., Miami, Fla. 33138. Office: Dept. of History, U. of Miami, Coral Gables, Fla. 33138.

WRIGHT, JAMES LEITCH, JR., b. Ashland, Va., Aug. 9, 1929. HISTORY. B.S., Va. Military Institute, 1950; M.A., U. of Va., 1956; Ph.D., 1958. Asst. prof., Va. Military Institute, 1958-61; PROF., HISTORY, RANDOLPH-MACON COLL., 1961- . American Philosophical Society and University Center in Va. grants (Mexico, England, and Spain). Membership: American Association of University Professors; American Historical Association; Southern Historical Association. Research: Anglo-Spanish rivalry in North America. Author: Sixteenth Century English-Spanish Rivalry in La Florida (Florida Historical Quarterly,

April 1960); Andrew Ranson, 17th Century Pirate (Florida Historical Quarterly, Oct. 1960). Language: Spanish 4,3,3,3; French 3,—,—,—; German 2,—,—,—. Home: Rt. 1 (Gwathmey), Ashland, Va. Office: Dept. of History, Randolph-Macon Coll., Ashland.

WRIGHT, WINTHROP ROBINS, b. Philadelphia, Pa., Mar. 31, 1936. HISTORY. B.A., Swarthmore Coll., 1958; M.A., U. of Pa., 1960; Ph.D., 1964. ASST. PROF., HISTORY, BIRMINGHAM-SOUTHERN COLL., 1963- . Rockefeller Foundation grant (Argentina), 1960-62. Membership: American Association of University Professors; American Historical Association; Conference on Latin American History. Research: 19th century Argentina; political and economic history of the Rio de la Plata area; Argentine nationalism. Language: Spanish 4,4,4,4; Portuguese 3,2,1,1; French 3,2,1,1. Home: 812-A 12th St. West, Birmingham 4, Ala. Office: Dept. of History, Birmingham-Southern Coll., Birmingham 4.

WYTHE, GEORGE, b. Weatherford, Tex., Aug. 29, 1893. ECONOMICS. B.A., U. of Tex., 1914; Ph.D., George Washington U., 1938. Dir., American Republics Div., U.S. Dept. of Commerce, 1920-60; commercial attaché, Embassy (Mexico), U.S. Dept. of State, 1925-31; professorial lectr., George Washington U., 1953-60; RETIRED, 1960- . Consultant, Journal of Inter-American Studies; contributing editor, Handbook of Latin American Studies; National Advisory Committee, Handbook of Latin American Studies. Membership: American Economic Association; American Geographical Society; Conference on Latin American History; Economic History Association; Royal Economic Society. Research: economic development. Author: Industry in Latin America (1945, 1949); Brazil: An Expanding Economy (1949); The United States and Inter-American Relations (1964). Language: Spanish 4,4,4,3; Portuguese 4,3,2,1; French 4,4,4,3. Home: 3042 Cambridge Pl., NW., Washington 7, D.C.

Y NSFRAN, PABLO MAX, b. Asunción, Paraguay, July 30, 1894. HISTORY. Ecribano Público, Facultad de Derecho y Ciencias Sociales, U. of Asunción, 1923. PROF., ROMANCE LANGUAGES, U. OF TEX., 1941- . Membership: Academia Española (Madrid). Research: Rio de la Plata history and government. Author: Sobre latinismo (1927); La expedición norteamericana contra el Paraguay, 1858-1859 (1954-58). Editor: The Epic of the Chaco (1950). Language: Spanish 5,5,5,5; Portuguese 4,—,—,—; French 4,—,—,—. Home: 403 East 32nd St., Austin 5, Tex. Office: Box 7791, University Station, Austin 12.

YOUNG, GEORGE FREDERICK WILLIAM, b. Buffalo, N.Y., Nov. 13, 1937. HISTORY. B.A., Harvard U., 1959; U. of Chicago. STUDENT, HISTORY, U. OF CHICAGO. Fulbright grant (Chile), 1964-65. Research: Latin American history; the history of the Germans in Chile,

1850-1965. Language: Spanish 4,3,3,3; Portuguese 2,2,2,2; French 3,2,2,2; German 4,3,3,3; Swedish 4,2,2,2. Home: 52 Clinton St., Batavia, N.Y.

YOUNG, JORDAN MARTEN, b. New York, N.Y., Sept. 25, 1920. HISTORY. B.A., U. of Calif., Berkeley, 1946; M.A., 1947; Ph.D., Princeton U., 1953. Public health work (Brazil), Coordinator of Inter-American Affairs, 1942-44; instr., Princeton U., 1950-53; trainee, Interamericana Investment Banking (Rio, Brazil), 1953-55; general manager, Industrias Consolidadas (Venezuela), 1955-56; ASSOC. PROF., SOCIAL SCIENCE, PACE COLL., 1956- ; vis. assoc., N.Y.U., 1959- . Doherty fellow (Chile), 1947-48; U.S. Office of Education fellow (Brazil), 1949. Membership: American Historical Association; American Political Science Association; Latin American Historians Association; Pan American Society of New York. Research: contemporary political affairs and history of Chile and Brazil; revolutions of 1930 and 1932 in Brazil. Author: The Brazilian Congressional Elections (Journal of Inter-American Studies, Jan. 1963). Language: Spanish 4,4,4,2; Portuguese 5,5,5,3. Home: 159 Meadowbrook Dr., Princeton, N.J. Office: Dept. of Social Science, Pace Coll., 41 Park Row, New York 38, N.Y.

ZIMDARS, BENJAMIN FRANK, b. Whitehall, Wis., May 20, 1927. HISTORY. B.A., North Central Coll., 1952; M.A., U. of Wis., 1954; Ph.D., U. of Tex., 1965. Teaching asst., U. of Tex., 1956-58; ASST. PROF., HISTORY, MARY WASHINGTON COLL. OF THE U. OF VA., 1965- . Southern fellow, 1959-60. Membership: American Historical Association; Conference on Latin American History. Research: colonial Latin American historiography; colonial social, economic, and intellectual history of Peru; independence period of Mexico. Language: Spanish 4,3,3,2; Portuguese 1,1,1,1; French 3,2,2,1; German 3,3,2,2. Home: 1712-E Rio Grande, Austin, Tex. 78701. Office: Dept. of History, Mary Washington Coll. of the U. of Va., Fredericksburg, Va.

ZOOK, DAVID HARTZLER, JR., b. Bellefontaine, Ohio, Jan. 22, 1930. HISTORY. A.B., Wittenberg U., 1950; M.A., Ohio State U., 1955; Ph.D., 1959; Universidad Nacional Mayor de San Marcos (Peru), 1960. Assoc. prof., U.S. Air Force Academy, 1959-63; INTELLIGENCE OFFICER, U.S. AIR FORCE, 1963- ; assoc. professorial lectr., U. of Md., 1964; professorial lectr., 1965- . Membership: American Historical Association; American Military Institute; Conference on Latin American History. Research: South American military and diplomatic history; west coast South America, Bolivia and Paraguay. Author: The Conduct of the Chaco War (1960; Spanish edition, 1962); Zarumilla-Marañon: The Ecuador-Peru Dispute (1964); U.S. Military Assistance to Latin America (Air University Review, Sept.-Oct. 1963). Language: Spanish 4,3,3,1; Portuguese 2,2,1,1; French 2,1,1,1. Home: R.F.D. 2, West Liberty, Ohio. Office: 1007th A.I.S.G., U.S. Air Force, Washington 25, D.C.

INDEX

INDEX

INDEX

MEXICO

INDEX